الطب النبوى

Healing with the

Medicine
of the
Prophet ﷺ

Second Edition: June 2003

© Maktaba Dar-us-Salam, 2003
King Fahd National Library Cataloging-in-Publication Data
Ibn Qayyim Al-Jauziyah, Mohd. Ibn Aby Bakr 751 H.
Healing with the medicine of the prophet-Riyadh.
359p., 14x21 cm. ISBN 9960-892-91-3
I-Faith (faith)   II-Title
214.61 dc.   1424/2881
Legal Deposit no. 1424/2881
ISBN 9960-892-91-3

Head Office: P.O. Box: 22743, Riyadh 11416, K.S.A. Tel: 00966-01-4033962/4043432 Fax: 4021659
E-mail: darussalam@awalnet.net.sa Website: http// www.dar-us-salam.com

K.S.A. Darussalam Showrooms:
Riyadh
Olaya branch:Tel 00966-1-4614483 Fax: 4644945
Malaz branch: Tel 4735220 Fax: 4735221
• Jeddah
  Tel: 00966-2-6879254 Fax: 6336270
• Al-Khobar
  Tel: 00966-3-8692900 Fax: 00966-3-8691551
U.A.E
• Darussalam, Sharjah U.A.E
  Tel: 00971-6-5632623 Fax: 5632624
PAKISTAN
• Darussalam, 36 B Lower Mall, Lahore
  Tel: 0092-42-724 0024 Fax: 7354072
• Rahman Market, Ghazni Street
  Urdu Bazar Lahore
  Tel: 0092-42-7120054 Fax: 7320703
U.S.A
• Darussalam, Houston
  P.O Box: 79194 Tx 772779
  Tel: 001-713-722 0419 Fax: 001-713-722 0431
  E-mail: sales@dar-us-salam.com
• Darussalam, New York
  572 Atlantic Ave, Brooklyn
  New York-11217, Tel: 001-718-625 5925
U.K
• Darussalam International Publications Ltd.
  226 High Street, Walthamstow,
  London E17 7JH, Tel: 0044-208 520 2666
  Mobile: 0044-794 730 6706 Fax: 0044-208 521 7645
• Darussalam International Publications Limited
  Regent Park Mosque, 146 Park Road,
  London NW8 7RG Tel: 0044-207 724 3363
• Darussalam
  398-400 Coventry Road, Small Heath
  Birmingham, B10 0UF
  Tel: 0121 77204792 Fax: 0121 772 4345
  E-mail: info@darussalamuk.com
  Web: www.darussalamuk.com

FRANCE
• Editions & Librairie Essalam
  135, Bd de Ménilmontant- 75011 Paris
  Tél: 0033-01- 43 38 19 56/ 44 83
  Fax: 0033-01- 43 57 44 31
  E-mail: essalam@essalam.com
AUSTRALIA
• ICIS: Ground Floor 165-171, Haldon St.
  Lakemba NSW 2195, Australia
  Tel: 00612 9758 4040 Fax: 9758 4030
MALAYSIA
• E&D Books SDN. BHD.-321 B 3rd Floor,
  Suria Klcc
  Kuala Lumpur City Center 50088
  Tel: 00603-21663433 Fax: 459 72032
SINGAPORE
• Muslim Converts Association of Singapore
  32 Onan Road The Galaxy Singapore- 424484
  Tel: 0065-440 6924, 348 8344 Fax: 440 6724
SRI LANKA
• Darul Kitab 6, Nimal Road, Colombo-4
  Tel: 0094-1-589 038 Fax: 0094-74 722433
KUWAIT
• Islam Presentation Committee
  Enlightment Book Shop
  P.O. Box: 1613, Safat 13017 Kuwait
  Tel: 00965-244 7526, Fax: 240 0057
INDIA
• Islamic Dimensions
  56/58 Tandel Street (North)
  Dongri, Mumbai 4000 009,India
  Tel: 0091-22-3736875, Fax: 3730689
  E-mail:sales@IRF.net
SOUTH AFRICA
• Islamic Da'wah Movement (IDM)
  48009 Qualbert 4078 Durban,South Africa
  Tel: 0027-31-304-6883
  Fax: 0027-31-305-1292
  E-mail: idm@ion.co.za

Printed in Lebanon

الطب النبوى

Healing with the
Medicine
of the
Prophet ﷺ

By: **Imam Ibn Qayyim Al-Jauziyah**
Translated by: **Jalal Abual Rub**
Edited by: **Abdul Rahman Abdullah**
Formerly **Raymond J. Manderola**
Fordham University U.S.A.

DARUSSALAM
GLOBAL LEADER IN ISLAMIC BOOKS
Riyadh • Jeddah • Al-Khobar • Sharjah
Lahore • London • Houston • New York

In the Name of Allâh,
the Most Gracious, the Most Merciful

CONTENTS

Part III. The Prophet's Guidance on using Divine Ruqyah

Part IV. Alphabetical Listing

Publishers Note

All Praises if for Allâh, Lord of the universe. We praise Him, and seek his help, and his forgiveness, and we seek His protection from the accursed Satan. Whoever Allâh guides will never be misguided, and whom He allows to be misguided will not be guided. I bear witness that there is no deity worthy of worship except Allâh, who is One alone and has no partners. I bear witness that Muhammad is His Servant and Messenger. May the blessings of Allâh be upon him and his family and his companions and the righteous who follow them until the Day of Judgement.

Throughout the history of mankind, man has been searching for those things which will heal his many ailments. The present book "At-Tib an-Nabawee" written by Sheikh Al-Islam Ibn Al-Qayyim Al-Jawziah (Healing with the Medicine of the Prophet) is presented to the readers in order to provide them with information, knowledge and wisdom in dealing with their many ailments brought about by their libertine life style devoid of faith and belief in their creator. Allâh has clearly indicated to mankind that: " Indeed in the Messenger of Allâh (Muhammad ﷺ) you have a good example to follow for him who hopes for Allâh and the Last Days and remembers Allâh much". (33:21)

Prophet Muhammad was sent as a guide, and mercy for all of mankind, and as such was given wisdom by Allâh that benefits man. Allah says: "O Mankind! There has come to you a good advice from your Lord, and a healing for that which is in your breasts, a guidance and mercy for the believer's." (10:57). The Prophets medicine is not restricted to spiritual healing, in fact it balances the healing of the soul and the physical man in order to prepare him for a better life in the Hereafter.

We at Darussalam are pleased and we thank Allâh for the opportunity he has given us to publish this authentic book about the medical treatment of Prophet Muhammad ﷺ who was a physician of the soul and the body. We also would like to thank brother Aqeel Walker for his tireless work in revising and editing the final draft of this projcet. We ask Allâh to accept this work, forgive us for our mistakes and to make this book a valuable asset for the believers of truth.

Abdul Malik Mujahid

General Manager

October 1999

Part I

Kinds of Diseases

Kinds of Diseases

There are two types of diseases that attack the heart, one doubt and error, and the second lust and desire, both are mentioned in the Qur'ān. Allāh says about the disease of doubt:

$$\text{﴿ فِى قُلُوبِهِم مَّرَضٌ فَزَادَهُمُ ٱللَّهُ مَرَضًا ﴾}$$

"In their hearts is a disease (of doubt and hypocrisy) and Allāh has increased their disease." (2:10)

And He said:

$$\text{﴿ وَلِيَقُولَ ٱلَّذِينَ فِى قُلُوبِهِم مَّرَضٌ وَٱلْكَٰفِرُونَ مَاذَآ أَرَادَ ٱللَّهُ بِهَٰذَا مَثَلًا ﴾}$$

"... and that those in whose hearts is a disease (of hypocrisy) and the disbelievers may say: 'What Allāh intends by this (curious) example?'" (74:31)

Allāh says concerning those who refuse to make the Qur'ān and *Sunnah* the basis of their judgments:

$$\text{﴿ وَإِذَا دُعُوٓا۟ إِلَى ٱللَّهِ وَرَسُولِهِۦ لِيَحْكُمَ بَيْنَهُمْ إِذَا فَرِيقٌ مِّنْهُم مُّعْرِضُونَ ۝ وَإِن يَكُن لَّهُمُ ٱلْحَقُّ يَأْتُوٓا۟ إِلَيْهِ مُذْعِنِينَ ۝ أَفِى قُلُوبِهِم مَّرَضٌ أَمِ ٱرْتَابُوٓا۟ أَمْ يَخَافُونَ أَن يَحِيفَ ٱللَّهُ عَلَيْهِمْ وَرَسُولُهُۥ بَلْ أُو۟لَٰٓئِكَ هُمُ ٱلظَّٰلِمُونَ ۝ ﴾}$$

"And when they are called to Allāh (i.e., His Words, the Qur'ān) and His Messenger (ﷺ), to judge between them, lo! a party of them refuses (to come) and turns away. But if the truth is on their side, they come to him willingly with submission. Is there a disease in their hearts? Or do they doubt or fear lest Allāh and His Messenger (ﷺ) should wrong them in judgement. Nay, it is they themselves who are the Zālimūn (polytheists, hypocrites and wrongdoers)." (24:48-50)

This is the disease of doubt and error.

Also, Allāh says about desire and lust, adultery in this case:

﴿ يَـٰنِسَآءَ ٱلنَّبِيِّ لَسْتُنَّ كَأَحَدٍ مِّنَ ٱلنِّسَآءِ إِنِ ٱتَّقَيْتُنَّ فَلَا تَخْضَعْنَ بِٱلْقَوْلِ فَيَطْمَعَ
ٱلَّذِى فِى قَلْبِهِۦ مَرَضٌ ﴾

"O wives of the Prophet! You are not like any other women. If you keep your duty (to Allāh), then be not soft in speech, lest he in whose heart is a disease (of hypocrisy, or evil desire for adultery) should be moved with desire..." (33:32)

Physical diseases that attack the body

Allāh's says:

﴿ لَّيْسَ عَلَى ٱلْأَعْمَىٰ حَرَجٌ وَلَا عَلَى ٱلْأَعْرَجِ حَرَجٌ وَلَا عَلَى ٱلْمَرِيضِ حَرَجٌ ﴾

"There is no restriction on the blind, nor any restriction on the lame, nor any restriction on the sick..." (24:61)

These Verses refer to ailments that might attack a person while performing the *Hajj*, while Fasting or making ablution. They contain a tremendous secret and wisdom, indicating the greatness and divine wisdom of the Qur'ān and its sufficiency for those who have sound understanding and comprehension.

The science of medicine consists of three basic rules preserving good health, avoiding what might cause harm (i.e. establishing immunity) and ridding the body of harmful substances. Allāh has mentioned these three basic principles in connection with the performance of *Hajj*, Fasting, and ablution mentioned above,

﴿ فَمَن كَانَ مِنكُم مَّرِيضًا أَوْ عَلَىٰ سَفَرٍ فَعِدَّةٌ مِّنْ أَيَّامٍ أُخَرَ ﴾

"But if any of you is ill or on a journey, the same number (should be made up) from other days." (2:184)

Allāh has allowed the sick to break their Fast because of their illness. Allāh has also permitted the traveler to break their fast in order to protect and preserve their health and strength while traveling. Traveling uses tremendous physical effort that requires nourishment to sustain the body's energy. This is why the traveler is given an exemption from fasting so his body can be supplied with the required nourishment. Further, Allāh said:

﴿ فَمَن كَانَ مِنكُم مَّرِيضًا أَوْ بِهِۦٓ أَذًى مِّن رَّأْسِهِۦ فَفِدْيَةٌ مِّن صِيَامٍ أَوْ صَدَقَةٍ أَوْ نُسُكٍ ﴾

"And whosoever of you is ill or has an ailment in his scalp (necessitating shaving), he must pay a Fidyah (ransom) of either observing Saum (fasts) (three days) or giving Sadaqah (charity - feeding six poor persons) or offering sacrifice (one sheep)."
(2:196)

Allāh has allowed the sick and those suffering from lice or sensitive scalp, to shave their head, which is normally prohibited, while wearing *Ihram*. Shaving the head and exposing the scalp in these cases removes the harmful substances and thus allows the sick person to get rid of whatever caused his illness and to recover from the condition that was aggravated because of the hair. This is an example of ridding the body of harmful substances which had a higher priority (thus the exemption) than the general rule, no shaving of the head while in the state of *Ihram*. There are ten things that might cause harm to the body when congested, unless the body eliminates them: blood when it is irritated, sperm when it is excessive, urine, excrement, air, vomit, the need to sneeze, sleep, hunger and thirst. When any of these ten things are not properly dealt with or satisfied, as in the case of sleep, they will cause a particular type of illness. When Allāh permitted shaving the head to remove harmful substances on the scalp, His statement inspired His slaves to use the same practice in removing harmful substances caused by other ailments.

As for observing a certain precautionary measure (i.e, diet, or other type of abstention), Allāh said:

﴿ وَإِن كُنتُم مَّرْضَىٰٓ أَوْ عَلَىٰ سَفَرٍ أَوْ جَآءَ أَحَدٌ مِّنكُم مِّنَ ٱلْغَآئِطِ أَوْ لَٰمَسْتُمُ ٱلنِّسَآءَ فَلَمْ تَجِدُواْ مَآءً فَتَيَمَّمُواْ صَعِيدًا طَيِّبًا ﴾

"And if you are ill, or on a journey, or one of you comes after answering the call of nature, or you have been in contact with women (by sexual relations) and you find no water, perform Tayammum with clean earth and rub therewith your faces and hands (Tayammum)." (4:43)

Allāh has allowed the sick person to use clean earth instead of water to perform his ablution for prayer; this spares his body from the repercussions of using water while ill. This *Ayah* sets the precedent for every type of precautionary or preventive measure (diet etc.) that protects the body from harmful substances that one consumes or his body produces.

Allāh, all praise is due to Him, has emphasized the three basic rules of the science of medicine that we mentioned above.

We will now give several instances and examples that prove Prophetic medicine is superior and more comprehensive than any other method.

Providing proper remedies for ailments of the heart (referring to spiritual or emotional ailments) only occurs at the hands of Prophets عليهم السلام and Messengers of Allāh. The heart becomes well when it acquires knowledge of its Lord and Creator and in His Names, Attributes, Actions and Commandments. The heart also becomes well when it prefers acquiring Allāh's Pleasure and prefers what He likes, all the while avoiding His prohibitions and what might lead to His displeasure. There is no life, health, or wellbeing for the heart except by this method, which only the Messengers can provide. It is wrong to think that one can ever attain the heart's wellbeing through any other way than through the guidance of the Messengers of Allāh. These errors result from confusing the heart's true wellbeing with satisfying and strengthening its lower animal lusts and desires. By this way the heart will be far from acquiring its true wellbeing, strength and even its very existence will be in danger. Those who do not distinguish between these two paths should grieve for their heart's life and health, or in fact for the lack of it. Let such people also grieve because of their lacking the light of true guidance and because they are completely submerged in an ocean of darkness.

Remedies for physical illnesses are divided into two categories

One depends on instinct, which all species have. There is no need for the doctor to cure this type of illness, which entails responding to hunger, thirst, cold and fatigue.

The second, requires deep thought and analysis and entails subduing and resisting the ailment, and moderating the patients condition (temperament), which can result from fever, heat, coldness, dryness, or a combination of these symptoms. These ailments have two types of causes: physical and one that relates to temperament. These ailments are the result of a physical cause or are due to changes that affect the mood and the temper (of the body). The difference between the two types is that the ailments of the temperament occur after the physical causes are eliminated. Their effects remain and alter the temperament. The ailments that are caused by physical elements have their causes with them. In these cases of physical disease we should look at the cause first, the ailment second and the cure third.

Further, deep thought and careful analysis are also required concerning repelling and removing the ailments that affect the various organs and cause some alterations in the organs whether in the shape, cavity, vessel, roughness, touch, number, bone, and so forth. When these organs, which collectively constitute the body, are working properly, they are described as being connected. Otherwise, they are described as having lost their proper connectivity.

These ailments that affect and alter the organs are included in the general ailments that affect the body.

As we have stated, these same ailments negatively affect the mood and temperament. The changes that accompany such ailments come in eight types, four simple types and four compound types. The simple types include coldness, hotness, wetness and dryness. The compound types include being hot and wet, hot and dry, cold and wet or cold and dry. The causes of these ailments are either physical or due to changes in the mood or temperament as we have stated.

Also, there are three states that the body can be in normal, abnormal and in the middle (between normal and abnormal). When the state of the body is normal, the body is healthy. The second state occurs when the body is ill, while the third is in the middle, as one extreme does not become the opposite extreme except after passing through a middle stage.

There are internal reasons for the abnormal state the body passes through, for the body consists of coldness, hotness, wetness and dryness. Also, there are external reasons for the abnormal state, which could find the body susceptible and affect it.

The potential harm inflicted on the body could result from bad temperament that was not moderated, an ailment that attacks an organ, or a general weakness in the overall power of the body, or even the soul, which sustains such power. The ailment could be caused by an increase in what should not be increased, or a decrease in what should not be decreased. Also, a break in the connection could be the cause, where the connection is essential, or due to a connection between that which should not be connected. The ailment could also occur due to an extension of what should not be extended or an alteration and change in the shape or place of some of the body organs.

The doctor is able to distinguish between what might harm the body when connected and what should be connected. The doctor also distinguishes between what might cause harm if increased and what might cause harm if decreased. The doctor helps bring about good health or what preserves good health, and helps fend off the ailment with its antidote (opposite) or by using a corrective diet. You will see that all these guidelines are met by the guidance and advice of the Prophet ﷺ, by Allāh's Will, Power and Support.

The Prophet (ﷺ) used medicine himself and prescribed medicine for his family and Companions

Yet, the type of medicines that the Prophet (ﷺ) and his companions used to take was nothing like the chemical mixtures that are called, "Aqrabathayn (Pharmacopoeia)". Rather, the majority of their medicine consisted of only one ingredient. Sometimes, they would take another substance to assist the medicine or make it taste better. This was, and still is, the case with most of the medicine used by many cultures such as Arabs, Turks, Indians and nomads. The Romans and the Greeks, on the other hand, use a mixture of substances or remedies in their medicine.

The medical authorities agree that whenever an illness could be fought with nourishment and diet, then medicine should be avoided. Also, they agree that whenever it is possible to use only one substance or ingredient as a remedy, a compound remedy should not be used. They agree that the body will be harmed if doctors over prescribe medicine. This is because the remedy might not find an illness to cure, or might find an illness that it cannot cure, or might be suitable for the illness, but an excess dose may be given, thereby compromising the health of the body.

The most experienced doctors use medications that contain one ingredient. The medication should be similar or related to regular foods that the patient is used to eating. Cultures that consume one or only a few types of food in their regular diet, generally suffer from few illnesses, they should not use compound medicines. Those who live in cities and whose diets are complex need medicines that are a mixture of several substances or ingredients, as these are the types of medicines that most suit their illnesses. The ailments of the people who live in the deserts are usually simple and thus simple medications are suitable for them. These arguments entail facts that are known in the medical profession.

Prophetic medicine has a divine element to it. This element makes comparing Prophetic medicine to the medicines offered by regular doctors similar to comparing the medicine offered by doctors to folk medicine. The best medical authorities agree to this fact, since the science that they excel in is a result of comparisons, experimentation, inspiration, visions and hypothesis. Some of them state that their knowledge is acquired through the animal kingdom, for example they observe cats swallowing a venomous creature and then observe it lick the oil in the lamp, thus neutralizing the effect of the venom. They also observe a snake that has something wrong with its eyes. The snake then wipes its eyes on fennel leaves and cures its condition. Also, they observe some birds that sip seawater when constipated. There are many similar examples that doctors mention concerning their observations of nature.

This type of knowledge cannot be compared to revelation from Allāh to His Messenger and which informs him of what is good for him and what is not. Comparing scientific knowledge to revelation is like comparing the rest of the sciences to what the Prophet ﷺ has been sent with. In fact, the Prophets provide us with a kind of medicine that the doctors can barley understand or reach by their experimentation, hypothesis and theories. The Prophets deliver remedies that cure the heart from whatever attacks it. These Prophetic remedies strengthen the heart and increase the reliance and dependence on Allāh. It also aids in seeking refuge, being humble and showing meekness before Him, begging Him, giving charity and supplicating to Him. It also includes repenting to Allāh, seeking His forgiveness, practicing kindness towards His creation and aiding those in desperate need and those who have suffered a calamity. These cures have been tried by various nations who have indeed found them to carry the cure doctors can never prescribe on their own, whether by experimentation or scientific observations.

We have tried the Prophetic cures and found that they are more powerful than any type of regular medicine. Further, it is a fact that comparing the Prophetic medicines to the medicines that doctors prescribe is just like comparing regular medicine to folk medicine.

The hearts that are connected with the Lord of the Worlds – the Creator of the illness and its cure and He Who governs the affairs of everything and everyone – require special types of remedies that are nothing like those required for the hearts that are far away from their Lord. Furthermore, whenever the soul and the heart become stronger (spiritually), they will cooperate to defeat the illness. How can anyone deny that the most effective cure for the ailment that afflicts the heart and soul occurs by feeling delight and joy when drawing closer to the Lord, loving Him, remembering Him, being totally dedicated and attentive to Him, depending on Him and seeking His help? Only the most ignorant people deny these facts, especially those who have the dullest intellect, the worst comprehension and who are the farthest from Allāh and from knowing the true reality of mankind. Soon after, Allāh willing, we will mention the reason why reciting Al-Fatihah (the first chapter in the Qur'ān) has removed the effects of a poisonous sting, enabling the poisoned person to stand up as if he never suffered pain.

We will mention two types of Prophetic medicine in as much detail as possible, according to the limited strength, knowledge and resources available to us. We rely only on Allāh for every type of good and righteous matter, while seeking His Bounty, for He is the Cherished Who grants favors without limit.

Every sickness has a cure

Muslim narrated in his *Sahih* that the Prophet ﷺ said:

«لِكلِّ دَاءٍ دواءٌ؛ فإذا أُصِيبَ دَواءُ الدّاءِ: بَرأَ بإذن اللهِ عزَّ وجل»

"Every illness has a cure, and when the proper cure is applied to the disease, it ends it, Allāh willing."

Also, it is narrated in the *Sahihān* that the Messenger of Allāh said:

« ما أنزل اللهُ من داءٍ، إلا أَنزل لهُ شِفاءً »

"Allāh has not sent down a disease except that He has also sent
down its cure."

Further, Imam Ahmad narrated that Usamah bin Shuraik said:

«كنتُ عند النبي صلى الله عليه وسلم، وجاءت الأعرابُ، فقالوا: يا رسول
الله؛ أَنتَدَاوَىٰ؟ فقال: نعم يا عباد اللهِ؛ تَدَاوَوْا: فإن الله عز وجل لم يَضَع داءً
إلا وَضعَ له شِفاءً؛ غيرَ داءٍ واحدٍ. قالوا: ما هو؟ قال: الهَرَم».

"I was with the Prophet ﷺ when the Bedouins came to him and
said, 'O Messenger of Allāh, should we seek medicine?' He said,
'Yes, O slaves of Allāh, seek medicine, for Allāh has not created a
disease except that he has also created its cure, except for one
illness.' They said, 'And what is that?' He said, 'Old age.'"

In addition, it is related in the Musnad (by Imam Ahmad) that the
Prophet ﷺ said:

« إنَّ الله عزَّ وجل لم يُنزل داءً، إلا أنزل له شفاءً: عَلِمَه مَنْ عَلِمَه، وَجَهِلَهُ مَنْ جَهِلَهُ»

"Allāh has not sent down a disease except that He also sent
down its cure; whoever knows it (the cure), knows it, and whoever
is unaware of it (the cure), he is unaware of it." (the medicine)
while those who are ignorant of it are unaware of it." [An-Nasai'î,
Ibn Mājah, Al-Hakim and Ibn Hibban].

Also, it is narrated in the Musnad (by Imam Ahmad) and the Sunan (of
At-Tirmidhî and Ibn Mājah) that Abu Khuzamah said:

« قلتُ يا رسول اللهِ؛ أرأيتَ رُقًى نَسترَقيهَا، ودواءً نَتداوَىٰ به، وتُقاةً نَتقيِهَا؛
هل تَرُدُّ من قَدِرِ اللهِ شيئًا؟ فقال: هي من قدرِ اللهِ »

"I said, 'O Messenger of Allāh ﷺ, about the Ruqya (divine
remedies - Islamic prayer formula) that we use, the medicine we
take and the prevention we seek, does all this change Allāh's
appointed destiny?' He said, 'They are a part of Allāh's appointed
destiny.'"

These Ahadith indicate there are causes for whatever occurs in this
world and also removal of these causes.

The Prophet's statement that there is a cure for every disease might include both the curable and the humanly incurable diseases, for Allāh may have hidden these types of cures from mankind and blocked their path to acquiring them. Allāh knows best. The Prophet ﷺ said that the disease ends when the proper cure is applied to it, indicating that there is an opposite for every creation and thus there is an antidote for every disease. The Messenger of Allāh ﷺ has stated that when the two opponents meet, meaning, the proper remedy and the disease, recovery from the illness occurs. When the medicine is given in a dosage higher than what is needed, or when it is not the required medicine, it might lead the body to another type of disease. When the dosage is less than what is needed, it will not be sufficient to cure the disease. When the sick person and the disease are not treated with the suitable medicine, cure and recovery does not occur. Also, when the time is not suitable for the cure, or when the body is unable or unsuitable for the prescribed medicine, the cure will not be effective. When all circumstances are favorable, the cure will surely be effective. This is the best explanation available for these *Ahadith*.

On the other hand, these *Ahadith* might be specific, in that Allāh has not created a disease that can be humanly cured but has sent down a cure for it. This is similar to what Allāh said:

$$\text{﴿ تُدَمِّرُ كُلَّ شَيْءٍ بِأَمْرِ رَبِّهَا ﴾}$$

"Destroying everything by the Command of its Lord!" (46:25)

This *Ayah* means that everything prone to be destroyed was destroyed by the wind. In this case, the *Ahadith* do not include incurable diseases.

Those who observe various substances and their opposites in this world, and analyze the pacifying effect, opposing nature and resistance in relation to each other, would appreciate Allāh's perfect power, eternal wisdom and perfect creation and His Oneness in the Lordship and in His Actions. Everything else except Allāh has an opponent or an antidote, but Allāh Alone is the Self Sufficient and Irresistible, while everything and everyone stands in need of Him.

These authentic *Ahadith* command Muslims to seek and take the appropriate medicine, while indicating that this action does not contradict dependence on Allāh Alone for everything. Just as one satisfying his hunger, thirst or reacts to being hot or cold does not contradict the dependence on Allāh. On the contrary, the belief in *Tawhid* (Oneness of Allāh) can only be complete by pacifying and responding to the various harmful elements in the manner and method that Allāh has commanded and that which will help in such cases. Furthermore, refraining from using these cures or antidotes is, in fact, contradictory to total dependence on Allāh, along with contradicting the Commandments and the Wisdom (of Allāh). Not using these cures will also weaken our Tawakkul (reliance and dependence on Allāh) even though the person might be thinking that he is strengthening his reliance and dependence by abandoning seeking the cure. Abandoning the cure is in fact contradictory to the true reliance and dependence, in that, reliance and dependence in essence includes the heart of the slave relying on Allāh in acquiring what benefits him in his life and his religious affairs, while fending off what harms his life and religion. The correct method of reliance and dependence includes seeking these benefits for the slave; otherwise one will not be implementing the Commandments and the Wisdom. The slave should not call his inability, dependence on Allāh, nor consider his true reliance and dependence as an inability.

These *Ahadith* also contradict those who do not seek medicine, saying:

"If the cure has been written or is destined to occur, then the medicine will be of no use. If the cure was not destined, then the medicine will not be useful."

Also, one might say:

"The disease has occurred by Allāh's will, and no one and nothing can resist Allāh's will."

The last statement is similar to the question that the Bedouins asked the Messenger of Allāh. As for his close companions, who had more knowledge of Allāh, His Wisdom and His Attributes, they did not think the way the Bedouins did.

The Prophet ﷺ gave the Bedouins an answer that comforted their heart, saying that these *Ruqya* (Islamic prayer formulas), medicines and preventative measures, are all part of Allāh's Appointed Destiny. Therefore, nothing escapes Allāh's Destiny, except by Allāh's Destiny.

Taking medicine is a part of Allāh's Destiny and it also repels a part of Allāh's Destiny. In short, there is no way that the creation can escape Allāh's Destiny no matter what they do. This is the exact same case with ending the hunger, thirst, warm or cold conditions with what satisfies or pacifies them. Also, it is similar to repelling the enemy, which is a part of Allāh's Destiny, with Jihad, which is also Allāh's Commandment and appointed Destiny. Thus, the cause, its removal and those who remove it are all a part of Allāh's appointed destiny.

Another way of answering those who ask similar questions (concerning taking medicine) is that this logic requires them to then refrain from seeking their benefit or fending off harm. Following their logic, if the benefit or harm was destined to occur, then it would surely occur, and if it were not destined, then it would never occur! This method, if implemented, would bring utter destruction to life, religion and the entire world. Furthermore, this rhetoric only comes from those who arrogantly deny the truth and reject it, and this is why they mention destiny concerning this subject so as to refute the truth when it is offered to them. This is the exact case with the polytheists, who said:

$$\text{﴿ سَيَقُولُ ٱلَّذِينَ أَشْرَكُوا۟ لَوْ شَآءَ ٱللَّهُ مَآ أَشْرَكْنَا وَلَآ ءَابَآؤُنَا ﴾}$$

"If Allāh had willed, we would not have taken partners (in worship) with Him, nor would our fathers..." (6:148)

And:

$$\text{﴿ لَوْ شَآءَ ٱللَّهُ مَا عَبَدْنَا مِن دُونِهِۦ مِن شَىْءٍ نَّحْنُ وَلَآ ءَابَآؤُنَا ﴾}$$

"If Allāh had so willed, neither we nor our fathers would have worshipped aught but Him." (16:35)

The polytheists issued these statements to refute Allāh's proof against them when He sent the Messengers to them.

Also, those who utter this question, concerning destiny, medicine and true reliance and dependence should know that there is an argument that they did not mention. Allāh has decided that such and such matters will occur when such and such causes occur. Thus, if the cause is implemented or practiced, what was destined would also occur.

If one asks, "If I was destined to practice the cause, I would practice it. Otherwise, I would not be able to bring it into existence." We answer this claim by saying, "Would you accept such reasoning from your servant, children or workers if they deny what you have ordered them to do or commit an act that you have forbidden for them? Because if you accept such reasoning, then you have no right to blame those who disobey you, steal your property, question your honor, or transgress against your rights. If you chastise such persons for these acts, then how can you use the same logic to deny Allāh's rights and Commandments on you?"

Jewish tradition states that Ibrahim عليه السلام once asked Allāh, "O my Lord! Where does the disease come from?" He said, "From Me." Ibrahim عليه السلام said, "Where does the cure come from?" He said, "From Me." Ibrahim عليه السلام said, "What is the role of the doctor then?" He said, "A man in whose hands I send and cause the cure."

The Prophet's statement that there is a cure for every illness should strengthen the resolve of the sick person and the doctor, encouraging them to seek medicine. When the sick person feels that there is a cure for his illness, his heart will be full of hope, rather than despair, and thus the doors of positive anticipation will be wide open before him. When the resolve of the ailing person is strengthened, the various powers that exists within the person, the instinctive energy (or heat as Ibn Al-Qayyim puts it), the soul and the psyche, will also be strengthened. These powers will in turn strengthen that part of the body affected and the disease will be more easily dissipated and defeated.

In addition, when the doctor knows that there is a cure for that illness, he actively and energetically pursues that cure.

The diseases that attack the body are similar to diseases that attack the heart. Just as Allāh has sent down a cure for every disease that strikes the heart, He has sent down a cure for every disease that attacks the body. If the person acquires knowledge of this cure and applies it in the proper manner, his heart will regain its health by Allāh's Leave.

The Prophet's guidance concerning food and drink

Including observing diets, refraining from excessive eating and the general guidelines that should be observed regarding eating and drinking.

Al-Musnad (by Imam Ahmad) narrated that the Prophet ﷺ said:

« ما مَلأَ آدَمِيٌّ وِعاءً شرًّا مِنْ بطْنٍ، بِحَسْبِ ابنِ آدَمَ لُقَيْماتٌ يُقِمْنَ صُلبَه، فإن
كان لابدّ فَاعلًا : فثُلُثٌ لطعامِهِ، وثلثٌ لشرابِه، وثلثٌ لنَفَسِه »

"The son of Adam never fills a vessel worse than his stomach. The son of Adam only needs a few bites that would sustain him, but if he insists, one third should be reserved for his food, another third for his drink and the last third for his breathing."

Physical aliments

Physical aliments attack and harm the body and alter its normal functions, because of an excess amount of a substance. This type constitutes the majority of diseases and occurs because of overeating or consuming more than what the body needs, that which brings about little benefit or is not digested easily, or due to complex meals. When the son of Adam habitually fills his stomach with these types of foods, he will end up with various types of illnesses, some of which take a long time to remedy. On the other hand, when one consumes moderate amounts of food and eats sensibly, the body will get the maximum benefit from this diet, as opposed to when one overeats.

The foods we eat are either for necessity, sufficiency or excessiveness. The Prophet ﷺ told us that one only needs a few bites to sustain him, so that his strength does not fail him. When one wishes to exceed what is barely enough, he should reserve a third of his stomach for his food, another third for the water or drink and the last third for breathing. This is the best method of eating, both for the body and the heart. When the stomach is full of food, there will not be enough space for drinking. When one consumes something to drink on a full stomach, one's breathing will be difficult, thus bringing about laziness and fatigue. One will feel heavy, as if carrying a load on his stomach. Consequently, one will be lazy fulfilling his obligations and will seek other desires now that his stomach is full!

Eating until one is full harms the body and the heart, when it becomes a habit. There is no harm if one occasionally eats his fill. For example, Abu Hurairah رضي الله عنه once drank some milk in the presence of the Prophet ﷺ until he said, "By He Who has sent you with the Truth! I do not find a place for it." The Companions at times used to eat their fill in the presence of the Prophet ﷺ. Eating until full as a matter of habit weakens the strength and the body, even as one becomes fatter. The body will be strong when it gets the nourishment it needs and can utilize, not from the quantity of food one eats.*

The human body consists of three basic elements: water, solids and air (whereas the fourth basic element is fire, according to the Greeks). This is why the Prophet ﷺ gave each of these elements its due share in the body (the stomach being part of the body — editor). If someone asks about the share of fire in the body, we say that doctors confirm that heat is used in reactions that occur in the body. Other people disagree with this opinion and state that there is no firey part in the body. They reached these conclusions based on the following assumptions.

First, the firey part could either descend from the air and be mixed with the watery and solid parts (of the human body), or it could exist within the watery and solid matter.

The first assumption is not plausible, because fire naturally ascends and does not descend, otherwise it would depart from its center and descend to the earth. Also, if in fact fire descends, it would have to pass through spheres of bitter cold that exist on earth and it would still have to remain intact. However, what we in fact observe in this world is that a great fire is extinguished with a little amount of water. Thus if the fire were to descend from its center, it would certainly be extinguished due to the bitterly cold spheres it would pass through.

The second assumption is that fire is formed inside the solid and watery bodies. This is even less plausible, because the body that has turned to fire must have been watery, earthly, or composed of air beforehand, along with being surrounded by such elements. In this case, the element that is surrounded and interconnected with the watery or solid elements would not turn to fire on its own, because it is not

---

* **Editor's note**: The science at the time of the author 691-751 *Hijriah* (1364-1423 Gregorian approx.) understood creation consisting of 4 basic elements: water, earth, fire, and air. There was a dispute between the scientists of this time concerning whether the element of fire was part of the human body or not. From the prescription of the Prophet ﷺ concerning the proper proportions of food and drink our author seems to have brought this *Hadith* as evidence that fire was not part or the human body. The rest of the chapter is a divergence on this subject in support of his theory and not part of the Prophetic medicine.

composed of fire in essence. Also, the elements that surround it are cold. How can the solid and watery body turn to fire under these conditions?

Some might suggest that parts of these elements are composed of fire and thus turn parts of the body to fire upon mixing with it.

We answer by stating that the refutation of this theory is explained in the refutation we offered regarding the first theory.

Some people might say that when they pour water on slaked lime, it causes fire to emerge from it. They might also say that sunrays start a fire when they pass through a crystal and that when they strike a stone on an iron rod, fire bursts occur. All these fiery parts occur when such substances are mixed, they might say, adding that this conclusion refutes what we stated in the beginning.

Those who reject this opinion say that they do not deny that violent impacts could sometimes start a fire, as when one strikes a stone with iron, or when the sun heats an object such as a crystal, causing fire bursts to emerge. Yet, they refute the opinion that this might occur inside the bodies of animals and plants. The bodies of the animals and plants are not susceptible to produce fire upon violent impacts, because they are neither smooth nor polished enough to act like a crystal. In fact, sunrays fall on the outer bodies of the animals and plants, and do not cause them to burst into flames. So, how can sunrays that might or might not reach their interior start a fire inside their bodies?

Further, doctors agree that the older the drink gets, the hotter it gets. It is not possible that this inner warmth in the drink could be caused by fire, otherwise the fiery part would be extinguished by the much larger watery part and would not remain intact for a long time. In fact, we notice that a great fire is usually extinguished by a little amount of water.

Thirdly, if the animals and the plants have fiery parts within them, then the fiery parts would be overwhelmed and dissipated by the watery parts. Some elements are superior to others in nature, and thus the weaker element succumbs to the stronger element. If such fiery parts exist in the body, they will certainly be turned into watery parts, which is the opposite of and superior to fire.

Fourthly, Allāh has mentioned the creation of mankind in His Book in many instances. Sometimes Allāh would inform us that He has created mankind from water. Sometimes He would state that he created them from soil, a mixture of both and from clay that the sun and wind strike until it becomes just like a clay pot. All of these statements are true and describe the stages that mankind pass through. Allāh never stated that He has created mankind from fire, as in the case with the creation of Satan, being of the Jinn.

Imam Muslim narrated that the Prophet ﷺ said:

« خُلِقَتِ الملائكةُ من نورٍ، وخُلِقَ إبليسُ من مارجٍ من نارٍ، وخُلِقَ آدمُ مما وُصِفَ لكم »

"The angels were created from light, while Satan was created from the smokeless flame of fire. As for Adam, he was created from what has been told to you."

This statement is clear in its indication that Adam was created from what Allāh has stated in His Book about this subject. Allāh did not state that He created Adam from fire or that fire exists within him.

Fifthly, the best evidence they rely on, to prove that there are fiery parts in the body, is the warmth in the bodies of animals which they claim proves that the bodies are partly fire. We say that there is no proof in this observation, because there are several other causes for inner heat. For instance, fire produces heat, and so does movement, reflection of sunrays, the heat of the air and from being close to the fire, as the fire transmits the heat through the air. There are several causes behind the inner heat, but not necessarily fire.

The followers of the fire theory say that fire is necessary for sand and water to be mixed and blended. Otherwise, they would not blend or produce a compound. Also, they say, if the seed is buried in the mud so that the air and the sun could not penetrate the mud to reach the seed, it would get spoiled. Therefore, the seed should have an inner part that leads it to maturity, and later on to spoil, that is, the fire, they claim. Otherwise, the seed would only mature and then spoil due to an outside effect or else it would be in a state of deep freeze. They say that when the outside effect ends, the body will not be heated unless there is an inner fiery part in it that matures it, such as the case with some foods and medicines that are warm by nature.

They also say that if the body did not consist of a fiery part that produces heat, the body would be cold. If the nature of the body is susceptible to coldness and the surrounding environment does not have the opposite effect, the body will reach the coldest degree there is. In this state, the body would not feel the coldness because it would have reached such coldness that it would be in fact frozen. Therefore, the state of coldness and the body would be in the same cool degree and thus the body would not feel the cold nor would it feel any pain because of the extreme cold. The same argument can be said when the body is in a lower temperature than the cold substance itself. Thus, if the body did not have any fiery part, it would not normally feel the cold nor be affected by it.

They also say that, "Your proofs only serve to refute the opinion that the fiery parts remain as fire within the bodies. We do not support this statement. Rather, we say that fire changes when it is mixed with the body."

Those who oppose this idea reply, "Why not say that the heat of the sun blends the earth, water and air? Then, when the resulting mixture reaches maturity, it would be ready to take new shapes whether these shapes are plants, animals or minerals, with the heat as the medium. Why not say that the inner heat and warmth that exist in the body are the result of certain qualities and powers that Allāh brings into existence upon blending the mixture, not that they actually contain fiery parts? You have no way of denying this possibility, as some of the best medical authorities agree."

Also, the fact that the body feels the cold only indicates that there is an inner heat in body. Who denies this fact anyway? But, what is the evidence that this heat is only produced by fire? Yes, the fire radiates heats, but not every type of heat is the result of fire. Rather, the correct statement in this regard is that some types of heat are produced by fire.

Also the statement that the fire's essence changes when it mixes with the body is not supported by the opinions of the best doctors, or by fact. Also, some of your (those who say that the body is part fire) best supporters (i.e. Ibn Sina, the misguided philosopher) has admitted in his book Ash-Shifaa (The Cure) that the four essential elements (water, fire, earth and air) retain their essential qualities when blended in a compound.

The Prophet ﷺ used three types of remedies for various ailments: natural, divine and a combination of both natural and divine

We will mention the three types of remedies that the Prophet ﷺ prescribed and used, starting with the natural medicines, then the divine remedies and lastly those composed of the two types.

The Prophet ﷺ was sent as a guide and a caller to Allāh and to His Paradise. He acquainted the people with Allāh. He also informed them of what pleases Him and commanded them to implement these actions, and informed them of what angers Allāh and ordered them to avoid these actions. He told them stories of the Prophets and Messengers عليهم السلام and what occurred between them and their nations. He also acquainted the people with the creation of the world, its beginning, Resurrection and how and the reasons why souls will either acquire misery or happiness.

As for the remedies of the bodies, this is a part of the Prophet's Law that completes it and makes it whole. The remedies of the body should be used when needed. Other than that, it is better to spend the time and energy curing the ills of the heart and soul, preserving their health, and preventing any harm from touching them. This is the ultimate goal that the Prophet's mission seeks to achieve. It is a fact that curing the ills of the body without curing the heart does not work or benefit anyone. However, curing the heart while the body is ill does not cause extensive harm since soon after, this harm will be removed and will be replaced with the ultimate, eternal benefit. All success comes from Allāh.

Part II

Using Natural Medicines

Curing fever

It has been narrated in the *Sahihān* that the Prophet ﷺ said:

« إِنَّمَا الحُمَّى – أَو شِدَّةُ الحمَّى – مِن فَيحِ جَهنمَ؛ فَابْرُدُوهَا بِالماءِ »

"Verily Fever- or severe fever - is a breath of the Hell Fire, so cool it using water."

This *Hadith* has caused confusion for many ignorant doctors as they thought it contradicts the common method of treating fever. We will explain this *Hadith* in detail, Allāh willing.

When the Prophet ﷺ issues a statement, it is either general for all people or for specific people and conditions. The majority of the Prophet's statements are of the first type. As for the second type, it is similar to the Prophet's statement:

« لا تَسْتَقْبِلُوا القبلةَ بغائطٍ ولا بولٍ، ولا تَستدبِرُوها؛ ولكن شرِّقوا أَو غَرِّبُوا »

"Do not face the Qiblah with urine or feces, nor leave it directly behind you. Rather, face either the East or the West."

This statement (facing the East or the West) is not for those who reside in the East, the West or Iraq, but for those residing in Al-Madinah and Ash-Sham (Syria). It is the same case with the Prophet's statement:

« ما بينَ المشرقِ والمغربِ قِبلَةٌ »

"What is between the East and the West is a Qiblah."

Understanding this fact, we can realize that what the Prophet ﷺ said regarding fever is particularly for the people of Hijaz (Western Arabia), for the people in this area are susceptible to a type of fever that results from sunstroke. This type of fever requires cold water, either by drinking it or taking a bath. Fever causes rising temperatures in the body that emanates from the heart and which spreads throughout the entire body via the blood vessels and the soul, which disrupts the proper functioning of the body.

There are two types of fever, accidental that is a result of tumors, sunstroke, movements, or intense heat and another type that results from an ailment that usually starts at a particular organ and then heats up the entire body. When the fever is of the first type, it ends in one to three days. If the fever is a result of harmful mixtures, it is called septic (or toxic) fever, which is divided into four types: bilious, melancholic, phlegmy and sanguinary. If the fever originated in the basic organs of the body, it is called hectic fever, which has many types also.

The body benefits from the fever more so than it benefits from taking medicine. This is because, the fever heats up and matures harmful substances, which it could not have done without the fever. Also, the fever causes various blockages to open especially those that medicines can not reach.

As for simple and chronic conjunctivitis, fever helps cure most of its types quickly, as well as, helping against facial paralysis, hemiplegia, paralysis affecting only one side of the body, spasms and many other ailments that result from thick substances or excesses.

Some of the best doctors feel a bit relieved when fever breaks out in an ailing body, just as the sick person rejoices upon recovering from illness. This is because fever is more efficient than medication in some cases, since it matures the spoiled and septic substances that harm the body. When such substances reach maturity, the medicine will reach it, as the substances are ready to be discarded out of the body, bringing this process to a successful conclusion. Thus the fever becomes a part of the cure.

Based on these facts, it appears that the *Hadith* is talking about the accidental type of fevers that are relieved by being submerged into cold water or by drinking cold water. In this case, the sick person does not need any other medicine, because this type of fever is composed of heat that is connected to the soul. When a cold substance is introduced, the heat produced by the fever will be eliminated without having to get rid of any mixtures of substances or to wait for these substances to mature.

Galinus, one of the renowned doctors, admitted that cold water helps relieve this type of fever. He stated in the tenth article in his book, Healing Methods, "If a young, healthy man, who does not suffer from an internal tumor, took a bath in the heat of the day or swam in it, he will gain a benefit." He also stated that he used to prescribe this remedy on a regular basis.

Also, Ar-Razi said in his book, Al-Kabir:

> *"If the strength is normal, but the fever is very intense and the maturity (of the harmful substances) is apparent, while not suffering from any internal tumors or any type of ruptures, then drinking cold water becomes beneficial. If the ailing person is fat, the weather is hot and the person is used to taking cold showers, let him do just that."*

In the Prophet's statement: "The fever is a breath of Juhannam's fire." There are two possible meanings.

First, the fever is a breath that was released from Hell so that the slaves are aware of it and thus learn a lesson from this fact. Therefore, Allāh has created reasons and causes for the fever to appear and breakout. Similarly, comfort, joy, enjoyment and elation are a part of Paradise's joys that Allāh has allowed to appear in this world as an example and a lesson, and He has allowed such feelings to be connected to reasons and causes behind their appearance.

Secondly, the *Hadith* equated fever and the heat of day, to the intense heat of Hellfire, so that our hearts could imagine the intense torment of the Fire and the heat that emits from it.

The Prophet's statement, 'Cool it off with water' might entail all types of water, and this is the correct opinion. Another opinion states that the water here means *Zamzam* water. Supporters of this opinion used as evidence what Al-Bukhāri narrated in his Sahih that Abu Jamrah, Nasr bin 'Imran Adh-Dhuba'i said, "I used to be in the presence of Ibn 'Abbās in Makkah until one day, I was struck by fever. He said to, 'Cool it off with Zamzam water, for the Messenger of Allāh said:

$$« الحمَّىٰ مِن فَيْحِ جهنمَ »$$

"Fever is a breath of Hell's fire."
therefore, cool it with water, or said with Zamzam water."'

The narrator of the *Hadith* was in doubt as to the exact words of the Prophet ﷺ. Otherwise, it would be established that the Prophet meant *Zamzam* water for the people of Makkah, because it is available. All others can use whatever water is available to them.

There is a difference of opinion concerning if the Prophet ﷺ meant by this *Hadith* to encourage giving away some water as a charity, or to actually use it. The correct opinion is that the *Hadith* means using it. I believe that those who thought the *Hadith* means giving away some water as a charity did not understand the goal behind using cold water for fever. Yet, there is a good explanation for the Prophet's statement, for the reward is of a type comparable to the deed. Since thirsty people drink cold water to quench their thirst, Allāh dissipates the fever with cold water, as well. Yet, this is an implication of the Hadith, as for the ruling contained in it, it simply means to use the water (not give it away in charity).

Abu Nu'aym said, Anas رَضِيَ اللهُ عَنْهُ narrated that the Prophet ﷺ said:

« إِذَا حُمَّ أَحَدُكم: فَلْيُرَشَّ عليه الماءُ الباردُ ثلاثَ ليالٍ مِن السَّحَرِ »

"If any of you comes down with fever, let him sprinkle cold water on himself for three consecutive nights before daybreak."

Ibn Mājah narrated that Abu Hurairah related from the Prophet ﷺ that he said:

« الحُمَّى مِن كِيرِ جهنمَ؛ فَنَحُّوهَا عَنكُم بالماءِ الباردِ »

"Fever is a bellow of Hell's heat, so remove it from you with cold water."

It is also narrated in the *Sunan* that Abu Hurairah رَضِيَ اللهُ عَنْهُ said:

"Fever was mentioned in the presence of the Messenger of Allāh and a man cursed it. The Messenger of Allāh said,

« لا تَسُبَّهَا؛ فإنها تَنْفِي الذنُوبَ كما تَنفِي النارُ خَبَثَ الحَدِيدِ »

'Do not curse it, for it removes the sins, just as fire removes the impurity of the iron." [Also refer to Sahih Muslim].

Fever is usually followed by a diet avoiding improper foods and requires consuming beneficial foods and medicines. The sick person's body will be cleansed from all impurities and septic elements and materials, having a similar purifying effect as the fire has when it removes the impurity of the iron. The benefits that fever has are already known to the medical authorities.

As for cleansing the heart from its ills and impurities, only doctors of the heart (this does not refer to cardiologists-Editor) have access to this type of knowledge. Such experts will find that whatever the Prophet ﷺ stated in this regard is the plain truth. However, when the heart's ills become chronic, hope diminishes that it will ever be cured!

Fever thus helps the body and the heart. Therefore, cursing such a beneficial matter would be an act of injustice and transgression.

Abu Hurairah رَضِيَ الله عَنْهُ said:

"No ailment that I might suffer from is dearer to me than fever, because it enters every organ of my body, and Allāh gives each organ its due share of the reward."

Therefore, using cold water to relieve fever during summer and in hot areas is beneficial, because the water would be the furthest from the rays of the sun just before daybreak (at its coolest). Also, just before daybreak the body is at its strongest, for the ailing person would have taken his due share of sleep and relaxation also they would have less polluted air to breathe. The strength of the body will be added to the strength of the medicine - water in this case - and they will both relieve the fever that is not a result of malignant tumors or septic substances or conditions. Allāh will then extinguish the heat of the fever by His will.

The Prophet's guidance on curing diarrhea

It is narrated in the *Sahihān* that Abu Sa'id Al-Khudri رَضِيَ الله عَنْهُ said:

« أن رجلًا أتى النبيَّ صلى الله عليه وسلم، فقال: إنَّ أخي يَشْتكِي بَطنَهُ، وفي رواية: استطلقَ بَطنُهُ، فقال: اسقِهِ عسَلًا. فذهب ثم رجعَ، فقالَ: قد سَقيتُهُ فلم يُغنِ عنه شيئًا. وفي لفظ: فلم يزدهُ إلا استِطْلاقًا» ... « اسقِهِ عسَلًا» ...

«صَدَقَ اللهُ وكَذَبَ بطنُ أخيكَ »

"A man came to the Prophet ﷺ and said, 'My brother is complaining about his stomach, or he is complaining about diarrhea.' The Prophet ﷺ said, 'Give him some honey.' The man went and came back later, saying, 'I have given him some honey, but it did not help,' or he said, 'It made his diarrhea worse.' He repeated this twice or three times, all the while the Prophet ﷺ continued saying to him, 'Give him some honey.' In the third or fourth time, the Prophet ﷺ said, 'Allāh has said the truth while your brother's stomach has lied.'"

Honey has tremendous medicinal value, because it washes away the harmful substances that might be collected in the veins and the intestines. Honey also dissolves excess moisture, is beneficial as a drink and as an ointment, it is of great value for the elderly, and those suffering from phlegm and cold moods or condition (chills). Honey is nutritious, softens one's bowel movement and is a good preserving agent. Also, honey reduces the bitter taste of other medicines, cleanses the liver and the chest, aids in producing urine, and dissolves the phlegm that is accompanied by coughing. When honey is consumed hot and mixed with rose oil, it cures animal bites and the effects of opium. Taking honey mixed with water helps against the bite of a rabid dog and the effects of eating poisonous mushrooms. If fresh meat is kept in honey, it preserves its freshness for three months. Likewise if gourds, cucumbers and eggplants are kept in honey, they too will be preserved.

Further, honey will keep some types of fruit fresh for six months. It preserves dead corpses, thus deserving to be called, "The true preserver." When honey is applied to someone that is infected with lice, it will kill both the lice and the eggs. Honey will also add softness and beauty to the hair while allowing it to grow longer. When honey is applied to the eye as a Kuhl, it will strengthen weak eyesight. Honey also whitens the teeth, preserves their health and the health of the gums, opens the orifice of the veins along with causing the flow of menstruation. Furthermore, licking honey on an empty stomach will help the body get rid of mucus and phlegm. It cleanses the stomach and rids it of harmful substances or mixtures, heats the stomach mildly and opens up the pores. Honey has similar effects on the kidneys, the prostate and the liver. Furthermore, honey is the least harmful sweet substance for congesting the liver and kidneys.

Adding to all these benefits that we mentioned, honey does not have any side effects, nor harm except for those suffering from bile and who should take it with vinegar to neutralize its harm.

Honey is also a food, a drink, a sweet, a remedy, a type of refreshment and an ointment, along with its numerous medicinal values. Therefore, there is no other substance that is more beneficial than honey or that even rivals its value. This is why the people of old relied on honey, for most of the books of old do not mention sugar, as this was discovered in modern times.

The Prophet ﷺ used to drink some honey mixed with water on an empty stomach. There is a wonderful secret behind this practice regarding preserving the health. Only those who enjoy sound comprehension will be able to recognize such a secret. We will mention this subject again when we explain the Prophet's guidance regarding persevering good health.

A *Hadith* [narrated by Ibn Mājah and others] stated that the Prophet ﷺ said:

« عَلَيْكُم بالشِّفَاءَين : العسَلِ والقرآن »

"Make use of the two cures: honey and the Qur'ān."

This *Hadith* joins the material and the divine cures, the medicine of the body and the soul, the earthly medicine and the heavenly cure.

Understanding these facts, let us go back to the man to whom the Prophet had prescribed honey to cure his diarrhea, which was caused by overeating. The Prophet ﷺ prescribed honey for him to rid his stomach and intestines from accumulating harmful substances or excretions that prevents the food in the stomach from being digested, because honey has a cleansing effect. The harmful, viscid substances were adhering to the stomach walls, which is similar to the material of a towel, polluting both the stomach and the food. Honey removes these substances that engulf the stomach, and it is the best cure for this condition. Honey is a potent cleanser and is effective in treating cases of diarrhea, especially when the honey is mixed with warm water.

The Prophet ﷺ repeated his command to the man to give some honey to his sick brother for a good reason. The prescribed medicine should be in sufficient doses; otherwise the ailment will not be fully cured. When the prescribed medicine is in a larger than necessary dose, it will weaken the body and cause side effects. When the Prophet ﷺ first ordered the man to give his brother honey, he did not give him a sufficient amount to cure his condition. When the man said that his brother was not cured, the Prophet ﷺ knew that the dose was not sufficient, so he told the man several times to give his brother more honey, so that the dose would reach a sufficient amount. When the sick person has several doses of honey in a sufficient amount to fight the disease, the cure occurs by Allāh's permission. Giving the correct dose of the proper medicine is a major part of the science of medicine.

When the Prophet ﷺ said to the man:

« صَدَقَ اللهُ و كَذَبَ بطنُ أخيكَ »

"Allāh has said the truth and your brother's stomach has lied."

This indicates the sure effectiveness of the honey. It also indicates that the illness remained not because the prescribed medicine was not effective, but because the stomach had a large amount of spoiled substances in it. Therefore, the Prophet ﷺ ordered the man to take more medicine because his stomach contained excessive amounts of spoiled substances.

Prophetic medicine is not similar to that offered by doctors and physicians. Prophetic medicine is indeed the effective treatment and cure provided by the revelation and the guidance of the Prophet ﷺ that is coupled with a sound and perfect mind. In comparison, the majority of remedies prescribed by other than a Prophet ﷺ are built on hypothesis, observation and experimentation.

It is a fact that many people do not benefit from Prophetic medicine, because it will help only those who acknowledge and have faith in it. Thus, they believe that it will help them and they then submit to it. If the Qur'ān, which is a cure for whatever the heart conceals, is not acknowledged and accepted with faith, it will not provide a cure for the heart. In fact, the Qur'ān will only add more evil and disease to the hearts of the hypocrites.

Prophetic medicine is only suitable for good and pure bodies, just as the Qur'ān is only suitable for righteous souls and feeling hearts. Therefore, when the people ignore Prophetic medicine, it is like ignoring the help and guidance of the Qur'ān, which is the most effective medicine. Again, when the medicine (the Qur'ān and the Prophetic medicine) do not work, it is due to the negativity in the body and soul that are not suitable for accepting the medicine, not because the medicine does not work. All success comes from Allāh.

Wherein is healing for men

There is a conflict of opinion concerning what Allāh said:

﴿ يَخْرُجُ مِنْ بُطُونِهَا شَرَابٌ مُّخْتَلِفٌ أَلْوَانُهُ فِيهِ شِفَاءٌ لِّلنَّاسِ ﴾

"There comes forth from their bellies, a drink of varying color wherein is healing for men." (16:69)

The disagreement revolves around the words "wherein is healing for men" if they refer to the drink or the Qur'ān? There are two opinions on this matter, the closest to the truth is what Ibn Mas'ud, Ibn 'Abbās, Al-Hasan, Qatadah, and the majority of the scholars stated, that these words refer to the drink. The *Āyah*, (Verse) is talking about the drink and not the Qur'ān. Adding to this fact, the Prophet ﷺ said in the previous *Hadith*, "Allāh has said the truth," as it is clear in determining that the verse is referring to the drink. Allāh knows best.

The Prophet ﷺ commanded Muslims not to enter a plague-infested area

In the *Sahihān* it is narrated that Sa'd bin Abi Waqqas رَضِيَ الله عَنْهُ asked Usamah bin Zayd رَضِيَ الله عَنْهُما about what he heard the Prophet ﷺ say concerning the plague. Usamah رَضِيَ الله عَنْهُ said that the Messenger of Allāh ﷺ said:

« الطَّاعُونُ رِجْزٌ أُرْسِلَ عَلَىٰ طَائِفةٍ من بني إسرائيلَ، وعلى مَن كان قبلكم؛ فإذا سمعتم به بأرضٍ : فلا تدخلوا عليه؛ وإذا وقع بأرضٍ - وأنتم بها - فلا تخرُجوا منها فِرَارًا مِنْهُ »

"The plague is a punishment that was sent down on some of the Children of Israel and on those who were before your time. So if you hear that it has struck a land do not enter that land, and if it breaks out in a land that you are residing in, do not go out of that area escaping from it."

Furthermore, in the Sahihān it is narrated that the Messenger of Allāh ﷺ said:

« الطاعونُ شهادةٌ لكلِّ مسلِمٌ »

"The plague is a martyrdom for every Muslim."

Linguistically, Ta'oon, the plague, is a type of disease. In medical terms, the plague is a fatal, vicious tumor that causes a very strong and painful infection, quickly turning the infected area into black, green or brown color. Soon afterwards, ulcers start to appear around the infected area. The plague usually strikes three areas, under the arms, behind the ear and the tip of the nose, and/or, the soft (flaccid) tissues of the body. 'Āishah رضي الله عنها narrated that she asked the Prophet ﷺ about the plague, and he said:

« غُدَّةٌ كَغُدَّةِ البَعِيرِ يَخْرُجُ في المَرَاقِّ والإبْطِ »

"A gland that is similar to the camel's gland and which appears in the tender parts of the abdomen and under the arms."

Doctors say that when a septic infection occurs in the soft flesh, such as under the arms or behind the ears, it is called the plague. The plague is caused by spoiled, septic blood [infected by a bug that carried the disease from infected rodents]. The infected blood spoils the part of the body that it strikes, sometimes causing blood hemorrhaging and pus. In this case, the inflicted organ sends the infected blood to the heart, thus causing vomit, unconsciousness and rapid heartbeat. Although the plague describes every infection that sends septic blood to the heart, becoming fatal sometimes, it particularity describes the infection that attacks the soft tissues of the body. Since the infected blood is septic, the various organs reject the blood, except those that have become weak. The worst types of the plague are those that strike behind ears and under the arms, because they are closer to the essential organs of the body. There is little chance to be cured from the black plague, while the red plague then the yellow plagues are the least dangerous. Since the plague breaks out in polluted areas, it is called a plague, although this word describes every epidemic, as we have stated, and as Al-Khalil has concurred.

The word epidemic is more general than the plague.Every plague is an epidemic while not every epidemic is a plague.

The plagues cause infections, ulcers and malignant growths in the areas of the body we described. It is my judgment that these are only the symptoms of the plague, since this is what doctors visibly observe, thus prompting the doctors to call them symptoms of the plague.

There are three meanings for the word plague. First: the symptoms of the disease that the doctors observe and record.

Second, the death that occurs to those inflicted by the plague, as the Prophet ﷺ said:

« الطَّاعونُ شَهَادةٌ لكلِّ مُسلِمٍ »

> *"The plague is a martyrdom for every Muslim."*

Third, the reason behind the outbreak of the plague, which is mentioned in the *Hadith*,

« إنهُ بَقِيَّةُ رِجزٍ أُرسِلَ عَلى بَني إسرائيلَ »

"The plague is the remnant of a punishment that was sent on the Children of Israel."

Also, the plague was described in another *Hadith* that:

« إنَّهُ وَخْزُ الجنِّ »

"It is a result of the Jinn's touch."

Further, the Prophet ﷺ said that the plague is:

« أنهُ دَعوةُ نبيٍّ »

"A Prophet's supplication."

The doctors cannot refute the reasons we have mentioned explaining why the plague breaks out, although they feel that there is no physical proof that supports them. The Messengers informed us of matters of the Unseen, while the doctors' expertise deals with the physical symptoms of the plague. However, the symptoms of the plague that doctors are familiar with do not provide them with any material evidence that the plague does not engage the soul in some manner, for there is a tremendous connection between the soul and what the body suffers due to disease and ultimately death. Only the most ignorant people will deny the effects of the soul on the body and on human nature as a whole. Allāh gives the soul certain powers over the body of the sons of Adam, at such times when an epidemic breaks out or when the air is unhealthy. Also, the soul has certain effects on the body when it experiences the ailments that are caused by septic substances, especially when blood, semen or black bile is irritated. Evil forces take control of the body when it experiences such emotions and ailments, unless the person repels it with an even stronger power, such as remembering Allāh, supplicating to Him, invoking and pleading to Him, giving in charity and reciting the Qur'ān. In this case, angels will descend and will defeat and neutralize the evil effects of the devilish souls (evil forces). We have successfully tried this method many times, that which only Allāh is Able to count, and we witnessed the wonderful effects of such positive forces (good souls) in strengthening one's resolve and ridding him of bad elements when in the early stages. This method almost never fails.When one feels that evil is close-by him, he should turn to good deeds as we have explained, so that they deter and fend off the evil forces (souls). This is the best medicine in such cases for those whom Allāh leads to success. But when Allāh decides that His appointed destiny takes over, He draws the slave's heart away from knowing and intending to perform these good deeds. In this case, the slave does not decide or intend to perform these good deeds, so that what Allāh has decided takes over.

Allāh willing, we will elaborate further on this subject when we discuss the divine remedies of Islamic prayer formulas (*Ruqya* literally: incantations), the Prophet's supplications, the various types of *Du'ā* (supplications and prayers), specific forms of remembering Allāh and performing righteously good deeds. We will also affirm that comparing Prophetic medicine to regular medicine is just like comparing folk medicine to that provided by doctors, as some of the best doctors have conceded. We will also elaborate on the fact that bodies are more affected by the soul and that Islamic prayer formulas and supplications are better and more powerful than the most powerful medicines; that they can even neutralize the effect of deadly poisons.

We must reemphasize the fact that unhealthy air plays a major role in causing the plague. Air becomes unhealthy when it becomes polluted because of septic materials or pollutants, no matter what time of year, although it usually happens in the latter part of the summer and in the autumn. This is because during these times of the year (and when the air is most polluted), acute bilious excretions will accumulate during the summer, yet would not have matured by the end of the season. In autumn, the air is usually cold and thus the immature excretions that accumulated in the summer will heat up and start to get spoiled and decayed, thus causing putrid illnesses. This is especially the case when the body is ready to accept such ailments, being inactive and having abundant septic materials, both of which rarely spare the body from ailments.

We should state that the best season of the year is spring especially regarding the air. Hippocrates said, "Autumn carries the worst types of ailments and deadly sicknesses. Spring, on the other hand, is the best season and has the least occurrences of death." Pharmacists and those who prepare dead bodies for burial usually borrow money during spring and summer, rather than autumn. This is because to them, autumn is their spring that they are eager for its coming and feel happy when it starts (due to the increased number of deaths in the autumn).

It was reported in *Hadith* that:

« إذا طَلَع النَّجْمُ: ارْتَفَعَت العَاهَةُ عن كلِّ بَلَدٍ »

"When the Najm (literally: star) appears, every epidemic is removed from every land."

The *Najm* is said to mean the star, or the plants that appear in spring.

﴿ وَٱلنَّجْمُ وَٱلشَّجَرُ يَسْجُدَانِ ﴾

"And the herbs (or stars) and the trees both prostrate themselves (to Allāh)." (55:6)

Meaning during spring, because it is the season when the trees are at their prime and thus the epidemics are removed.

As for the *Najm* (North star in this case), ailments intensify when it rises and then sets just about dawn. At-Tamimi said in his book, 'The Secret of the Existence', "The worst two times of the year and the most harmful for the body are: when the North star sets just before dawn, and when it appears from the east before the sun rises on the world. This is the time when spring is about to end. Yet, the harm that occurs when it appears is less than the harm caused by its setting." Further, Abu Muhammad bin Qutaibah said:

"Whenever the Pleiades (in astronomy, the star cluster was named by the ancient Greeks after the "Seven Sisters" of mythology, the Arabs called it Atharaiya) rises or sets, it brings about an epidemic for people and camels. Yet, its setting is worse than when it is rising."

There is a third opinion regarding the meaning of the *Hadith*, that is, the star means the Pleiades and the epidemic is that which attacks the plants and fruits during winter and in the beginning of spring. When the star rises, the plants will be safe from such epidemics during that time. This is why the Prophet ﷺ disallowed selling or buying fruit before it is apparent that they are good.

The Prophet ﷺ commanded Muslims not to enter a plague-infested area and to remain in the infected area

Once there was an outbreak of the plague where one happened to be. This is the best type of prevention, for when one enters a plague infested area, he exposes himself to the risk of infection and harm. Exposing oneself to such danger defies religion and a sound mind. Staying away from plague infested areas is a type of prevention that Allāh has directed and guided the people to. In this case, one observes a form of diet or prophylactic by avoiding contaminated areas and air.

As for the Prophet's prohibiting the Muslims from escaping from the epidemic infested area, it has two possible meanings.

1. Encouraging the heart to depend and rely on Allāh while observing patience and being content with what Allāh has decided.

2. The best medical authorities say in order to avoid becoming sick during an epidemic requires helping the body to get rid of harmful fluids and moisture, observing a diet and preserving the body's dryness in general, they warn against sports activities and taking baths. The human body usually contains harmful substances that are idle and which sometimes become activated by sports and taking a bath. They would then mix with the beneficial substances in the body and cause several ailments. Therefore, when the plague strikes a land, the best thing one can do is to remain idle in that land, so that the harmful substances in his body are not aroused or irritated. Leaving the plague-infested area requires motion and physical effort, both of which are very harmful in this case.

These are the statements of the best medical authorities of old and present, helping to shed light on the correctness of the Prophet's commands that assure the wellbeing of the heart and body.

If someone asks, "When the Prophet ﷺ said: 'Do not abandon it and take flight,' Refutes the meaning that has been stated. Leaving the infested land for another purpose than escaping, such as travelling, is exempt from the prohibition."

We answer this question by stating that no person, whether a doctor or otherwise, said that all types of motion is prohibited when the plague strikes a land, for the people cannot act as if they were fixed objects. Rather, engaging in excessive physical movements and activities that are not necessary is discouraged during the outbreak of an epidemic. There is no reason behind abandoning the plague-infested land other than escaping from the plague, whereas being idle and calm are better for the people's hearts and bodies in this situation. Also, staying inactive satisfies the required dependence and reliance on Allāh and submitting to His decisions. As for those who need to move about, such as hired hands, manufacturers and travelers, they are not required to remain completely inactive, but to refrain from any unnecessary movements such as traveling to escape the plague.

There is a great wisdom behind commanding the people to remain in the plague-infested area, as follows.

1. Avoiding harm and the paths that might lead to harm.

2. Preserving one's health, which is the vehicle that people rely on to acquire life's necessities and to fulfil the requirements of the Hereafter.

3. So that the people do not fall sick upon breathing polluted and contaminated air.

4. Avoiding close association with those afflicted with the plague, so as not to catch the plague themselves.

5. Preserving the body and soul from contamination and superstition, which only harms those who believe in it.*

In short, prohibiting entering plague-infested areas is a preventive measure and a type of diet (prophylactic) that leads away from the paths of harm. Prohibiting leaving the area where the plague has struck entails submitting to Allāh's will and decisions. The first order teaches and trains, while the second order entails submission and referring all matters to Allāh's will.

"Umar رَضِيَ الله عَنْهُ was on his way to Ash-Sham when he reached the area of Sargh where he met Abu Ubaydah bin Al-Jarrah رَضِيَ الله عَنْهُ with some people. They told 'Umar رَضِيَ الله عَنْهُ that there was a outbreak of the plague in Ash-Sham. They disputed among each other about what to do. So 'Umar رَضِيَ الله عَنْهُ said to Ibn 'Abbās رَضِيَ الله عَنْهُما, 'Summon the

---

* **Editor's note**: The medical concept of quarantine was not yet established at the time of our author although this *Hadith* preceded the author by approximately 700 years. This *Hadith* established quarantine through faith before the knowledge required was available to medical scholars even seven centuries later.

early Migrants.' Ibn 'Abbās رَضِيَ الله عَنْهُما said, 'I summoned them and they also disputed, as some of them said (to Umar) you went out for a certain purpose and we recommend that we do not go back until it is fulfilled.' Other Migrants said, 'You have the best of the people in your company and the remainder of the Companions of the Messenger of Allāh ﷺ. Therefore, we do not recommend that you send them towards the epidemic.' 'Umar said, 'Go away from here.' He then said, 'Summon Al-Ansar for me.' I (Ibn 'Abbās) summoned them and Umar asked for their opinions. The Ansar disputed just as the Migrants disputed and copied their behavior. 'Umar said, 'Go away from here.' 'Umar then said, 'Summon whoever is present from the leaders of Quraish from those who embraced Islam in the aftermath of the Fath (conquering of Makkah).' I (Ibn 'Abbās) summoned them and no two among them disputed, as they all said, 'We recommend that you go back with the people and do not expose them to the epidemic.' 'Umar then ordered the people to leave, saying, 'In the morning, I will be riding on my animal's back, and so you too should.' Abu 'Ubaydah bin Al-Jarrah said, O leader of the believers! Do you run away from Allāh's appointed destiny?' Umar said, 'I wish that somebody else had uttered these words, O Abu 'Ubaydah! Yes, we run away from Allāh's appointed destiny to Allāh's appointed destiny. If you had a herd of camels that arrived at a valley that has two slopes, one fertile and the other barren and you let your camels graze on the fertile slope, you will do so by Allāh's leave, will you not? And if you allow them to graze on the barren slope, you will do so by Allāh's Leave, will you not?' Soon after, Abdur Rahman bin 'Awf came back from attending to some of his needs and said, 'I have knowledge regarding this matter. I heard the Messenger of Allāh ﷺ said:

« إذا كان بأرض وأَنْتُمْ بها : فلا تخرُجوا فِرارًا منه ؛ وإذا سمعتم به بأرضٍ : فلا تَقْدَموا عليه »

"If you hear about it (the plague) in a land that you are in, do not run away from it, and if you hear that it broke out in a certain land, do not enter that land." [Al-Bukhāri, Muslim, Abu Dawud, At-Tirmidhī, An-Nasa'ī, Ibn Mājah and Ahmad].

The Prophet's remedy for dropsy

In the *Sahihān* it is narrated that Anas bin Malik رَضِيَ الله عَنْهُ said:

> "Some people of (the tribes of) 'Ukl and 'Uraynah tribe came to
> Al-Madinah and its climate did not suit them. So the Prophet ﷺ
> ordered them to go to the herd of camels reserved for charity, and
> to drink their milk and urine (as a medicine). So they went as
> directed. After they became healthy, they killed the shepherds of
> the Prophet's camels and drove away all the camels, thus
> becoming aggressors against Allāh and His Messenger ﷺ. The
> Prophet ﷺ sent (men) in their pursuit and they were captured.
> The Prophet ﷺ then ordered that their hands and feet to be cut
> off (and it was done), and their eyes were branded with heated
> pieces of iron. They were then kept in the sun until they died."

The proof that these people were complaining from dropsy, is from Imam Muslim who narrated in his *Sahih* from the same *Hadith* above that the Bedouins said, "We have not found Al-Madinah suitable for us and our stomachs swelled, our organs became weak..." until the end of the *Hadith*.

Dropsy is a physical disease that occurs when a harmful cold substance penetrates the external organs of the body and also the body organs other than those that are used in digestion, causing them to swell. There are three types of dropsy: in body tissue (fleshy), which is the most serious of the three, in a body cavity (ascites), and in an organ (drum). The remedy required for this disease includes mild laxatives and diuretic medicines that help rid the body of fluids. These diuretic qualities exist in the milk and urine of camels and that is why the Prophet ﷺ ordered them to drink them. Camel milk is a mild laxative, diuretic, cleanses and opens that which is closed and removes the obstructions and soothes the body. This is especially the case when the camels graze on beneficial herbs, such as wormwood, lavender, chamomile, daisy and lemongrass. These herbs help against dropsy.

Dropsy is usually symptomatic of an ailment in the liver, especially due to congestion in the liver. The milk of the Arabian camels helps in this

case, because of its many benefits as mentioned and which help open
the clogged passages and the obstructions. Ar-Razi said, "The she-camel's
milk soothes the liver and the effects of a spoiled constitution." Al-Israili
also said, "The she-camel's milk is the softest, least concentrated and
lightest milk. It is the best choice for moving the bowels, as a laxative
and for opening the clogged passages and obstructions. What makes this
evident is the fact that this type of milk is mildly salty, as a result of the
animal's instinctively hot nature. Therefore, the she-camel's milk is the
best remedy for the liver as it soothes it, opens its pores and veins and
softens the hardness of fresh food. Fresh, warm camel's milk is beneficial
against dropsy, especially when taken with fresh, warm camel urine, thus
making the combination more salty and adding strength to its
effectiveness in dissolving harmful fluids and as a laxative. If the
[combination of milk and urine] did not purge the stomach, then one
should take a stronger laxative.' The author of Al-Qanon also
commented, "Do not listen to those who claim that milk does not
provide cure from dropsy. Rather, know that camel's milk is an effective
cure, because it cleanses gently and easily, due to its other qualities. This
type of milk is so beneficial that if a person substituted water and food
with camel's milk, he would be cured [from dropsy and other ailments].
Some people tried this remedy and were soon cured. We should state
that the best camel urine is that of the camels of Bedouin people."

The story that was mentioned in the last Hadith has several areas of
interest, as follows. The Hadith encourages the use of medicines and
cures. The Hadith also indicates the purity of the milk of the animals that
Muslims are allowed to eat, for using what Allāh has prohibited in
medicine is disallowed. Further, the people mentioned in the Hadith
were not commanded to rinse their mouths or their clothes for the
prayer, although they were new Muslims [indicating that rinsing the
mouth and the clothes in such cases is not necessary]. The Prophet ﷺ
cannot delay the necessary details of a religious command when such
elaboration is necessary. Also, this story emphasizes the fact that the
aggressor is punished by the same method he transgressed. The people
mentioned in the Hadith killed the shepherd and branded his eyes, as
evident in another narration of this Hadith by Imam Muslim. The Hadith
also mentioned that the entire group was killed for killing one person.
Also, this story indicates that whereas the aggressor deserves to be

punished for multiple crimes, one punishable according to the law of equality and the other for an act of aggression, then both laws are applied. The Prophet ordered that the hands and feet of the aggressors be cut off, as a punishment from Allāh for their audacious raid and aggression. They were also killed because they had killed the shepherd. Also, the *Hadith* indicates that when armed aggressors steal money and also commit murder, their hands and feet are cut off, and they are then executed. The *Hadith* also indicates that the punishment for multiple crimes is multiplied, because the people who were mentioned in the story reverted from Islam, killed a human being, disfigured the dead shepherd, stole other people's property and announced their armed aggression. Also, the entire armed band mentioned in the story were executed, not only those who actually committed the murder, as the Prophet ﷺ did not consider this fact, nor did he ask about who actually committed the murder. Furthermore, assassination warrants capital punishment and cannot be pardoned [by the relatives of the deceased] or compensated, according to the scholars of Al-Madinah and the *Mathhab* of Imam Ahmad, which our Shaikh (Ibn Taymiyyah) has chosen.

The Prophet's guidance on treating wounds and cuts

In the *Sahihān* it is narrated that Sahl bin Sa'd رَضِيَ الله عَنْهُ was asked about how the Messenger's injuries in the battle of Uhud were treated. Sahl said, "The Prophet's face was injured, his tooth was broken and the helmet he was wearing was smashed on his head. Fatimah رَضِيَ الله عَنْها, the daughter of the Messenger of Allāh ﷺ, was washing the blood off while 'Ali رَضِيَ الله عَنْهُ was pouring water on her hands with his shield. When Fatimah رَضِيَ الله عَنْها realized that the bleeding did not stop, she took a burned mat (of palm leaves) and inserted the ash in the wound of Allāh's Messenger and the bleeding stopped." The ashes of burnt palm leaves are very effective in stopping bleeding, because it is a strong drying agent and because it has the least burning effect (on the exposed skin). Other strong drying remedies have a burning effect on the skin and cause the blood to be irritated and the bleeding to intensify. Further, when the ashes of palm leaves are applied alone or mixed with vinegar in a bleeding nose, it will stop the bleeding. The author of *Al-Qanūn* said, "Al-Baradii (Papyrus) is effective in stopping bleeding and coating exposed flesh when it is placed on a wound. In old Egypt, paper was made of the

Baradii, which has a cold, dry condition. Baradii ash is effective in treating oral fungus and infection, hemoptysis (spitting up blood) and also prevents malignant infections from spreading."

The Prophet's guidance using honey, cupping and cauterizing as remedies

Al-Bukhāri narrated that the Prophet said:

« الشِّفاء في ثَلاثٍ: شَرْبَةِ عَسَلٍ، وشَرْطةِ مِحْجَمٍ، وكَيّةِ نارٍ. وأنا أَنْهَى أُمَّتِي عنِ الكَيِّ »

"There is cure in three substances, a drink of honey, a slash with a knife used for cupping and cauterizing by fire. I forbid my Nation from cauterizing by fire."

Abu 'Abdullāh Al-Maziri said, Plethoric (excessive substances) conditions are either sanguineous (bloody), bilious, phlegmy, or melancholic. Curing sanguineous plethora entails extracting the blood. If plethora was from the other three types, its cure is in softening the stool as warranted for each disease. The Prophet ﷺ has indicated that honey is used as a laxative and that cupping is used to extract [septic] blood. Some people said that when the slash by a cupping knife does not work, the last resort is branding by fire (cauterizing). The Prophet ﷺ mentioned branding by fire as a last resort when the body has a strong resistance against medicine, rendering it ineffective. The Prophet ﷺ then said: "I forbid my Ummah (Muslim Nation) from branding by fire (cauterizing)," and in another narration, "I do not like to be branded by fire." Cauterizing by fire should be the last resort and only used when warranted. The fire should not be the first choice because of the intense pain it causes and which will be used to remove a lesser pain!

Some doctors said that diseases related to the temperament are either material or non-material. The material types are either cold, hot, wet or dry or a combination of these conditions. The four conditions, hotness and coldness are effected, while the other two, wetness and dryness, are usually affected. When one of the two effective temperaments is stronger than the other, it is usually accompanied by one of the affected temperaments. Every type of temperament in the body has two parts, effective and affected.

Temperamental ailments are usually caused by whichever effective condition is stronger, hotness or coldness. The Prophet's statement directs us to the origin of ailments, hotness and coldness. If the ailment was hot, the cure entails extracting the blood by cupping or puncturing the veins, both of which help extract the septic matter, cooling the temperament. If the ailment is cold, we treat it with heat, such as by taking honey. If we also need to extract the cold material that has caused the ailment, honey also helps in this case because it leads the various substances to maturity along with its other qualities of cleansing, softening, soothing and purging the affected organs. In this case, the septic material will be gently extracted while saving the body the annoyance of using strong laxatives.

Physical ailments are either acute, not needing cauterization because they would soon be neutralized, or chronic ailments, for which cauterizing the proper organ is the best remedy after extracting the septic substances. Chronic diseases usually result from thick, cold septic substances residing in the affected organ, ailing it, spoiling its constitution and, thereby, inflaming the parts of the body that are directly connected to the affected organ. Therefore, cauterizing should be used to dissipate and extract the septic substances in the affected organ with fire.

The *Hadith* explains treatments for all type of physical ailments, just as we learned the treatment method for all simple ailments (accompanied by fever) from the *Hadith*,

« إنّ شِدَّةَ الحُمى مِن فَيْحِ جَهنمَ، فَأَبْرِدُوهَا بالمَاءِ »

"The heat of the fever is a breath of the Hell Fire; cool it with water."

Cupping continued

As for cupping, Ibn Mājah narrated in his *Sunan* that the Messenger of Allāh ﷺ said:

« مَا مَرَرْتُ ليلةَ أُسريَ بِي بمَلَإٍ، إلا قالُوا: يَا مُحمَّدُ؛ مُرْ أُمتكَ بالحِجامةِ »

"During the night of Isrâa' *(the overnight journey from Makkah to Jerusalem and then to the heavens), every company (of angels) that I passed by would say, 'O Muhammad! Order your nation to*

use cupping.'''

Also, in the *Sahihān* it is narrated that the Prophet ﷺ once had his blood cupped (medically) and paid the person who applied the cupping.

Further, in the *Sahihān* it is narrated:

Abu Taybah cupped Allāh's Messenger ﷺ, who then ordered that Abu Taybah be paid one *Sā'* (a measure pertaining to food) of dates and ordered his masters to reduce his tax (as he was a slave and had to pay a tax to them). The Prophet ﷺ then said:

« خيرُ مَا تَدَاوَيْتم بِه الحِجَامة »

"Cupping is among your best remedies."

The benefits of cupping include cleansing the exterior parts of the body more than puncturing the veins

Venesection, or puncturing the veins, is better when used to extract blood from the internal parts of the body. Cupping entails removing blood from the various parts of the skin.

Using either cupping or puncturing the veins depends on the time of year, the area, the age and state of the ailing person. For instance, cupping is more beneficial than puncturing the veins in warm areas, warm weather and hot tempered people, whose blood is near maturity (concerning the septic substances in the blood). In this case, the septic, maturing blood will collect near the skin. Cupping extracts the septic blood more efficiently than puncturing the veins. This is why using cupping for children and those who cannot bear puncturing the veins is better and more useful.

Doctors affirm that cupping is better used in warm areas than puncturing the veins and that cupping is preferred in the middle of the month or soon after, especially in the last quarter in the month. In the beginning of the month, the blood will have already become irritated (thus carrying septic materials that need to be cupped). In the end of the month, the blood will be idle, unlike the case in the middle and last quarter of the month when the blood is agitated and sufficiently produced.

The author of *Al-Qanūn* said, 'Cupping is not preferred in the beginning of the month, because the body's various conditons will not be agitated then, nor is it preferred in the end of the month, because by then the conditions would have decreased. Cupping is preferred in the middle of the month when the substances (of the constitution, or condition) accumulate and become agitated.' It was reported that the Prophet ﷺ said:

« خيرُ مَا تَدَاوَيْتم بِه الحِجَامة »

"Cupping and puncturing the veins are your best remedies."

This *Hadith* is directed at the people of Hijaz and warm areas in general, for their blood is delicate and circulates closer to the surface of the skin, while the pores on their skin are wide and their strength weakened (i.e., during summer). Puncturing the veins is harmful for them. Puncturing of each of the veins usually has a special benefit. For instance, puncturing of the basilic vein (the large vein running on the inner side of the upper arm) is useful against the heat of the liver and spleen and various blood-related tumors in these two organs. It is also useful for tumors of the lungs (emphysema), arterial pulsation, pleurisy and all blood-related diseases of veins in the lower part of the knee to the hip. Further, puncturing of the median vein helps against the various swellings that appear throughout the entire body, especially when the swelling is blood-related, and contains spoiled blood in general. In addition, puncturing of the arm's vein helps against the ailments in the head and neck that result from excessive amounts of blood or from septic blood. Puncturing of the jugular vein helps against the ailments of the spleen, asthma, thoracic cavity and forehead pain.

Cupping the upper section of the back helps against the aches of the shoulder and the throat. Further, cupping the two jugular veins helps against the ailments of the head, face, teeth, ears, eyes, nose and throat, if these ailments were caused by excessive presence of blood, soiled blood or both.

Anas رَضِيَ الله عَنْهُ said:

« كَانَ رَسُولُ الله صلى الله عليه وسلم يَحْتجِمُ فِي الأَخْدَعَيْنِ والكَاهل »

"The Messenger of Allāh used to apply cupping on the two jugular veins and the upper part of the back." [Abu Dāwud, At-Tirmidhî, Ibn Mājah, Ahmad and Al-Hakim].

"The Messenger of Allāh ﷺ used to apply cupping on three areas, his upper back area and the two jugular veins." [Al-Bukhāri and Muslim].

It is also narrated in the Sahih that the Prophet ﷺ used cupping on his head when he was in a state of Ihrām (for Hajj or Umrah) due to a headache.

In addition, Abu Dāwud narrated that Jabir رَضِيَ الله عَنْهُ said that the Prophet ﷺ used cupping on his hip because of a debilitation he suffered from.

Doctors have conflicting opinions regarding cupping on the nape cavity

Some doctors approved of this form of cupping, saying that it helps against exophthalmos, the abnormal protrusion of the eyeballs, the heaviness in the eyebrows and the eyelids and against eyelid mange. A Hadith states:

« عَلَيْكُم بالحِجَامة في جَوْزِةِ القَمَحْدَوَةِ؛ فإنَّها شِفاءٌ مِنَ اثْنَين وسَبِعين داءً »

"Use cupping on the nape cavity, for it cures seventy two kinds of ailments."

Further, it was narrated that when Ahmad bin Hanbal needed cupping on the nape cavity, he did it on the two sides of the nape but not on the cavity itself.

The author of the Qanūn also disliked cupping the cavity of the nape saying that, "It causes forgetfulness just as our Prophet Muhammad ﷺ has stated. This is because the back of the brain is the location of the memory power and cupping it affects that power."

Other people did not approve of his opinion though, saying that the Hadith that he referred to is not authentic. They said that even if the Hadith is authentic, cupping weakens the brain if cupping occurs without a necessity that warrants it. When warranted, cupping the nape cavity is medically and religiously useful against the pressure of the blood on the cavity. Authentic narrations have stated that the Prophet ﷺ used cupping in many areas on the back of his neck and in other areas of his body as much as was needed.

Cupping under the chin helps against toothache, face ailments and throat infections when used at the proper time

Cupping under the chin also cleanses and purifies the head and the jaws. Further, cupping on top of the foot substitutes for the puncturing of the saphena, which is a vein on the heel. This kind of cupping also helps against the ulcers that occur on the thighs and legs, the interruption of monthly periods and skin irritation on the testicles.

Cupping on the lower part of the chest helps against spots, sores and mange on the thigh. It also helps against gout, hemorrhoids, elephantiasis and itchiness on the back.

When is cupping preferred

Anas رَضِيَ الله عَنْهُ related from the Prophet ﷺ that he said:

« كَانَ رَسُول الله صَلَّى الله عليه وسلم: يَحْتَجِمُ فِي الأَخدَعَين والكَاهل؛ وَكَانَ يَحتَجِم لِسَبعة عَشَر، وَتسعَة عَشَر، وَفِي إحدى وَعِشرين »

"The Messenger of Allāh ﷺ used to have cupping on the jugular veins and the upper part of the back on the seventeenth, nineteenth or twenty-first (day of the month)." (At-Tirmidhi)

Anas رَضِيَ الله عَنْهُ related from the Prophet ﷺ that he said:

« مَن أراد الحجَامة: فَليَتَحَرَّ سَبعةَ عشرَ، أو تسعَةَ عَشرَ، أو إحدى وَعِشرين؛ وَلَا يَتَبَيَّغْ بأحدكم الدمُ، فَيقتلَه »

"Those who intend to have cupping let them do that on the seventeenth, nineteenth or twenty-first (of the month), to prevent the septic blood from causing death to one of you." (Ibn Mājah)

Also, Abu Dāwud narrated that Abu Hurairah رَضِيَ الله عَنْهُ related from the Prophet ﷺ that he said:

« مَن احتجم لِسبْعَ عشرةَ، أو تسعَ عشرةَ، أو إحدى وعشرين -: كانت شِفاءً من كلِّ داءٍ »

"Those who have cupping on the seventeenth, nineteenth or twenty-first will be cured from every disease."

"Every disease" mentioned in the *Hadith* means the blood-related diseases. [Both of the last two Ahadith are weak].

These Ahadith conform to the position taken by doctors that cupping is preferred in the latter half of the month and the third quarter, rather than the beginning or the end of the month. However, if cupping is necessary, it will be useful during any part of the month including the beginning and the end. It was reported that Imam Ahmad Ibn Hanbal used to practice cupping during any part of the month when the spoiled blood became agitated.

The author of Al-Qanūn said, "Cupping is preferred during the day, the second or the third hour and after one takes a bath. When warranted, one should take a bath then rest for an hour or so and then use cupping." Cupping is not preferred when the stomach is full, for it might cause various ailments, especially after taking a heavy meal.

It was said that cupping on an empty stomach is a cure, and when one's stomach is full is a disease, and when it is done on the seventeenth [of the month] it becomes a remedy. Choosing the best time for cupping preserves good health and helps prevent harm from occurring to the body. However, when the illness intensifies, cupping becomes warranted and needed whatever the circumstances, for the Prophet ﷺ said:

《 لا يَتَبَيَّغْ بأحدِكم الدمُ، فيقْتُلَهُ 》

"So that the septic blood does not cause death to one of you."

We stated before that Imam Ahmad used to use cupping during any time of the month if cupping was medically warranted.

As for the best days of the week to have cupping, Al-Khallal said that Imam Ahmad was asked about the days when cupping is not preferred, and he said, "Wednesday and Saturday." Also Al-Khallal narrated that Imam Ahmad was once asked about the days when cupping is disliked and Imam Ahmad answered, "Saturday and Wednesday, and also Friday as was reported." [However, all the Ahadith that state the time when the cupping is either preferred or disliked are weak, according to the scholars of Hadith].

The previous Ahadith we mentioned state that seeking the cure, including cupping, is preferred. Also, cupping is done in the part of the body that most needs it. In addition, those who have assumed Ihrām are allowed to use cupping, even if it involves cutting some hair and they do not have to pay a penalty. Further, it is allowed for those who are fasting to use cupping as Al-Bukhāri narrated that the Messenger of Allāh ﷺ used cupping while he was fasting.

There are several *Ahadith* that state that cupping breaks the Fast. The only *Hadith* that appears to contradict this ruling is the Hadith that the Prophet ﷺ had cupping while fasting. In this case, for the *Hadith* to mean that cupping does not break the Fast, it should satisfy one of the following four conditions.

First, Fasting should have been obligated by the time the incident in the *Hadith* [narrated by *Al-Bukhāri* above] occurred. Second, it should be proven that the Prophet ﷺ was not traveling [when he had cupping]. Third, that the Prophet ﷺ was not suffering from an illness that warranted cupping. Fourth, that this *Hadith* came after the Prophet ﷺ said, "Those having cupping and those who do it have both broken their Fast." If these four conditions are satisfied, only then can we say that cupping does not break the fast relying on the *Hadith* [that the Prophet ﷺ had cupping when he was fasting]. Otherwise, the Fast mentioned in the Hadith might have been a voluntary fast that one is allowed to break when cupping is warranted. Or it could have occurred during Ramadān but while the Prophet ﷺ was traveling. Or, the *Hadith* could be talking about a compulsory Fast during Ramadān but that it was necessary to have cupping due to an illness. Or, cupping could have been done during Ramadān and without a necessity that warrants it, but before the Prophet ﷺ issued his statement that cupping breaks the Fast of those involved in it. There is no proof that any of the four conditions we mentioned above were satisfied, so how about all four of them? [That is why Ibn Al-Qayyim asserts that cupping breaks the Fast of those who are doing it and those who are having it done].

Also, the *Hadith* proves that one is allowed to hire a doctor for a certain purpose and then pay him for his services without a service contract.

The *Hadith* [that the Prophet ﷺ paid the person who performed cupping for him] also indicates that some people are allowed to make cupping their profession. The Prophet ﷺ gave the man who performed cupping some money and that person spent that money on his necessities. Furthermore, cupping is similar to garlic and onion in that they are described as being impure. But we are still allowed to use them.

Finally, the *Hadith* proves that one is allowed to collect reasonable taxes from his slave and that the slave is allowed to use whatever is left after paying the tax. Otherwise, if the master is going to take all the money anyway, it will not be called a tax any more! Therefore, whatever is left with the slave beyond the required tax is his property and he can do whatever he wishes with it.

The Prophet's guidance regarding cauterization and puncturing of the veins

"Jabir bin 'Abdullāh عَنْهُ اللهُ رَضِيَ narrated that the Prophet ﷺ once sent a doctor to Ubay bin Ka'b and that the doctor used puncturing on one of Ubay's veins and then cauterized the wound." (*Al-Bukhāri*)

Further, when Sa'd bin Mu'ādh was injured in his medial arm vein, the Prophet ﷺ had it cauterized and then cauterized again when the wound became swollen. In another narration of this *Hadith*, the Prophet cauterized Sa'd bin Mu'ādh in his medial arm vein using the tip of an arrow. Afterwards, Sa'd bin Mu'ādh, or someone else, cauterized the wound again. Another narration states that one of the Ansar was injured in his medial arm vein and the Prophet ordered that he be cauterized. [These *Ahadith* are narrated by *Muslim*, Abu Dāwud, and others].

Abu 'Ubayd also narrated that a man, who was prescribed cauterization, was brought to the Prophet ﷺ and the Prophet ﷺ ordered that he be cauterized. Then hot stones were applied on the wound to close it. Also, Jabir narrated that the Prophet ﷺ once cauterized him in his medial arm vein.

Al-Bukhāri narrated that Anas عَنْهُ اللهُ رَضِيَ said that he was once cauterized because he was complaining from pleurisy while the Prophet ﷺ was still alive. At-Tirmidhī also narrated that Anas عَنْهُ اللهُ رَضِيَ said, "The Prophet ﷺ cauterized As'ad bin Zurarah when he came down with a septic finger."

We have mentioned that the Prophet ﷺ said in the *Hadith* narrated by *Al-Bukhāri* and *Muslim*,

« وَمَا أُحِبُّ أن أَكتوِيَ »

"I do not like to be cauterized."

and in another narration:

« وأنا أَنْهَىٰ أَمّتِي عن الكَيِّ »

"I forbid cauterizing for my Nation."

Further, [At-Tirmidhī, Abu Dāwud and Ahmad] narrated that one of the Companions said that the Prophet ﷺ has disallowed cauterizing, "But we were tested (i.e., with various ailments) and we did have cauterization, so we neither were successful nor did we acquire an advantage."

Al-Khattabi commented, "The Prophet ﷺ only cauterized Sa'd to stop the bleeding, because he feared that bleeding would not stop until Sa'd died. Cauterization is usually used in drastic cases, such as when a hand or a leg is amputated. As for prohibiting cauterizing, it might be specifically directed at whoever was seeking a cure with it (not to close an open wound). In early times, the people used to superstitiously believe that whoever did not have cauterization would certainly die and this is why the Prophet ﷺ disallowed it. It was also said that the Prophet ﷺ disallowed 'Imran bin Husayn in particular from using cauterization because he was suffering from a sore in a delicate place. That is why the prohibition could be specific to cases where cauterizing is dangerous. Allāh knows best.

Further Ibn Qutaybah said that cauterizing is of two types. The first type entails a healthy person using cauterization to fend off illness and it is this type that is referred to by the statement, 'Whoever reverts to cauterizing would not have practiced *Tawakkul* (depending on Allāh),' as such people seek to fend off whatever is destined for them in the future. The second type entails cauterizing infected wounds and amputated limbs, and cauterization is effective in these cases. As for the type of cauterization that might or might not work, it is apparently disliked.

There is a *Hadith* narrated in the *Shahihān* [Al-Bukhāri and Muslim] about the seventy thousand Muslims who will enter Paradise without reckoning, describing them as:

« إنهم الذينَ لَا يَسْتَرْقُونَ، وَلَا يكتَوُونَ، ولا يتطَيَّرُونَ؛ وعَلى ربهم يتوكَّلُونَ»

"They are those who do not seek prayer formulas (Ruqyah literally

incantations), nor cauterization, nor are they superstitious, and they depend on their Lord (for each and everything)." [Also narrated by *At-Tirmidhī, An-Nasa'ī* and *Ahmad*].

In short, the *Ahadith* that discussed the subject of cauterization fall under four categories: practicing it, disliking it, praising those who do not revert to it and disallowing it. There is no contradiction between these categories. When the Prophet ﷺ had someone cauterized, he indicated that practicing it is allowed. Further, the Prophet's disliking cauterization for his *Ummah* (Muslim Nation) does not indicate that it is prohibited. In addition, the Prophet's praising those who avoid cauterization indicates that avoiding it is better. Finally, disallowing cauterization can either be explained that in general, cauterization is disliked, or that it is directed at those who revert to cauterizing to fend off a future illness. Allāh knows best.*

---

* **Editor's note**: *Ruqyah* (incantations / prayer formulas) and cauterization were practiced in pre-Islamic times based on superstitions, it was these practices that the Prophet ﷺ stopped. The benefit in these practices was rehabilitated by Islam and they were practiced only when necessary in the correct way according to Islamic law, without superstition. *Ruqyah*, Islamic prayer formula, is recited for a certain number of times according to the specific *Ruqyah* or Islamic prayer formula. The one reciting the Islamic prayer formula will spit (without saliva) after each recitation on the target of the prayer formula. This is a standard Islamic practice to preserve spiritual and physical health.

There is another point that needs to be clarified and that concerns the word prayer. What we call prayer in English has two different words to describe it in Arabic. *Salat*, the formal prayer with specific movements and *Du'a*, the informal prayer in which one asks the Creator for what they want in their own words or according to formulas set by the Prophet ﷺ or the Qur'ān. One of the pillars of Islam is the five daily prayers. This is a formalized system of praying that has specific movements and times. In Arabic this is called *Salat*. The other form of prayer, when we ask Allah for anything, in our own words or in prayer formulas set by the Prophet ﷺ or by the Qur'ān, is called *Du'a*. This form of prayer is sometimes referred to as supplication in English, which is a very good word to describe this form of prayer. The only problem with translating *Du'a* as "supplication" is that the word "supplication" is very formal and rarely used in verbal communication. *Du'a* is used constantly throughout the day. Any English speaking person who is continuously calling on God, will describe what they are doing as praying, which is the simple common way to describe this act. When we call *Ruqyah* (literally incantations) Islamic prayer formulas, we are using the word prayer in its informal meaning (*Du'a*) and not the formal meaning (*Salat*).

The Prophet's guidance on treating epilepsy and spiritual possession*

In the *Sahihān* it is narrated that 'Ata bin Raba'h said, "Ibn 'Abbās رَضِيَ اللهُ عَنْهُما said to me, 'Should I tell you about a woman from among the people of Paradise?' I said, 'Yes.' He said, 'That black woman, who came to the Prophet ﷺ and said, 'I suffer epileptic fits during which I inadvertently take off my clothes. So invoke Allāh on my behalf.' He said,

« إنْ شِئْتِ صَبَرْتِ ولكِ الجنةُ؛ وإن شئتِ دعوتُ اللهَ لكِ أن يُعافِيَكِ »

'If you wish, be patient and you will acquire Paradise; and if you wish, I will supplicate to Allāh to cure you.'

She said, 'Rather, I will observe patience.' She then said, 'I keep taking off my clothes during these fits, so supplicate to Allāh for me that I do not do so. The Prophet ﷺ supplicated (to Allāh) on her behalf.'"

Epilepsy is two kinds, one that results from negative forces and the second type is physical that results from bad mixtures (chemical and material imbalance). The doctors often talk about the second type and explain its causes and how to cure it.

As for the epilepsy that results from negative forces, the best doctors and the wise ones among them affirm that it exists. They also confirm that curing this type of disease occurs by the support of the righteous, exalted souls so that they neutralize the effect of the evil and render its efforts harmless. When Hippocrates explained the cures for epilepsy he stated that, "These cures are effective in treating the epilepsy that results from chemical and material causes. As for the epilepsy that results from negative forces, these remedies (that he explained and detailed) do not cure it."

As for the most ignorant, unknowing and immoral doctors, and those

---

* **Editor's note:** The name of epilepsy in Arabic is *Sarâ*; It is derived from the word *Sara'a* meaning to knock down, strike down, or bring to the ground. This is the classic symptom of epilepsy and thus in Arabic its name was derived from it. Possession by evil spirits or jinn, which requires exorcism for its cure, has the same classic symptom and was called by the same name. Epilepsy in Arabic therefore is described as being of two types, the classic physical epilepsy and spiritual possession.

who consider heresy a virtue, they deny the type that occurs by negative forces and deny that it has any effect on the body. They have only ignorance to support them, because the medical authorities cannot actually disprove the epilepsy that is caused by these negative forces. Fact and experience assert and prove the existence of this type of epilepsy. That is why when the doctors explain the reason behind epilepsy as being natural or physical, their statement is true regarding some types of epilepsy but not all of them.*

The doctors of old used to call epilepsy, 'The divine disease', stating that it is caused by negative forces. On the other hand, Galinus and other doctors misinterpreted the term divine ailment, saying, "They called it divine because it attacks the head and thus causes harm to the apparent divine organ where the brain resides." This explanation, however, resulted from their ignorance of the soul and its effects.

As for the heretical doctors, they only confirm the kind of epilepsy that results from physical causes. Whoever has a sound mind and good knowledge of the soul and its effect, will laugh at the ignorance shown by these doctors and at their weak minds.

Curing the type of epilepsy caused by negative forces has two parts, a part that involves the person afflicted with epilepsy and a part that involves those who treat them.

The part that the person afflicted with epilepsy plays in his treatment involves strengthening his heart and being sincere in repentance to the Creator from the negative forces and seeking sincere refuge with Him both by heart and tongue. This is a type of warfare that the person afflicted with epilepsy engages in against evil. To defeat the enemy, warfare requires the warrior to acquire beneficial, suitable weapons and to have a strong arm. When one of these two elements does not exist, the effort will not be very effective. The situation becomes more difficult when the person is missing both essential requirements, in this case, the heart will be lacking Tawhid (Oneness of Allāh), Tawakil (trusting in Allāh), Taqwa (righteousness), and Tawajhu (awareness of Allāh's Presence), plus the person does not have sufficient material armament.

---

* **Editor's note**: The author is referring to a type of spiritual possession.

The second part of epilepsy treatment involves the person who is treating the ailment and who is also required to have the same necessary weapons mentioned above. When these weapons are ready, one sometimes merely needs to say (to the evil spirit), 'Get out of him,' or, 'In the Name of Allāh,' or, 'There is no power nor strength except with Allāh.'

The Prophet ﷺ used to say in such cases:

« أُخْرُجْ عَدُوَّ اللهِ؛ أَنَا رَسُولُ اللهِ »

"O enemy of Allāh, Depart! I am the Messenger of Allāh."

I once witnessed our Shaikh (Ibn Taymiyyah, the renown Imam of Islam) send someone to speak to an evil spirit that had possessed a person, saying, "The Shaikh says this to you: get out of this body for you are not allowed therein." The person afflicted with epilepsy (possession) then woke up from his seizure. Sometimes, our Shaikh would even speak to the evil spirit directly, or would use physical punishment to repel the rebellious evil spirit. When the patient would wake up, he would not feel any pain, as we have ourselves witnessed on numerous occasions. The Shaikh would sometimes read the following *Āyah*, verse, in the ear of the person afflicted with epilepsy (possession),

﴿أَفَحَسِبْتُمْ أَنَّمَا خَلَقْنَاكُمْ عَبَثًا وَأَنَّكُمْ إِلَيْنَا لَا تُرْجَعُونَ﴾

"Did not think that We had created you in play (without any purpose), and that you would not be brought back to Us?"
(23:115)

The Shaikh once told me that he read this *Āyah*, verse, in the ear of the person afflicted with epilepsy and that the evil spirit that possessed him answered by saying, 'Indeed,' extending her voice (mocking the Qur'ān). So the Shaikh said, "So I took a stick and beat the sick person on his neck with it until my hands became tired. Those present did not doubt that the patient would die from this severe beating.

While beating the patient, the she-devil said, 'I love this person.' I said, 'But he does not love you.' She said, 'I want to accompany him to perform *Hajj*. I told her, 'He does not want to go to Hajj with you.' She said, 'I will leave him in your honor.' I said, 'No, but as an obedience to Allāh and His Messenger ﷺ.' She said, 'Then, I will leave him alone.' The patient then woke up and started looking around, saying, 'What brought me to the presence of the Shaikh?' They asked him, 'What about the beating you took?' He said, 'Why would the Shaikh beat me while I have not done anything wrong?' He had no idea that he had been beaten.'''

Further, the Shaikh used to recite *Ayat Al-Kursi* [2:255] and would order those who suffer from and those who cure epilepsy (possession) to recite it along with the last two chapters of the Qur'ān [113 and 114].

In general, no one can deny the type of epilepsy that is caused by negative forces except those who have little knowledge and comprehension. We should also state that the majority of those afflicted by the touch of evil spirits are themselves in error due to weak Faith and hearts and tongues that don't remember Allāh, they fail to seek refuge with Him and they fail to use Prophetic guidance, (supplications and remedies). The evil spirits find the people that are vulnerable and take advantage of them.

If the truth was uncovered, we would discover that the majority of mankind is under the influence of negative forces which guides the people according to their evil wishes. The people are unable to set themselves free from this control or even oppose it. Most people suffer from this common type of possession (epilepsy), from which the afflicted person cannot wake up. And unless the veil that obstructs their sight is removed, they will not realize that it is they who are actually afflicted by epilepsy. We seek Allāh Alone for His help.

Curing (epilepsy) possession that results from the touch of evil requires the cooperation of a sound mind and sincere faith in what has been sent down to the Prophets عليهم السلام. Then one would act as if both Heaven and Hell are right in front of his eyes and heart. They would remember that the people of this earthly life suffer calamities and trials that come down on their homes just as the rain does, all the while being unaware of what is going on around them.

The epilepsy that evil causes is truly severe, but since it touches so many people and is so common, the people are no longer surprised by it. Since they are so many, it is strange to see someone who is not touched by it.

When Allāh wills that a certain slave should acquire what is good for him, that slave will wake up from these fits of epilepsy and will realize that the children of this life are suffering from epilepsy. He will discover that some of them have surrendered to insanity and that some of them might briefly recover from a bout to fall back into another bout soon after. Some of them would be awake from a bout and would act like sane people, but when he falls into another bout, he would act confused. [This is the state of those who do not have the correct Faith.]

The epilepsy that results from physical causes

This type of epilepsy alters the constitution and is accompanied by spasms that prevent the limbs from functioning normally or from normal movements. The physical or constitution related epilepsy occurs due to the accumulation of thick, viscous substances near the brain that partially obstructs the cerebral cavities. In this case, the area of the brain responsible for the senses and the various movements are impeded, and accordingly, the organs (including limbs) of the body suffer from the same condition. There are other causes for this type of epilepsy, such as the accumulation of thick flatulence that impedes the soul in some manner, or a viscous vapor accumulates in an organ of the body and ascends to the brain, or from an acute ailment. The brain suffers from spasms due to fighting the harmful substances that are affecting the brain, and accordingly, the various organs of the body suffer from spasms. The person will not be able to stand up straight for very long he or she will fall down and foam accumulates in and around the mouth.

This type of epilepsy causes intense pain during seizures. It is also a chronic illness that is hard to cure and that remains for many years, especially if the person afflicted by it is more than twenty-five years old, who repeatedly falls into epileptic fits. Hippocrates said that epilepsy remains with such people until they die.

As for the woman mentioned in the Hadith who suffered from epilepsy and who used to take off her clothes because of epileptic fits, she might have been suffering from the physical type of epilepsy. That is why the Prophet promised her Paradise if she observes patience, or otherwise, the Prophet would have asked Allah to cure her without guaranteeing her that she will be cured. She chose Paradise, but the Prophet asked Allah on her behalf not to take off her clothes during these fits.

The *Hadith* indicates that it is allowed for Muslims to forgo the use of a remedy. Furthermore, the Hadith indicates that the cure of the soul is exclusively tied to invoking Allah and turning to Him sincerely and that this type of medicine has such profound effects on the human body that no regular medicine prepared by any doctor could ever compare to it. We have tried this medicine on numerous occasions [and witnessed its success].

The best medical authorities confirm the fact the psyche has an effective role in curing disease. The medical profession suffers from some ignorant, heretic doctors who do not do service to their profession.

As we have stated, it appears that the woman mentioned in the Hadith suffered from the epilepsy that is caused by a physical condition (chemical imbalances). Yet, she might have been suffering from the type that is caused by evil negative forces. We stated that the Messenger of Allah gave her the choice to observe patience and then acquire Paradise or that he would invoke Allah to cure her. She chose the first option but asked to be relieved from discarding her clothes because of the epileptic fits.

The Prophet's guidance on curing sciatica

Ibn Mājah narrated in his *Sunan* (collection of *Hadith*) that Anas bin Malik رَضِيَ الله عَنْهُ said, I heard the Messenger of Allāh ﷺ saying:

« دواءُ عِرقِ النَّسَا : أَلْيَةُ شاةٍ أَعْرابيَّةٍ تُذابُ، ثمَّ تُجَزَّأُ ثلاثَةَ أجزاءٍ، ثُمَّ تُشرَبُ
على الرِّيقِ: في كُلِّ يوم جزءٌ »

*"Curing sciatica is accomplished by melting the fat from the tail of
a nomad's ewe. Then, the fat is divided into three parts and one
part per day is drunk on an empty stomach."*

Sciatica is an ailment that starts from the hip's joint, then descends to the thigh from the backside of the body. Sometimes, sciatica reaches the ankles and the longer the ailment remains, the lower it descends and the weaker the legs and thighs become.

There are two beneficial understandings in the *Hadith* mentioned, medical and linguistic.

Linguistically, the *Hadith* proves that we are allowed to call this ailment a '*Irq* (nerve) *Nasa* (sciatic nerve), to the contrary of the opinion of some people. They said that the *Nasa* is the nerve itself and thus the two words together are redundant.

Answering this claim takes two forms. First, the word *'Irq* (nerve) is more general than the word *Nasa* (sciatic nerve). Hence the term *'Iraq An-Nasa* gives the general and the specific meanings desired. Second, the *Nasa* is an ailment that attacks the nerve and thus the word Nasa should be included in the name given to the ailment [as it specifies the area where the nerve is causing pain]. It was reported that the name *'Irq Nasa* is called as such because it makes the people forget (*Nasa*) any other pain. The sciatic nerve starts from the hips until the bottom of the foot from behind the ankles.

The Messenger of Allāh ﷺ, as we have noticed in previous *Ahadith*, may use two types of meanings in his expressions. One meaning may be general, for all conditions and people, while the other specific, its meaning and indications are specifically directed at some particular people or situation. The *Hadith* in this section is the specific type, it is directed at Arabs and the people of Hijaz in particular, including the Bedouins of those areas. The remedy mentioned in the *Hadith* is the best cure for the people of those areas as *'Irq An-Nasa* is caused by dryness or thick, septic accumulations. The best treatment for this ailment is using a laxative. The fat on the ewe's tail has two qualities: bringing the septic substances to maturity and softening (the stool in this case), both are required to cure *'Irq An-Nasa*.

Also, the nomad's ewe has several qualities, such as being small in size, producing lesser excrements and having a soft essence. The nomad's ewe also grazes on beneficial wild plants, such as wormwood and lavender cotton, and so forth. When the ewe feeds on these wild plants, they will mix with and soften the ewe's flesh, especially the fatty tail. Although the ewe's milk carries in it the effective ingredients of the wild plants, the tail has two qualities that the milk does not have, being a laxative and leading the septic substances to maturity [making them ready to be extracted from the body].

We mentioned before that the regular medicines and remedies of different nations and peoples is based on the type of diet that the people are used to. Indians and Bedouins have a simple diet therefore the do not use complex medicines. As for the Romans and the Greek, they use compound medicines. They all agree, however, that the best treatment for an ailment is a specific diet. Otherwise, the doctors will first prescribe simple and then compound medications, when necessary.

If the diet is simple, simple medications are suitable for the simple ailments. The compound ailments, on the other hand, usually occur due to a complex diet and this is why compound medicines are suitable in those cases. Allāh knows best.

The Prophet's guidance on treating constipation

At-Tirmidhi and Ibn Mājah narrated that the Messenger of Allāh ﷺ asked Asmā' bint 'Umais,

« بماذا كنت تَسْتَمْشِينَ ؟ قالت : بالشُّبْرُم قال : حارٌّ جارٌّ . ثم قالت :
استَمْشيْتُ بالسَّنا . فقال : لو كان شيءٌ يشفي من الموتِ لكان السَّنا »

"How do you deal with constipation?" She said, "By using Shubrum (euphorb piteous)." The Prophet ﷺ said, "(It is) hot and to strong laxative." She then said, "I also use Senna," and the Prophet replied, "If there is a cure that prevents death, it would be Senna."

Further, Ibn Mājah narrated that 'Abudllāh ibn Umm Haram said that he heard the Messenger of Allāh ﷺ saying:

« عليكم بالسَّنا والسَّنُّوت فإن فيهما شِفاءً من كلِّ داءٍ إلّا السَّامَ . قيل : يا
رسول الله وما السامُ ؟ قال : المَوْتُ »

"Use Senna and Sanoot (cumin), because they cure every disease, except Saam." He was asked, "What is Saam?" He said, 'Death'."

The Prophet ﷺ asked the woman about what she uses to treat constipation, meaning what cure she uses to help soften the stool, so that the body is able to get rid of its harmful waste.

In another narration of the *Hadith*, the Prophet ﷺ asked Asmā' about what she uses to cure constipation, and she mentioned the *Shubrum* (euphorb piteous), which is the bark of the root of the euphorbic tree and which is dry and hot in the forth degree. The best type of *Shubrum* is the one reddish in color, which is soft and feels like wrapped skin.

Shubrum is among the medications that doctors do not advise people to use because it is a very strong laxative. In the *Hadith*, the Prophet ﷺ described *Shubrum* as being hot and a strong laxative.

Senna is a plant that grows in Al-Hijaz (Western Arabia) and the best kind of it grows in Makkah. *Senna* is hot and dry in the first degree and it is a good, mild medication that does not cause any side effects. *Senna* helps against bile and black bile ailments and strengthens the heart, which is another good quality that this medication contains. *Senna* is useful against melancholic obsession and corporal incisions, relaxes the muscles and improves the hair. *Senna* also helps against lice, headache, mange, pustules, rashes and epilepsy. It is better to cook the *Senna* whole and drink three measures of its soup than cooking it crushed. Also, it is better to cook the *Senna* mixed with violet flowers and red raisins, after removing the seeds.

Ar-Razi said, "*Senna* and fumitory help extract mature humors (bodily wastes) and helps against leprosy and rashes, when one takes four to seven measures of each remedy."

As for *Sanoot* (cumin), there is a difference of opinion concerning its nature. Umar bin Bakr As-Saksaki, for instance, said that *Sanoot* is either honey or butter extract. Another opinion suggests that *Sanoot* is a seed that resembles the Kammon (cumin), as Ibn Al-'Arabi has asserted. The fourth and fifth opinions suggest that *Sanoot* is the Persian cumin or fennel, according to Abu Hanifah Ad-Daynoori. The sixth opinion suggests that it is the Shibitt (dill), and the seventh opinion suggests that it is the date, according to Abu Bakr bin As-Sunni. The eighth opinion suggests that it is honey that exists in butter-skin, according to Abdul-Latif Al-Baghdadi. Some doctors also stated that the last meaning is the most probable. In this case, the *Sanoot* is prepared by blending *Senna* powder with some honey mixed with ghee, as this is better than taking the *Senna* by itself. Then one licks the mixture that contains the *Senna*, as in this case the *Senna* taste will be made milder, because of the honey and butter, which will also assist the laxative power of the *Senna*. Allāh knows best.

The Prophet's guidance on treating skin rashes and scabies caused by mites

In the *Sahihān* it is narrated that Anas رَضِيَ اللهُ عَنْهُ said, "The Messenger of Allāh ﷺ has allowed Abdur Rahmān bin 'Awf and Az-Zubayr bin Al-'Awwam to wear silk garments because of a skin rash they had." In another narration, "Abdur Rahman bin 'Awf and Az-Zubayr bin Al-'Awwam complained to the Prophet ﷺ during a battle that they had mites, and he allowed them to wear silk garments which I saw them wearing."

There are two areas of interest regarding this *Hadith*, one in the area of *Fiqh* (Islamic Jurisprudence) and another medical.

In the area of *Fiqh* (Islamic Jurisprudence), the *Sunnah* of the Messenger of Allāh is that wearing silken garments is allowed for women and disallowed for men, except when there is a legitimate need. For instance, [men are allowed to wear silken garments] in cold weather, when one has only a silken garment to wear and when complaining from mange, rashes, mites or lice, as evident by the last *Hadith*.

According to Imam Ahmad and Shāfi'i, wearing silken garments is allowed [for men if a necessity warrants it]. The permission given to some Muslims [such as wearing silken garments for men in this case] due to special circumstances applies to all those who face similar circumstances.

Several scholars said that the *Ahadith* that disallow silken garments for men apply in general. They said that the *Hadith* (narrated above) might entail a specific permission for only 'Abdur-Rahmān bin 'Awf and Az-Zubayr. They say that it is possible, though, that this permission applies to other Muslims. When there is a probability, adhering to the general text is warranted. This is why some of the narrators of this *Hadith* commented, "I do not know if the permission applies to whoever comes after them ('Abdur-Rahmān bin 'Awf and Az-Zubayr)."

The correct opinion is that the permission is general in its indication and that there is no evidence that it is specific or restricted. Similarly, the Prophet ﷺ once said to Abu Burdah, "This permission applies to you and none else after you." Also, Allāh said to His Prophet 🌿 regarding the woman who offered herself in marriage to the Prophet 🌿:

$$﴿ خَالِصَةً لَّكَ مِن دُونِ ٱلْمُؤْمِنِينَ ﴾$$

"A privilege for you only, not for the (rest of) the believers."

Since disallowing wearing silken garments for men is a precautionary measure, it is allowed in certain situations and for a benefit that warrants it. For instance, gazing at women is disallowed as a precautionary measure, but it is allowed when there is a real need. Such is the case with disallowing performing voluntary prayers at certain times [while the sun is rising or setting], to prevent even a hint of resemblance between Muslims and sun worshippers. Yet, in some cases, it is allowed for Muslims to offer voluntary prayers during these times for a real need and benefit. We have explained the cases when wearing silken garments is allowed in our book on this subject, *At-Tabiri*.

Medically, silk is produced by an animal and is a remedy. Silk has many benefits, such as soothing and strengthening the heart and helping relieve several of its ailments. Silk also helps against black bile and whatever ailments it might cause. Further, silk strengthens the eyesight when used as eyeliner. Raw silk, which is used in preparing medications and remedies, is hot and dry in the first degree. When silk is used in clothes, it is mild and heats the body. Sometimes it could chill the body.

Ar-Razi said, "Silk is hotter than linen, colder than cotton and develops the flesh. Every type of thick clothes weakens the body and hardens the skin."

There are three types of clothes, one that brings warmth and also heats the body. Another type of clothes brings warmth but no heat to the body. The third type does not bring warmth or heat. There is no type that brings heat but not warmth to those wearing it. For instance, clothes made of wool and animal hair elevate body temperature and bring warmth to the skin. On the other hand, silk, Kittan (linen) and cotton garments only bring warmth to the skin. Kittan clothes are cold and dry, wool clothes are hot and dry, while cotton garments are moderate. Silken garments are softer and less hot than wool. The author of *Al-Minhaj* stated that wearing silk, "Does not bring as much warmth as cotton, because it is milder."

Every type of soft, polished clothes heat the body less and is less effective in helping the decomposition process. That is why it is better that this type of clothes is worn during summer and in hot areas.

Since silken garments are neither dry nor thick as the other types of clothes, they help as a treatment for skin rashes that result from dry, thick material. Hence, the Prophet ﷺ allowed Az-Zubair and 'Abdur-Rahmān to wear silken garments due to their skin rash. Also, silken garments are the least hospitable to mites or lice, for it is not the best environment where mites live and thrive.

The types of body wear that neither elevates the body temperature nor brings warmth are made of iron, lead, wood, sand, and so forth.

If one asks, "Since silk provides the best type of clothes and the most suitable for the body, why was it prohibited for men) by the Islamic legislation, which is the mot honorable, perfect legislation and which allows the good and pure things and only disallows the impure things?" We should mention that this is a question that the Muslims differ regarding its answer.

Those who deny that there is wisdom behind the Islamic legislation do not even need to answer this question.

As for those who affirm that there is a wisdom behind the Islamic legislation, who are the majority, say that Islam disallowed silken garments for men so that they observe patience and abandon wearing them for Allāh's Sake. In this case, they will be rewarded by Allāh, especially since there are other types of clothes to wear.

Some people say that silk was created for the benefit of women, such as the case with gold. Hence, silk is prohibited for men so that they do not imitate women. Some Muslims say that silk was prohibited because it leads to arrogance and pride.

Others say that silk was disallowed because of its softness on the skin that leads to feminine behavior while weakening manhood and masculinity. Hence, you rarely see a man wearing silken garments who is not affected by its softness by inadvertently imitating feminine behavior and softness, even if he was among the most masculine men. Wearing silken garments will certainly diminish the manly qualities and masculinity, although these qualities will not disappear all together. As for those who do not comprehend these facts, let them submit to Allāh's wise decisions. Finally, we should state that according to the correct opinion, young boys should not be allowed to wear silken garments, because they will acquire feminine behavior.

An-Nasa'î narrated that the Prophet ﷺ said:

$$ \text{« إِنَّ اللهَ أَحَلَّ لِإِنَاثِ أُمَّتِي الحَرِيرَ وَالذَّهَبَ، وَحَرَّمَهُ عَلى ذُكُورِها »} $$

"Allāh has allowed silk and gold for the females of my Ummah (Muslim Nation) and disallowed them for the males of my Ummah (Muslim Nation)." In another narration, the Prophet ﷺ said:

$$ \text{« حُرِّمَ لِبَاسُ الحَرِيرِ والذَّهَبِ عَلى ذُكُورِ أُمَّتِي، وأُحِلَّ لِإِنَاثِهِم »} $$

"Wearing silk and gold is disallowed for the males of my Nation and allowed for the females."

Al-Bukhāri also narrated that the Messenger of Allāh ﷺ has disallowed wearing and sitting on silken garments and *Dibaj* (pure silken clothes), and then added, "It is for them (whoever wears them among men) in this life and for you in the Life Hereafter."

The Prophet's guidance on treating pleurisy

The doctors divide pleurisy into two types, real and unreal. The first type is an infected growth that appears in the pleura that coats the ribs. The second type causes a similar pain and attacks the pleura as a result of thick, congested flatulence between the peritoneum's (smooth transparent membrane that lines the abdominal cavity and part of the pelvic region). The pain caused by the unreal pleurisy is acute while the real pleurisy causes stinging pain.

The author of the *Qanoon* said, "Sometimes, the flank (of the body), the peritoneum, chest muscles and ribs and surrounding areas suffer from an extremely painful growth called pleurisy. Sometimes, there could be pain in these same areas of the body but not as a result of growth but of accumulating harmful gasses (flatulence), and thus, the people think that it is the first type when in fact it is not."

He also said, "Know that every type of disease that attacks the side or the flank is called *Thatul Janb* (pleurisy), which is derived from the place where it appears (i.e., the *Janb*, the flank). That is why every type of pain on the side or flank is called *Thatul Janb* regardless of the cause of the ailment. This is the meaning of Hippocrates' statement that those suffering from That *Al-Janb* will benefit from taking a bath. It is said that his statement includes those who suffer from pleurisy, as well as, lung disease (pulmonary) pains that result from a bad constitution, congested conditions without tumors or fever."

Some doctors said that in Greek, the term pleurisy means the warm growth that appears on the side and also the tumors of all internal organs. The tumor of any organ is called pleurisy when it is a warm tumor only. Further, there are five symptoms that accompany the real pleurisy: fever, coughing, stinging pain, hard breathing (dyspnea) and pneumonia.

Sea-costus (Indian costus) is used to treat the unreal pleurisy. When the Indian costus is ground to fine powder, blended with hot oil and then used as an ointment on the affected area, or when the ailing person licks it, it will be a good cure for that ailment. In this case, the costus decomposes the septic substances, strengthens the internal organs and opens the obstructions or clogs. Al-Masi'hi said, "Costus is hot and dry and constipates, strengthens the internal organs, dissipates the wind, opens the clogs, helps against pleurisy and dries out excess moistures. Also, costus is good for the brain and might help against the real pleurisy, if a phlegmy substance had caused it, especially when the illness is weakening. Allāh knows best."

Thatul Janb is a dangerous disease. An authentic *Hadith* related by Umm Salamh رَضِيَ الله عَنْها reads, "The final ailment that the Messenger of Allāh ﷺ suffered from started while he was in Maymunah's house. Whenever the Prophet ﷺ felt the pain had eased, he would go out and lead the people in prayer. Whenever the pain intensified, he would say, 'Order Abu Bakr رَضِيَ الله عَنْهُ to lead the people in prayer.' The pain kept intensifying until the Prophet ﷺ lost consciousness. When the pain intensified, his wives, his uncle 'Abbās, Umm Al-Fadhl bint Al-Harith and Asmā' bint 'Umais رَضِيَ الله عَنْهم discussed among each other about giving a medicine to the Prophet ﷺ, and they did just that while he was unconscious. When he woke up, he said, 'Who did this to me. This is the work of some women who came from there, pointing to the direction of Ethiopia with his hand.' Umm Salamah and Asmā' were the ones who had administered the medicine to the Prophet ﷺ (they were among those who had migrated to Ethiopia), and they said, 'O Messenger of Allāh! We were afraid that you were suffering from *Thatul Janb*.' He said, 'What medicine did you give me?' They said, 'Some Indian costus, Wars and some drops of oil.' He said, 'Allāh would never inflict this type of disease on me.' He then said, 'I order you that every person present in this house take some of the same medicine, except for my uncle Al-'Abbās."

Further, in the *Sahihān* (Al-Bukhari and Muslim) it is narrated that 'Āishah رَضِيَ الله عَنْها said:

«لَدَدْنَا رسول الله صلى الله عليه وسلم؛ فأشار: أن لا تُلُدُّونِي. فقلنا: كراهِيةُ المَرِيض للدَّواءِ. فلما أَفَاقَ قال: ألم أَنْهَكُمْ أن لا تَلُدّونِي؟! لا يبقَىٰ مِنكم أحد إلا لُدَّ، غيرُ عَمِّيَ العباس: فإنه لم يَشْهَدْكُم»

"*We administered some medicine to the Messenger of Allāh ﷺ although he indicated that he did not want to be given medicine. But we attributed his refusal to what the sick usually feel about taking medicine. When he woke up, he said: "Did I not disallow you from giving me this medicine? Therefore, everyone present should take some of that medicine, except for my uncle Al-'Abbās because he was not with you."*

The last *Hadith* allows treating the aggressor in the same manner he treated others, as long as what the aggressor has committed is not prohibited by Allāh, and there are more than ten proofs to this ruling that we elaborated on in another book. Also, this ruling confirms the rulings of the Four Guided Caliphs and Imam Ahmad. Also, this *Hadith* indicates that reprisal for striking the face and hitting is of the same nature, as there are several *Hadith* on this subject that are unequivocal.

The Prophet's guidance on treating headaches and migraines

Headaches resemble a pain that appears in some part of the head or all of it, but when the headache attacks one side of the head, it is called migraine. The type that attacks the entire head is sometimes called a helmet, for it resembles the helmet that covers the head. Furthermore, headaches sometimes attack only the back or the front side of the head.

There are many types of headaches that result from various conditions. Headaches usually start when the head becomes hot due to the pressure of a septic vapor that accumulates near the head and which seeks a way out of the body but fails. Then, the pressure of the vapor intensifies, just as a pot when it is heated but the steam is not able to escape from it. It is a fact that when moisture heats up, it seeks more space to expand. Similarly, the vapor accumulates near the head and then causes a headache in the entire head because it is unable to expand or escape from the body as it heats up. This condition causes a type of dizziness.

There are various specific causes for headaches. First, when one of the four essential conditions (coldness, hotness, dryness and wetness) becomes predominant. Second, ulcers of the stomach cause headaches, because the cephalic (relating to the head) nerves and the stomach are connected. Third, thick flatulence might accumulate in the stomach then later ascend to the head and cause headaches. Fourth, headaches are sometimes caused by a tumor in the gastric veins that cause pain in the head, because the stomach and the head are connected. Fifth, when the stomach is full of food it sometimes provokes headaches, as some of the food remains undigested. Sixth, headaches sometimes occur after sexual intercourse because the body will then be weakened and thus exposed to the heat of the air. Seventh, headaches sometimes occur after vomiting due to excessive dryness, or to accumulating gaseous materials (flatulence) that ascend to the head from the stomach. Eighth, sometimes the hot weather and air provoke headaches. Ninth, headaches are sometimes caused by the cold weather and from the vapor that accumulates in the head and which is unable to decompose. Tenth, not having enough sleep also causes headaches. Headaches are sometimes caused due to the pressure exerted on the head, such as when one carries a heavy object on his head. Twelfth, excessive talking sometimes weakens the mind in a way that causes headaches. Thirteenth, excessive movements and sports activity can also provoke headaches. Fourteenth, sadness, depression, obsession and evil thoughts also provoke headaches. Fifteenth, excessive hunger provokes headaches, as in this case; the excess gaseous materials (flatulence) that accumulate in the stomach ascend to the brain and provoke headaches. Sixteenth, those who suffer from a tumor in the cerebral lining sometimes feel as if hammers are constantly pounding on their heads. Seventeenth, fever also provokes headaches because of the intense heat that the body suffers from them. Allāh knows best.

Headaches result from changes in the system that affects the cerebral arteries

The weaker side of the brain will accept septic material and the migraine headache will be accompanied by pulsation in the arteries. The pain could be relieved in this case when one ties a bandage so that the pulsing of the arteries is stopped and thus the pain is lessened.

Abu Naʿim said in his book on Prophetic medicine that the migraine type of headache used to attack the Prophet ﷺ and that it would prevent him from going out of his house for one or two days at a time. Also, Abu Naʿim related from Ibn ʿAbbās رَضِيَ الله عَنْهُما that he said, "Once, the Messenger of Allāh ﷺ delivered a speech while a cloth was tied around his head."

Also, the *Sahih* states that the Prophet ﷺ said during the illness that preceded his death: "O my head!" He used to tie a piece of cloth around his head.

Tying a piece of cloth around the head helps soothe the pain of headaches and migraines.

Treating headaches varies according to their type and causes

Hence, headaches could be relieved by vomiting, eating, being calm and idle, using cold rags, cooling the body, elevating the temperature, avoiding noise, etc.

Knowing these facts, we should mention that treating headaches with Henna is partial and that it treats some types of headache. If the headache is caused by high fever and not a spoiled substance that requires extraction, Henna helps soothe the headache somewhat. Crushed Henna blended with vinegar and applied to the forehead will relieve the headache. Henna also soothes the nerves when used as a bandage. Finally, Henna is not only favorable to relieve headaches, but also for the various organs of the body and for the hot tumors and inflammations when used as a bandage.

Henna is cold in the first degree and dry in the second degree

The Henna tree has two special qualities, decomposing due to its warm watery essence, and constipating due to the cold earthly essence it contains.

Henna is useful in treating burns and soothes the nerves when used as a bandage, as we have stated. When chewed, Henna helps treat the cankers and thrush that appear in the mouth. Henna also heals stomatitis (inflammation of the mucous membranes of the mouth) that appear in the child's mouth. Using the Henna to bandage hot tumors also helps, as it has a similar effect on open sores as the dragon's blood tree has on them. When the Henna flower is blended with pure wax and rose oil, it will help against the aches of the side (Thatul Janb).

When the symptoms of smallpox start to break out on children and Henna is then applied on the bottom of their feet, the eyes will be immune from the sores that accompany smallpox. Also, when the flower of the Henna is placed between wool clothes, it will perfume it and will prevent mold or mite. Furthermore, when the leaves of the Henna are submerged in fresh water, then squeezed and drunk for forty days, twenty measures each day along with ten measures of sugar while eating the meat of a young ewe, it prevents leprosy with its amazing qualities.

We were told that a man once complained from fissuring in his fingers and that he offered monetary rewards to whoever could cure him, but to no avail. Later on, a woman prescribed for him a drink of Henna for ten days but he could not stand the idea of drinking it. Later on, he soaked Henna leaves in water and drank the water and his fingers were healed and regained their beauty.

Henna is also used as an ointment for the fingers, as it polishes and strengthens them. Henna is also useful when blended with butter and then used as a bandage for the hot tumors that drain yellow residue. Henna also benefits against chronic mange, helps the hair grow, makes it stronger and also strengthens the head. Finally, Henna helps against the blisters and the pustules that appear on the legs and feet and the rest of the body in general.

The Prophet's guidance concerning feeding the sick with what they like and not forcing them to eat or drink

At-Tirmidhi and Ibn Mājah narrated that the Prophet ﷺ said:

« لا تُكرِهُوا مَرْضاكم عَلَى الطَّعام والشَّراب؛ فإن الله عز وجل يُطْعِمُهم ويَسقِيهم»

"Do not force your patients to consume food or drink, for Allāh, the Exalted and Most High, feeds them and gives them drink."

Some doctors commented, "How beneficial and true is this statement by the Prophet ﷺ that contains divine wisdom, especially for the doctors who treat patients. When the patient does not feel like eating or drinking, it is because the body is busy fighting the illness, or because the instinctive heat (or the appetite) becomes weaker. Either way, it is not allowed to give the patients food in this case."

The feeling of hunger results from the body's appetite for food so that it refuels itself with the needed energy replacing that which the body has spent. The various organs of the body will spend the available energy until it runs low on supply, the stomach will alert the person, who would then feel hungry. Food will then be distributed from the stomach to the rest of the organs of the body starting with the closest ones. When one is ill, the body will be busy maturating and getting rid of the alien, septic substances and does not require food or drink. When the sick person is forced to eat some food, the body's energy will be divided between digesting the food and concentrating on fending off the invading septic substances that caused the ailment. The patient will be harmed in this case, especially when one is suffering from acute ailments or lessening in the instinctive heat, as these conditions will only add strength to the ailment and bring about harm. The patient should only eat what is required to sustain his strength and should avoid what can aggravate his condition. The patient should consume light food and juices like nenuphar (similar to carrot), apples and tender rosewater drinks, etc. As for the types of foods the patient should consume, they should include aromatic chicken soup. Also, the patient should refresh his body with good scents and listen to good news. The doctor is the servant of nature not one who hinders it or obstructs its path.

We should state that fresh, healthy blood provides nutrition to the body. We should also know that phlegm is a type of blood that has not properly matured. Therefore, when the patient's body has excess phlegm on an empty stomach, the body will lead the phlegmy blood to maturity and then turn it into fresh blood that will supply energy to the organs of the body. The nature of the human body is the engine and vehicle that Allāh has entrusted with preserving the body and its health and guarding it throughout its term.

Sometimes, compelling the patient to eat and drink becomes warranted when the ailments involve sanity.

The *Hadith* indicates that the patient could live without nourishment for longer than a healthy person could.

The Prophet's statement: "For Allāh provides food and drink for them," entails more far-reaching implications than the doctors think. Only those who are experienced in knowledge of the heart and soul and in their effects on the nature of the body and vise versa will be able to uncover the implications of the Prophet's statement.

It is a fact that when the heart is busy with such feelings as joy, sadness or fear, it will be busy attending to these feelings, thus ignoring the need to eat or drink. In this condition, one does not feel hunger or thirst or even the cold or the heat. Rather, the body in this case will be busy attending whatever made it concerned and whatever caused it pain. Every person experiences such moods and thus would agree that when the heart is busy attending to a concern, it will not feel the need for food.

When the concern is a matter that brings joy, the feeling of elation will be a substitute for the food. Jubilation will fill the body and will energize it and the blood will be pumped to the various organs until it appears under the skin. In this case, the face will radiate with delight and life. Indeed, happy feelings relax the heart and fill the veins with blood. The organs do not require food in this case because they are busy dealing with what is even better for their nature than food. When human nature acquires what it likes, then it will disregard what is less favorable or important.

When the concern entails sadness, anguish or fear, the body will be busy attending to such concerns and will ignore seeking food in this case, because it is busy conducting its own war. When the body wins the war against such feelings, the feelings of joy will re-ignite the body's strength and will become a substitute for the regular energy through food and drink. When the war against these concerns is lost, the body will feel as low and weak as the size of defeat it suffered. If the war against such concerns is sometimes won and sometimes lost the body will feel energetic at times and weak at other times. Certainly, this type of war resembles the actual war between two enemies, where the upper hand belongs to the victorious, while defeat entails suffering casualties, dead, wounded or captured.

The sick person receives supplies from Allāh that provide nutrition for him, in addition to the nutrition that he receives through the blood which the doctors confirm. This divine help varies in amount according to the amount of submission and meekness that one shows before his Lord and which will earn him closeness to Him. The closest the slave will be to his Lord is when his heart submits to Allāh and in return Allāh's mercy will draw closer to the slave. When the slave is one of Allāh's, loyal supporters, his heart will receive sufficient support and aid that will nourish his body and strength more than the nourishment that his body receives through material nourishment. The stronger the slave's love, happiness, certainty, eagerness and contentment with Allāh becomes, the more divine strength he will feel. This cannot be described with words, nor can any doctor explain or attain knowledge of it on his own.

Those who do not have sound comprehension and thus are unable to understand the aforementioned facts, let them observe the miserable condition of whoever covets a part of the material existence, whether a picture, a position, money or knowledge. Many people have discovered amazing facts concerning their own selves and other people by deep observation.

In the *Sahih* it has been stated that the Prophet ﷺ used to continue fasting for days at a time, yet he would prohibit his Companions from imitating him, saying:

« لستُ كَهَيْئَتِكُمْ؛ إِنِّي أَظَلُّ يُطعِمني ربي ويَسقِيني »

"I am not like any of you, my Lord provides me with food and drink."

The food and drink mentioned in the *Hadith* is not the type that people eat with the mouth. Otherwise, the Prophet ﷺ would not have been continuing the Fast. Rather, the Prophet ﷺ said: "My lord provides me with food and drink," thus drawing a difference between him and the Companions in that he is able to bear what they cannot bear. If the Prophet ﷺ were talking about the regular food and drink, he would not have said:

"I am not like any of you." Those who understand regular food and drink from this *Hadith* do not have a significant supply from the true nutrition that the heart and soul require. Nor do they have knowledge of this divine nutrition's effect on the strength and revival of the body, along with providing it with the true sustenance that is much more powerful and sustaining than the material food.

The Prophet's guidance on treating tonsillitis and administering the medication orally

In the *Sahihān* it is narrated that the Prophet ﷺ said:

« خيرُ مَا تَدَاوَيْتُم به الحِجَامةُ، والقُسْطُ البَحرِيُّ ولا تُعذِّبُوا صِبْيانكُم بالغَمْزِ من العُذْرَةِ »

"Cupping and marine costus are among your best remedies; and do not torture your children by pressing their uvula to cure tonsillitis."

Also in the *Sunan* and the *Musnad* (by Imam Ahmad) it is narrated that Jabir said, "The Messenger of Allāh came to 'Āishah رَضِيَ الله عَنْها and saw a boy with a bleeding nose and said, 'What is this?' They said, 'He is suffering from tonsillitis, or a headache.' He said:

« وَيلَكُنَّ ! لا تَقْتُلْنَ أولادَكُنَّ؛ أيُّمَا امرأةٍ أصاب ولدَها عُذْرةٌ أو وَجَعٌ في رأسِه: فَلْتَأْخُذْ قُسطًا هِنْدِيًّا، فلْتَحُكَّهُ بماءٍ ثم تَسْعُطْهُ أيَّاهُ. »

"Woe unto you! Do not kill your children. Let the mother whose child is suffering from tonsillitis or headache scrub Indian costus (aloes) with water and then administer it to the child through the nose.'

When 'Āishah رَضِيَ الله عَنْها ordered that the prescription be followed, the boy was cured." [Ahmad, Al Hakim, Abu Ya'la and Al-Bazzar].

Abu 'Ubaidah said, "Tonsillitis, according to Abu 'Ubaidah, is a blood related throat irritation." It was also said that tonsillitis is an ulcer that appears between the ear and the throat that especially afflicts young boys.

Administering scrubbed aloes through the nose helps against tonsillitis, which is essentially composed of blood related phlegm that accumulates in the bodies of young boys. Costus or Aloes tighten the uvula and pulls it up to its proper place. Aloes also help against other hot ailments. The author of *Al-Qanoon* stated that costus, Yemeni alum and marjoram seeds help against tonsillitis.

The marine costus mentioned in the *Hadith* is the Indian aloes, particularly the one whitish in color, and it is sweet and has many benefits. Before, the people used to treat their children who suffered from tonsillitis by pressing the uvula and sometimes affixing an object to the uvula. The Prophet ﷺ disallowed this practice and guided the people to what is better, more beneficial and easier for the afflicted children.

Administering the medicine through the nose involves either simple or compound remedies that are ground and dried. Then, when warranted, the medication is administered through the nose of the afflicted person while he lay on his back and while his shoulders are elevated so that the head lay back. In this position, the medication would reach the head and extract the disease by sneezing.

The Prophet ﷺ has praised using this method when there is a need that warrants it. Further, Abu Dāwud mentioned in his *Sunan* that the Prophet ﷺ used this method himself.

The Prophet's guidance on treating diseases of heart

Abu Dāwud narrated that Sa'd said, "Once, I became ill and the Messenger of Allāh ﷺ came to visit me and placed his hand on the center of my chest, until I felt its coldness on my heart. He then said:

« إِنَّكَ رجُلٌ مَفْؤُودٌ؛ فأْتِ الحارثَ بْنَ كَلَدَةَ من ثَقِيفٍ، فإِنَّه رجلٌ يتطبَّبُ؛ فَلْيأُخُذْ سبعَ تَمَراتٍ من عجوَةِ المدينةِ. فليجأُهُنَّ بِنَوَاهُنَّ، ثم لَيَلُدَّكَ بهنَّ »

"You are complaining from your heart. Go to Al-Harith bin Kaladah, from (the tribe of) Thaqhif, for he knows about medicine. Let him take seven dates from Al-Madinah, grind them with their seeds and then give them to you."

Dates in general and dried dates in particular, especially from Madinah, posses tremendous qualities and are especially effective in treating heart aliments. Using seven dates is another quality that can only be known through the revelation.

In the *Sahihān* it is narrated that Sa'd bin Abu Waqqas said, "The Messenger of Allāh ﷺ said:

« من تصبَّحَ بسَبْعِ تَمَراتٍ من تَمْر العَالِيةِ، لم يضُرَّهُ ذلك اليومَ سُمٌّ ولا سِحْرٌ»

"Whoever eats seven dates from the area of Al-Aliah when he gets up in the morning then no poison or magic would harm him that day."

In another narration, the Prophet ﷺ said:

«مَن أكَلَ سبعَ تمَراتٍ ممّا بَيْن لَا بَتَيْها، حينَ يُصْبِحُ، لم يَضرَّهُ سمٌّ حتّى يُمسيَ»

"Whoever eats seven dates produced between the two areas in Al-Madinah that are covered with burned black stones in the morning, will not be harmed by poison until he reaches the night."

Dates are warm in the second degree and dry in the first degree. Dates constitute a good type of nutrition, especially for those whose regular diet contains dates, such as the people of Al-Madinah. Dates are the best type of food for the residents of the hot and mildly warm countries, more so than for the residents of cold areas who have an elevated inner temperature, whereas those in warm areas have a colder inner temperature. This is why the people in Hijaz, Yemen and Tai'f, and similar areas, eat hot foods such as dates and honey. They also use pepper and ginger in their food more than other areas; sometimes ten fold as much. Some of them even eat *Zanjabil* (ginger) just as other people eat sweets. They even transport these types of foods with them when traveling. As we have stated, these types of food are suitable for the residents of warm areas and do not harm them because of the lower inner temperature of their bodies. On a similar note, we should mention that well-water becomes colder during summer and warmer during winter. Further, the stomach digests because thick (or complex) foods in winter more than during summer.

For the people of Madinah, dried dates are their staple like wheat is to other people. Also, dried dates from the area of Al-'Aliyah in Madinah are one of the best kinds of dates because they are firm, delicious and sweet.

Dates are a type of fruit that is also used for its nutritional and medicinal value, being favorable for most bodies and for their role in strengthening the natural heat. Also, dates do not produce harmful wastes or excrements such as the other types of foods and fruits. Rather, dates preserve the bodily wastes from being spoiled and from rotting, especially for those used to eating dried dates.

The *Hadith* we mentioned about dried dates [in the beginning of the chapter] is specifically for the people of Al-Madinah and surrounding areas. It is a fact that the medicinal value of the herbs and plants that grow in certain areas is closely related to the quality of the air and the type of soil in those areas. A certain medicinal herb might be useful in its natural habitat but not if it is grown elsewhere. The various lands differ in their nature and characteristics, just as people differ from each other. Sometimes, a certain type of plant might be a regular staple in the diet in a certain area, while it is poisonous in other areas. Sometimes, certain remedies that people use in a certain land might be a regular staple for other people in another area. Some types of medicine might provide a cure for some illnesses for some people while curing other kinds of diseases for other people. Furthermore, there might be a beneficial cure in some area that does not work in other areas.

Using seven dates has a spiritual and material significance. Allāh has created seven heavens, seven earths, seven days in the week and made the creation of mankind pass through seven stages. Also, Allāh made the *Tawaf* seven circumambulations, and the *Sa'i* also seven trips between Safa and Marwah. Also, the Jamrat are stoned with seven pebbles each and the Takbir during the 'Eid prayer is made seven times. In addition, the Prophet ﷺ said about young children,

« مُرُوه بالصَّلاة لسَبْعٍ »

"Command him to pray upon reaching the age of seven."

Also, when the child reaches the age of seven, he is given the choice between his father and mother, according to some opinions. When the Prophet ﷺ was ill he ordered that water be poured on him from seven different water skins. Allāh has also sent the destructive wind on the people of 'Ad for seven consecutive nights. The Prophet of Allāh ﷺ also asked Allāh in supplication to test his people with a similar seven years of famine that the people of the Prophet Yusuf (Joseph) عليه السلام were tested with. Furthermore, when Allāh gave the example of charity, He compared it to a grain (of corn); it grows seven ears, and each ear has a hundred grains. Also, the ears of corn that the king saw during the time of Prophet Yusuf (Joseph) عليه السلام were seven and the number of the years during which the king's people would farm the land was also seven. Also, charity is multiplied seven hundred times, to much more. Further, there are seventy thousand members of the Muslim Nation who will enter Paradise without questioning. The number seven has a special significance more than other numbers and only Allāh has full knowledge of the wisdom behind choosing this number above other numbers.

The *Hadith* mentioned that eating seven dates from a certain area in Al-Madinah prevents poisoning and magic, indicating the special qualities of this type of date. Had it been Hippocrates or Galinus who issued this statement rather than the Prophet ﷺ, the doctors would quickly accept the statement without question, even though they would be issuing it based on guessing and not on fact. The statements that come from the Prophet ﷺ, whose words are certainly true and divinely revealed, deserve to be believed in more and submitted to, without any hesitation or denial.

The dried dates mentioned in *Hadith,* being useful against certain poisons and only in some areas

Further, we should state here that it is a condition that the sick person should believe that the medicine will help him, so that his body accepts it and benefits from it. It is a fact that sometimes merely believing that the medicine will work helps cure some ailments, as many people have witnessed in this regard. When the heart accepts that a certain medicine carries the cure, the body will feel an elevation in its strength and in the instinctive heat that will help the body get rid of and extract harmful substances. On the other hand, sometimes an effective medicine fails to work because the patient does not believe that it will cure him, and consequently, his body neither accepts it, nor benefits from it.

Even the Qur'ān, which is the best, most beneficial remedy ever, both in this life and in the Hereafter, and which is a cure for every disease, will not benefit the heart that does not believe in its value as a cure and a remedy. Rather, the Qur'ān only adds more disease to such evil hearts.

There is not a more effective cure for the diseases of the heart than the Qur'ān, for it completely eradicates the ills of the heart, preserves the heart's health and wellbeing and defends it against all that might bring harm to it. Yet, most of the hearts ignore the Qur'ān and do not believe in it, and thus refrain from using it. Instead, such people refer to other types of medicine that were prepared by their like from among mankind, thus preventing their hearts from benefiting from the Qur'ān. Consequently, the symptoms that attacked their hearts will persist and will expose their hearts to even more ailments. By the passage of time, both the doctors and the patients will get used to the medicines produced and prescribed by their like, leaders, or those whom they respect. In this case, disasters will accumulate and the diseases will become harder to cure. And the more they (those who ignore the Qur'ān) use these medicines, the more strength they will add to the ailment!

The Prophet's guidance on neutralizing the harm of various foods and fruits

In the *Sahihān* it is narrated that 'Abudllāh bin Ja'far رَضِيَ اللهُ عَنْهُ said, "I saw the Messenger of Allāh ﷺ eat ripe dates with cucumbers."

Ripe dates are hot in the second degree, increase sexual desire and add strength to the cold stomach. But, ripe dates rot quickly, bring thirst, harm the teeth, spoil the blood and cause headaches, various clogs and pain in the prostate. Cucumbers are cold and wet in the second degree and they prevent thirst, have a refreshing aroma and cool the stomach. When the seeds of the cucumbers are dried then crushed and are boiled with water, they produce a drink that will quench the thirst, help produce urine and soothe the pain in the prostate. When cucumber seeds are crushed and then sifted, it will whiten the teeth when brushed with it. Further, when cucumber plant leaves are crushed and blended with raisin jelly and used as a bandage, they will help against the bite of the hydrophobic dog.

In general, dates are hot while cucumbers are cool, and each is suitable for the other and also neutralizes each others harm. This is a type of balancing off the harm of one substance by combining it with its opposite or antidote, and these are the goals that preventive science seeks to achieve. In fact, these are the goals that the science of medicine as a whole seeks to achieve.

Combining the foods or medicines with their antidotes or opposites makes the product milder and rids it of any harmful side effects. Consequently, the body will preserve its health, strength and wellbeing.

'Āishah رَضِيَ اللهُ عَنْها once said, "They tried to make me fatter using every type of food, but I did not get fatter. But when they fed me ripe dates and cucumbers, I became fatter."

In short, neutralizing the effect of the hot substance with the cold, the cold with the hot, the dry with the wet and the wet with the dry produces a milder substance that is considered among the best remedies and preventive measures. We mentioned before the Prophet's guidance concerning blending *Senna* and *Sanoot* (honey and butter) and stated that this method will make the *Senna* milder. May Allāh bestow His peace and blessings on he who was sent with all that brings life to the hearts and bodies and what brings about their benefit in this life and the Hereafter.

The Prophet's guidance on observing a diet as part of the cure

All types of cures and medicines contain either a certain diet or preventive measures. When one feels ill, he will need to rid the body from harmful substances and bodily wastes. These three elements are what medicine is all about.

There are two types of diet, a diet from what might bring an illness and a diet from what might intensify the illness. The first type of diet is for the healthy and the second type is for those with an illness. When the patient observes a certain diet, the illness will not progress and thus the powers contained in the body will cooperate and collaborate towards ridding the body of the ailment.

The most basic element regarding the diet is what Allāh said:

﴿ وَإِن كُنتُم مَّرْضَىٰٓ أَوْ عَلَىٰ سَفَرٍ أَوْ جَآءَ أَحَدٌ مِّنكُم مِّنَ ٱلْغَآئِطِ أَوْ لَٰمَسْتُمُ ٱلنِّسَآءَ فَلَمْ تَجِدُواْ مَآءً فَتَيَمَّمُواْ صَعِيدًا طَيِّبًا ﴾

"And if you are ill, or on a journey, or one of you comes after answering the call of nature, or you have been in contact with women (by sexual relations) and you find no water, perform Tayammum with clean earth." (4:43)

Allāh has saved the sick person from using water when there is a chance that it might harm him.

Ibn Mājah narrated that Umm Al-Munthir bint Qays said, "The Messenger of Allāh ﷺ came along with 'Ali رَضِيَ الله عَنْهُ who was then recovering from an illness. At that time, we had some hanging clusters of dates. The Messenger of Allāh ﷺ started eating from them and then 'Ali رَضِيَ الله عَنْهُ joined him. The Messenger of Allāh kept saying to 'Ali عَنْهُ: You are still recovering, 'until 'Ali رَضِيَ الله عَنْهُ Stopped eating.' I then made some barley and chard (similar to spinach) and brought it to them. The Prophet ﷺ said, to 'Ali, 'Eat from this food, it is more beneficial for you." In another narration, the Prophet ﷺ said, "Eat from this food for it is more suitable in your condition." [*Abu Dāwud, Ahmad* and *Al-Hakim*].

Also, Ibn Mājah narrated that Suhayb said, "I came by the Messenger of Allāh ﷺ and found that there were some dates and bread in front of him. The Prophet ﷺ said, 'Come closer and eat.' I picked up some dates and started eating from them. Then the Prophet ﷺ said, 'Do you eat dates while you are suffering from conjunctivitis (an inflammation of the covering membrane of the eye)?' I said, 'O Messenger of Allāh, I am chewing on the other side.' The Messenger of Allāh then smiled.'" [*At-Tirmidhi* and *Al-Hakim*].

In another *Hadith*, the Prophet ﷺ said:

$$ \text{« إنَّ اللهَ إذا أحبَّ عبدًا : حماه من الدُّنيا . كما يَحْمِي أحدُكم مريضَه عن} $$
$$ \text{الطَّعام والشراب» « إن الله يَحْمِي عبدَه المُؤْمن مِنَ الدنيا»} $$

"When Allāh loves a slave, He helps him observe a diet from the life of this world, just as one of you puts his patient on a diet from food and drink. Allāh puts His believing slave on a diet from the life of this world."

The famous statement that: "Diet is the top medicine; and the stomach is the home of disease; give each person what he is used to [of food and medicine]," this is not a *Hadith*, according to the scholars of *Hadith*. Rather, it is the words of Al-Harith bin Kaladah, the renowned Arab doctor.

Al-Harith stated that, "Diet is the head of medicine." To doctors, observing a diet by healthy people is as harmful as unhealthy eating habits for patients. Consequently, the best type of diet is that observed by those recovering from an illness, because until then, their body organs would not have regained their normal strength and wellbeing. In this condition, the digestion process would not be at its normal efficiency while the various organs of the body would still be prone to sickness. At this time unhealthy eating habits might cause the disease to come back stronger than it was before.

Know that the Prophet's disallowing 'Ali رَضِيَ الله عَنْهُ from eating the hanging clusters of dates while still recuperating from an illness is one of the best preventive measures. Fruits are not beneficial for sick or recovering patients as they get digested quickly at a time when the body is still fighting the ailment and is not strong enough to deal with an excess amount of food. Ripe dates in particular are heavy on the stomach at a time when the body is still resisting the ailment and removing its effects. Whatever part of the ailment that remains would either dissipate or re-intensify, depending on the condition of the body.

Therefore, when cooked barley and chard were brought to the Prophet ﷺ, he ordered 'Ali رَضِيَ الله عَنْهُ to eat from it. Cooked barley and chard represent one of the best types of foods for the recovering patients and those with weak stomachs. It does not produce any harmful substances or bodily wastes. The water of cooked barley is cool and nourishing, along with its other qualities of soothing, relaxing the bowels and strengthening the body in general, especially when it is cooked with chard.

Zaid bin Aslam once said, "Umar رَضِيَ الله عَنْهُ once made a patient observe such a strict diet that he used to suck on date stones." In short, diet is one of the most beneficial preventive measures before and after the disease strikes, in which case diet will prevent the disease from spreading or progressing.

We should know that when healthy, recovering or sick people have a taste for a type of food or drink, it would not harm if one consumes little amounts of it. Rather, the food might even help and benefit the body, as the stomach will accept and easily digest the food, more so than when one takes a medicine that it detests. This is why the Prophet ﷺ allowed Suhaib to eat a few dates when he was suffering from conjunctivitis, since it was just a little and would not harm him.

It was reported that 'Ali رَضِيَ الله عَنْهُ said that he once came by the Prophet ﷺ, when he, ('Ali رَضِيَ الله عَنْهُ), was complaining from conjunctivitis, and found the Prophet ﷺ eating dates. The Prophet ﷺ asked him, "O 'Ali, do you have a taste for dates?" He then threw a date and then another date to 'Ali, until he threw seven. The Prophet ﷺ then said, "That is enough, O Ali." [Abu Na'im in his book on the Prophetic medicine].

Also, Ibn Mājah narrated that Ibn 'Abbās رَضِيَ الله عَنْهُمَا said:

« أَنَّ النبيَّ صلى الله عليه وسلم عادَ رجُلًا، فقال له: ما تَشتَهِي ؟ فقال: أَشتَهِي خُبزَ بُرٍّ، وفي لفظٍ: أَشتَهِى كَعْكًا، فقال النبيُّ صلى الله عليه وسلم:

مَنْ كَانَ عِنْدَهُ خُبْزُ بُرٍّ، فَلْيَبْعَثْ إِلَى أَخِيهِ. ثُمَّ قَالَ: إِذَا اشْتَهَىٰ مَرِيضُ أَحَدِكم
شَيْئًا، فَلْيُطْعِمْهُ»

"Once, the Prophet ﷺ visited a sick person and asked him,
"What do you have a taste for?" The man said, "I have a taste
for wheat bread, or I have a taste for a cake." The Prophet ﷺ
then said: "Whoever has wheat bread, let him send some to his
brother." He also said, "When your's sick have a taste for
something, give them some of it."

The last *Hadith* contains a secret, because when the sick person eats
what he has a taste for while also hungry, it will be less harmful than
what he does not have a taste for. If what he has a taste for is not
beneficial in his condition, then his preference for it will prevent its harm.
In addition, eating what one does not like will cause harm to the patient
even if the substance is beneficial itself. In general, the type of food that
is tasty and that the person likes will be accepted by the body and will
be digested in the best way, especially when the appetite for it is strong.

The Prophet's guidance on treating conjunctivitis with rest and observing a special diet

We mentioned that the Prophet ﷺ required *Suhaib* to observe a diet
from eating dates when he was suffering from conjunctivitis, and did the
same with 'Ali رَضِيَ اللهُ عَنْهُ when he was suffering from the same condition.
Furthermore, Abu Na'im narrated in his book, the Prophetic Medicine,
"Whenever any of the Prophet's wives would come down with
conjunctivitis, he would not touch her until her eyes were cured."

Conjunctivitis is an infection that attacks the conjunctiva, that is, the
white part of the eye. The disease is caused by one of the four
conditions [hotness, coldness, dryness and wetness], or by the
accumulation of hot flatulence in the head and body, that later reaches
the eye and cause conjunctivitis. Also, when the eye receives a hit, the
blood and the soul will rush to the aid of the affected eye, which then
becomes swollen.

We should know that there are two types of moistures that ascend to
the air. One is hot and dry and the other hot and wet. These moistures

form the clouds that shade the sky from our eyes. Likewise, gaseous substances and moistures ascend from the stomach to the upper parts of the body and cause many ailments, such as conjunctivitis. When the body's resistance is strong, it will push these gaseous substances to the nose and cause a congestion that usually accompanies colds. When these substances are pushed up through the uvula and the nostrils, they cause angina. When these moistures are pushed towards the side, they cause causes pleurisy, and when they reach the chest they causes pneumonia. When the moistures reach the heart they cause rapid pulse, and when they reach the eyes they cause conjunctivitis. When they reach the intestinal cavity, they cause diarrhea and when they reach the brain they cause forgetfulness. If the brain receives excessive amounts of these gaseous moistures, they might cause heavy sleeping. This is why sleep is wet while being awake is dry. When the septic gases unsuccessfully seek to depart from the body through the head, they will cause headaches and less sleep. When these gases attack one side of the brain, they cause migraines. If these gases reach the cerebral divider and cause it coldness, hotness or wetness, it will cause sneezing. If the gases cause the accumulation of phlegm in the cerebral divider, so that its hot nature becomes weak, they cause unconsciousness and stroke. If the gases excite the black bile, they will cause obsession, and if they reach the nerves, they will cause real epilepsy. When the cerebral nerves receive these gases they will suffer from facial paralysis. If these gases were caused by inflamed yellow bile that heats the brain, they will cause cerebral tumors, and when the chest receives a part of these gases, they will cause pleurisy.

In short, the condition of the head and body will be irritated because of conjunctivitis, and having sex in this state will only aggravate the condition even more. Sex entails a movement that is shared by the entire body, the heart and the soul. As for the body, it heats up due to the intense movements during sex, while the heart will seek to acquire its lust and pleasures. The soul will follow the lead of the body and the heart, as the first part that is connected to the soul is the heart, which in turn affects the rest of the body. As for the body, it sends the semen that is needed to bring the sexual intercourse to conclusion. Thus, sexual activity involves a movement by the entire body, the heart and the soul, and every move excites the various conditions and causes them to move to the weaker parts of the body, such as the eye when suffering from conjunctivitis.

We should state that the body benefits from conjunctivitis in that it helps the body extract harmful substances and cleanses the body and the head from septic elements. Also, conjunctivitis compels the affected person to observe a diet and avoid sadness, grief, strong movements and hard work. Further, one of our righteous predecessors said, "Do not hate conjunctivitis, because it prevents blindness."

In addition, conjunctivitis requires rest and avoiding touching the eye to prevent more harmful substances from accumulating in it. Some of the Salaf once said, "The example of the Companions of Muhammad ﷺ is the example of the eye: its cure is in avoiding touching it."

A *Hadith* that we are not sure about its authenticity states that sprinkling cold water on the eye helps cure conjunctivitis. The remedy mentioned in the *Hadith* is beneficial for hot conjunctivitis, since water is cold and thus cools down the heat that accompanies conjunctivitis. This is why when the wife of 'Abdullāh bin Mas'ud رَضِيَ الله عَنْهُ complained about her eyes, he said to her, "If you had done what the Prophet ﷺ used to do, it would have been better for you and would have brought fast healing to your eyes. Splash water on your eyes and then say, 'Cure the ailment, O Lord of the people! Bring about the cure, for You Alone bring the cure and there is no cure except that which you bring about. Bring a type of healing that eradicates every ailment."

We mentioned before that these types of remedies are suitable for certain areas and for some ailments that attack the eye. Do not understand the Prophet's statements that are specific to be general nor vise versa. Otherwise, mistakes will certainly occur.

The Prophet's guidance on treating narcolepsy

Abu Ubaid رَضِيَ اللهُ عَنْهُ said in his book on the unusual words used in some *Ahadith* that some people passed by a tree that they ate from and they were soon immobilized, just as if a wind had swept through by them and froze them. The Prophet ﷺ said:

« قَرِّسُو المَاءَ فِي الشِّنَانِ، وصُبّوا عليهِم فيما بين الْأَذانَيْن »

"Cool some water in water skins and then pour the water on them between the two Adhāns (the Fajr call to the prayer and the Iqāmah)."

The Prophet ﷺ mentioned the water skins because they cool the water more than clay containers. He also called the *Iqāmah* an *Adhān* in this *Hadith*.

Some doctors stated that the remedy that the Prophet ﷺ prescribed in the *Hadith* is the one of the most effective against narcolepsy if it occurs in the area of Hijaz, which is a hot dry land. The inhabitants of that area have a weak instinctive heat. Pouring cold water on the people afflicted by narcolepsy during the above mentioned time, which is the coolest time of the night, will cause the instinctive heat that is scattered throughout the body to be energized and accumulate in the inner parts of the body where the ailment resides. The powers of the body will then concentrate on expelling and resisting the ailment by Allāh's will.

If it were Galinus or Hippocrates who had prescribed this remedy, the doctors would have been amazed by its perfect effectiveness!

The Prophet's guidance on food and drink contaminated by flies

In the *Sahihain* [actually, only Al-Bukhari narrated it in his *Sahih*] it is narrated that the Messenger of Allāh ﷺ said:

« إذا وقعَ الذُّبابُ في إناءِ أحدِكم: فامْقُلُوه، فإن في أحدِ جناحَيْه داءً، وفي الآخَر شِفاءً »

"If a housefly falls in the drink of anyone of you, he should dip it (in the drink), for one of its wings has a disease and the other has the cure for the disease."

Also, Ibn Mājah narrated that the Messenger of Allāh said:

« أحدُ جناحَي الذُّبابِ سُمٌّ، والآخَرُ شِفاءٌ. فإذا وَقَعَ في الطعامِ: فامْقُلُوه لله؛ فإنه يقدِّم السمَّ، ويؤخرُ الشفاءَ »

"One of the fly's wings carries poison while the other carries a cure. When it falls in the food, dip it, for the sake of Allāh, for verily He (Allāh) makes the poison (take affect) first and He makes the cure come last."

This *Hadith* contains two areas of interest, *Fiqh* (Islamic Jurisprudence) and medicinal. As for the *Fiqh* part, the *Hadith* states that when a fly falls in water or fluids, it does not make it impure, according to the majority of the scholars. None among the early generations contradicted this ruling.

The Prophet ﷺ ordered the fly that falls on the food be dipped in it, thus killing the fly, especially if the food is hot. If the fly's death inside the food would make the food impure, the Prophet ﷺ would have ordered us to discard the food. On the contrary, the Prophet sought to salvage the food.

Bees, hornets, spiders and all similar insects are treated in the same manner as houseflies, because the ruling that we derived from the Prophet's commandment in this *Hadith* is general. Since the reason why dead animals are impure is that their blood remains trapped in their bodies, therefore the insects, which do not have blood are pure. The first person to use the words "What does not have a soul (meaning blood)" was Ibrahim An-Nukha'i and then the scholars used these terms after him.

As for the medicinal value contained in the *Hadith,* Abu 'Ubaidah رَضِيَ الله عَنْهُ said that the purpose behind dipping the fly [in the drink] is to extract the cure from [its other wing] just as the poison was extracted from [the wing that fell on the food].

Houseflies carry poisonous materials as evidenced by the effect of their bite, such as rash and infection, and this poison is the fly's weapon of defense. When the fly falls into what harms it, it tries to defend itself with the available weapons. The Prophet ﷺ ordered that we neutralize the poisonous substances produced by the fly with the cure that Allāh has kept on its other wing. The fly should then be submerged in the water or the food so that the cure could neutralize the effect of the poison. This is a remedy that the best medical minds would never be able to discover on their own, because it is coming from Prophetic knowledge. The doctors who have good knowledge and comprehension submit to this Prophetic remedy and admit that he who was sent with it, is indeed the perfect human being who is supported by divine revelation that is beyond human power.

Several doctors have stated that when one anoints the inflammation caused by scorpion and hornet bites with the housefly, it would calm down the pain due to the cure that the fly carries in its wing. When the head of the housefly is amputated and the body is used to scrub the tumor that appears in the eyelid, it will cure it, Allāh willing.

The Prophet's guidance on treating pimples

Ibn As-Sunni said in his book that one of the Prophet's wives said, "Once, the Messenger of Allāh ﷺ came by when I had a pimple on my finger. He said:

« عندكِ ذَرِيرة ؟ قلتُ : نعم قال : ضَعِيها عَلَيها . وقال قُولي : اللّهم مُصَغِّرَ
الكَبِير ، ومكبِّرَ الصَّغِير؛ صغِّر مابي »

"Do you have a Tharirah (arum)?' I said, 'Yes.' He said, Place it on the pimple. He then said, 'Say, O Allāh who transforms the big to small and the small to big, make what I am suffering from small."
[*Al-Hakim* also narrated the *Hadith*].

The *Tharirah* (Arum) is an Indian remedy made of arum cane. Arum is hot and dry and helps against stomach and liver tumors and dropsy and also strengthens the heart.

In the *Sahihain* it is narrated that 'Āishah رَضِيَ الله عَنْها said, "I perfumed the Messenger of Allāh ﷺ with my hand using *Tharirah* (Arum) during the Farewell *Hajj* during the state of *Ihram* and otherwise."

The pimple is a growth that results from hot harmful, septic substances that push towards the skin so as to find a way out of the body. The pimple needs to mature and to then be opened and extracted, such as by using the *Tharirah*, which helps extract the septic matter from the pimple, along with giving a good aroma. In addition, the Tharirah soothes the hotness of the pimple. This is why the author of the *Al-Qanoon* said, "There is no better remedy for fire burns than the *Tharirah*, when it is blended with rose essence and vinegar.

The Prophet's guidance in treating tumors and abscesses with surgery

Abu Hurairah رَضِيَ الله عَنْهُ narrated that the Prophet ﷺ ordered a doctor to incise an abscess on the abdomen of a man. He was asked, 'Does medicine help, O Messenger of Allāh?' He said:

« الذَّي أنزل الداء، أنزلَ الشفاء فيما شاء »

"He Who has sent down the disease has also sent down whatever He wills of the cure."

The tumor, which accompanies most ailments, is a growth in the organ due to the accumulation of unnatural, septic materials engineered by the four conditions hotness, coldness, dryness and wetness, plus water and wind. When the tumor swells with septic material, it is called an abscess. Every hot tumor ends up decomposing, or becoming pus, or hardening. If the body is strong enough, it dissolves the tumor, and this is the best end of tumors. If the body is not strong, it turns the tumor into a white substance, pus, and opens an exit for the pus to go out of the body. If the body is weak, the tumor will be full of immature pus and the body will not be able to open an exit to discard the pus. In this case, it is possible the tumor will spoil the affected organ. The doctor's help is then sought to incise the tip of the tumor to extract the septic substance.

Puncturing or incising the tumor has two benefits, extracting the harmful substance and preventing more harmful substances from accumulating around the tumor making it even worse.

The *Hadith* stated that the Prophet ﷺ ordered a doctor to incise a tumor on a man's abdomen that was filled with putrid or rotten liquid.

The scholars have conflicting opinions regarding incising tumors, some of them did not allow it because it is dangerous in their opinion. Other doctors said that there is no cure for dropsy except incision. As we have stated, dropsy is of three types: drum dropsy, which causes the stomach to swell with accumulated gases, that if one pounds on the stomach it will produce a similar sound as the drum.

Also, there is the fleshy dropsy that causes the flesh to swell accompanied by phlegm that spreads throughout the body through the blood. This type is worse than the first one.

Third, there is the dropsy that causes the accumulation of toxic materials in the lower part of the stomach. When one moves in this case, his stomach will produce a sound similar to the shaking of a water skin. Most doctors consider this type of dropsy the worst, while others consider the fleshy dropsy the worst of the three types.

Curing the third type of dropsy requires extracting the accumulating water by incision, which is similar to extracting spoiled blood by puncturing the veins. Yet, this procedure is dangerous, although the Hadith, if proven authentic, allows using this method. Allāh has the best knowledge.*

---

* **Editor's note**: By giving permission for this procedure the vision of modern surgery was opened even though after seven centuries these surgical operations were still doubted by many doctors. The field of surgery had not developed the proper techniques required to make this a universal standard procedure at the time of our author.

The Prophet's guidance on treating the sick by encouraging them and strengthening their resolve

Ibn Mājah narrated that Abu Sa'id Al-Khudri رَضِيَ الله عَنْهُ said, The Messenger of Allāh ﷺ said:

« إِذَا دَخَلْتُمْ عَلَى الْمَرِيضِ: فَنَفِّسُوا لَهُ فِي الْأَجَلِ لله فَإِنَّ ذَلِكَ لَا يَرُدُّ شَيْئًا، وهو يُطَيِّبُ نَفْسَ المريض »

"When you visit a sick person, say good words to him, for the sake of Allāh for although that does not prevent any harm, it still brings relief to the patient's heart." At-Tirmidhi also narrated the Hadith].

This *Hadith* contains one of the most honorable remedies, that is, relieving the anxiety of the sick with some good words that will enhance his resolve and strength. In this case, the inner energy would be elevated and would help the body against the disease, which is the best the doctor could wish for.

Relieving the anxiety of the sick person and bringing relief to his heart has a surprisingly good effect in curing the body and lessening the effects of an ailment. It will also bring strength to the heart and the soul of the sick person, further encouraging the body to fight the disease. People have witnessed that the sick feel refreshed and energized in the company of those they like and respect when they visit them. This is one of the benefits gained from visiting the sick, which carries four types of benefits: for the sick person, the visitor, the sick person's family and the general public.

We mentioned before that the Prophet ﷺ used to ask the sick about what they complain from and how they felt. He would also ask them about what they had a taste for and would place his hand on the forehead, or even on the chest, asking Allāh to bring about whatever benefits them in their condition. Sometimes, the Prophet ﷺ would perform ablution and then pour the water he used on the sick person. Sometimes, the Prophet ﷺ would say to the sick person:

« لَا بَأْسَ عَلَيْكَ؛ طَهُورٌ إِنْ شَاءَ الله تَعَالَى »

"It is alright. You will be purified (cured), Allāh willing."

This, indeed, is the kindest way to treat the sick when visiting them.

The Prophet's guidance on treating various illnesses with food and medicine the body is used to

This is also one of the major pillars and the most beneficial parts of the science of medicine. When the doctor errs in prescribing the correct medicine, the patient will be harmed while the doctor is thinking that he is benefiting him. Only the most ignorant doctors will fail to recognize the importance of using the most favorable types of foods and medicines that are the most suitable for different patients. For instance, the Bedouins neither benefit from *Nenuphar* (similar to carrot and used as a drink) or rose-syrup, nor do these remedies have any effect on them, nor would the majority of the medicines used in villages and cities have much effect on them. This fact is known through experience and observation.

Those who read through this book will find that the Prophetic medicine and remedies are all suitable and favorable to the sick person and what he is accustomed to of food and medicine. We have stated that this is a pillar of the science of medicine, as the best medical authorities concur. For instance, the renowned Arab doctor, Al-Harith bin Kaladah, said, "Diet is the best cure; and the stomach is the residence of ailment; and give each body what it is accustomed to (of food and medicine)." In another statement, Al-Harith said, '*Azm* is a cure,' meaning hunger. In fact, going on a diet is a better cure for plethoric illnesses (having an excess of blood in the body and therefore looking reddish), except when there is a fear that the condition would flare up with septic accumulation and aggravate the illness.

Al-Harith stated that the stomach is the residence of the disease. The stomach is a curved organ that looks like a gourd and consists of three layers of delicate and neural components called fibers and surrounded by flesh. The fibers of one layer are arranged longitudinally, while the second layer's fibers are horizontal and the third slanting. The tip of the stomach has more nerves, while the bottom has more flesh and its interior is coated and fuzzy. The stomach is located in the middle of the abdomen, leaning more to the right side, created in this shape by the wisdom of the All-Wise Creator.

The stomach is indeed the residence of the ailment, it is the center of the digestion and maturing process of all food and drink. After that, the digested food descends to the liver and the intestines. Meanwhile, excess amounts of partially digested substances that the stomach was not able to completely digest remain, either because the amount of nourishment was excessive, spoiled, or was not consumed in the proper order, or all of these reasons. Some of this excrement remains in the stomach and the body is not be able to completely discard them, and this is why the stomach is the residence of ailments. Al-Harith indicates the importance of eating less food and preventing the heart from fulfilling its desires.

As for one's being accustomed [to certain things and foods] it is a part of the human nature. Habit has such a great influence on the person and on his body, that if we conduct an experiment on several people who have the same characteristics, the result will vary considerably. For instance, three young, hot-tempered men, one of them is used to eating hot foods, the second is used to cold foods, while the third man is accustomed to mild foods. When the first person eats honey, it would not harm him, unlike the second person, while the third person would be slightly bothered. Habit, therefore, is an important basis on which preserving the health and healing ailments relies. That is why the Prophet ﷺ said that each person should be treated according to what he is accustomed to of medicine and food.

The Prophet's guidance on treating the sick with the simplest types of food

In the *Sahihain* it is narrated that 'Āishah رَضِيَ الله عَنْها said that when a relative of hers would die the women would gather on that occasion and then would depart except for her family members and close associates. She would then order that milk soup be prepared. Then, *Tharid* would be made and she would pour the milk soup on it. 'Āishah would then ask them to eat saying, "I heard the Messenger of Allāh ﷺ saying:

« التَّلْبِينَةُ مُجِمَّةٌ لِفُؤَادِ الْمَرِيضِ، تَذهبُ بِبَعْضِ الْحُزْنِ »

"Milk soup brings relief to the heart of the sick and takes away some of the anguish." '

Milk soup, means the kind of soup that is similar to milk in consistency. This is a beneficial food suitable for the sick, especially when well cooked until acquiring a soft consistency. The milk like soups, are as beneficial as barley soup, even better. Barely soup is made of whole barley grains, while the milk like soup is made of ground barley flour with its bran.

We mentioned that observing the habits and customs of a certain sick person benefits them with a favorable cure and nourishment. The people in Al-Madinah were accustomed to eating barley soup ground not whole, thus making it more nutritious and beneficial for them. The doctors in cities recommend the use of whole barley grains, because the soup in this case is lighter and easier for the ailing person to digest. The people who live in cities are used to comfort and easy life and that is why ground barley grain is heavy on their stomachs.

Whole grain barley soup digests quickly, provides good nutrition, and cleanses the stomach, especially when taken while it is still hot. In this case, it's cleansing and digestive qualities are stronger and the soup will also develop its instinctive heat quicker and will soften the outer layers of the stomach.

The Prophet's statement that the Milk like soup takes away some of the sadness refers to the effect of sadness on the mood and in weakening the instinctive well being, which in turn affects the soul and the heart. Milk like soup brings strength to one's inner energy and thus the body will be able to rid itself of the sadness and grief that took it over.

We could also say that some foods bring relief to the heart, such as the type of soup mentioned above, because they posses a special quality that effect people's mood and brings them relief and comfort. Allāh knows best.

We might also say that the sick person's strength becomes weaker because of his grief and sadness that will translate to dryness in the body and the stomach due to the scarcity of food. The milk like soup brings wetness and strength to the stomach, which will also bring relief to the heart. Also, the sick person may complain from an accumulation of harmful flatulence or phlegm in his stomach. The milk like soup will dissolve these harmful substances or dilute them, so that the pain and harm they cause are diminished, especially for those accustomed to eating barley bread, such as the people of Al-Madinah. During that time, barley bread was the staple diet for the people of Al-Madinah as wheat was scarce at that time.

The Prophet's guidance on treating poisoning

Abdul Razzaq narrated that, "A Jewish woman brought to the Prophet ﷺ a roasted sheep that she had poisoned, while he was in Khaybar. The Prophet ﷺ asked, 'What is this.' She said, 'A gift,' being careful not to say that it was from charity so that he would not eat it. The Prophet ﷺ and his Companions ate from the sheep, then the Prophet ﷺ said, 'Stop eating.' He said to the woman, 'Did you poison this sheep?' She said, 'Who told you that?' He said, 'This bone,' meaning the ewe's leg that he had in his hand. She said, 'Yes.' He said, 'Why?' She said, 'I thought that if you were a liar, the people would be relived from you. However, if you were a true Prophet ﷺ, it would not harm you.' The Prophet ﷺ then used cupping thrice on the upper part of his back and commanded that his Companions do the same. Yet, several of them died.'"

In another narration narrated by Musa bin 'Uqbah, "The Messenger of Allāh ﷺ used cupping on his back because of what he ate of the poisoned sheep. Abu Hind, a servant for Bani Bayadhah, used a knife to cup him. Three years later, when the Prophet ﷺ was suffering from the illness that he died from, he said:

« مَا زِلْتُ أَجِدُ فِي الْأُكْلةِ الَّتِي أَكَلْتُ مِن الشَّاةِ يَوْمَ خَيْبَرَ، حتى كان هٰذا أَوَانَ
انْقِطَاع الْأَبْهَر مِنِّي »

"I still feel the effects of the poisoned sheep I ate from during the Day of Khaybar, until now, when it is the time the aorta is cut off (meaning when death is near)".

Therefore the Messenger of Allāh ﷺ died as a marty.

Poisons are treated by extracting the poison and by using the proper antidotes to neutralize their effect. Whoever does not have access to the medicine, or the antidote, should use complete disgorging, the best method of which is cupping especially in warm areas and during hot weather. The poison passes through the veins and the blood vessels to the heart and then to the rest of the body, bringing certain death. Since the blood is the means that transports the poison to the heart and the organs, when the infected blood is extracted by cupping, the body will get rid of the poison. Also, when one resorts to complete disgorging, the poison does not cause any further harm, the body gets enough strength to fight it and then weakens or even completely dissipates the poison.

When the Prophet ﷺ used cupping, he did it in the upper part of the back, which is the most direct route to the heart, and so the poison was extracted with the blood, in this case only partially. A part of the poison remained in the Prophet's system, in order to fulfill what Allāh had decided for His Prophet so he would acquire every type of good and righteous reward there is.

When Allāh decided that it was time for His Prophet ﷺ to die as a martyr, the effect of the poison reappeared, so that Allāh's decision was fulfilled. Therefore the meaning of the following Âyah, becomes apparent where Allāh says,

$$\text{﴿ أَفَكُلَّمَا جَآءَكُمْ رَسُولٌ بِمَا لَا تَهْوَىٰ أَنفُسُكُمُ ٱسْتَكْبَرْتُمْ فَفَرِيقًا كَذَّبْتُمْ وَفَرِيقًا تَقْتُلُونَ ﴾}$$

"It is that whenever there came to you a Messenger with what you yourselves desired not, you grew arrogant? Some you disbelieved and some you killed." (2:87)

This *Ayah* uses the word disbelieve in the past tense and the word kill in the future tense, indicating an uncompleted action that would continue to occur [meaning the Jews would kill the Prophet]. Allāh knows best.

The Prophet's guidance on treating sorcery

Some people have erroneously denied that sorcery could effect the Prophet, they believed that it was not befitting his grade and status. Actually, being effected by sorcery illustrates the human side of the Prophet, just like he suffered from various other illnesses, and sorcery is an ailment just like poison.

In the *Sahihain* it is narrated that 'Âishah رَضِيَ الله عَنْها said:

« سُحِرَ رَسُولُ اللهِ صلى الله عليه وسلم، حتى إنْ كَان لَيُخَيَّلُ إليه أنه يأتي نساءَه، ولم يأتِهِنّ »

"The Messenger of Allāh was effected by sorcery until he thought that he had slept with his wives, while in fact he did not."

This is the worst type of magic spell.

Qadi 'Iyadh said, "Sorcery is just like any other ailment that the Prophet ﷺ suffered from, and this fact by no means affects his status as a Prophet ﷺ. Further, the fact that the Prophet ﷺ imagined something which he did not do, does not detract from his truthfulness regarding religion, there is a consensus that he is immune from error in this regard. Sorcery is just like any other matter of this life, which has nothing to do with the reason why he was sent and preferred above mankind. The Prophet was subject to come down with all types of ailments that would touch other people. Therefore, it is not surprising that he would imagine doing something which in fact he did not do, and that he was soon cured."

The Prophet ﷺ used two methods to treat sorcery, first by finding the spell and neutralizing it. The Prophet ﷺ supplicated to his Lord and Allāh showed him that the evil spell was hidden in a well. The Prophet ﷺ removed the evil spell, which consisted of a comb, combed material (hair) and a dry male spathe. When he discarded these objects, he was immediately cured, as if he was restrained and then suddenly released. This is the best cure from sorcery and is similar to removing septic materials by complete disgorging.

The second type, extracting harmful substances from the organ most touched by magic works. Evil spells aggravate nature, produce harmful substances and adversely affect the mood. Disgorging the alien substance that affected a certain organ as a result of evil spells becomes necessary.

The effect of the sorcery reached the Prophet's head and affected one of his senses, he imagined he did something while in fact he had not. The sorcerer, therefore, affects some of the natural powers of the body so that it does not function normally.

Sorcery is a combination of the powers of evil spirits and the adverse effects they have on the normal functions of the body. The worst type of magic is that which affects the senses of the affected organ. Drawing blood from the organ most affected by magic is the most beneficial cure, if used in the proper manner. Hippocrates said that, "Cupping (or disgorging) should be used on the part most affected using the most favorable means available."

Some people also said that when the Messenger of Allāh ﷺ suffered from this condition, he first thought that it was caused by spoiled blood that reached the brain and affected the senses. In such cases, cupping is the best medicine, and this is what the Prophet ﷺ did. Then, when Allāh revealed to him that it was the effect of magic that caused his condition, he asked Allāh to show him where the evil spell was hidden and then he retrieved and discarded it. When he did so, he was cured as if released after being restrained. Further, the magic spell only affected the Prophet's senses not his sanity or heart. This is why he did not believe what he imagined of sleeping with his wives because he knew that this sensation was not real.

Divine cures are the best remedies against sorcery. Since sorcery is the work of evil spirits, then its best cure is that which neutralizes it, such as certain prayers and recitations of the Qur'ān. The more powerful the defending army, the more powerful the adversary it will be able to remove and neutralize. This case is similar to two opposing armies, each of which carries its weapons and armaments. The army that has more weaponry and supplies, is the army that will prevail in the war. When the heart is full of Allāh's remembrance and invokes Him often for its needs, and when the heart is joined by the tongue and righteous deeds, these acts will be the best medicine there is against sorcery and magic spells.

The sorcerers and magicians admit that their magic is most effective against those who have weak hearts that are busy satisfying the desires and lusts of the life of this world. That is why magic usually affects women, children, nomads, ignorant people, those who have weak Faith, lack trust in Allāh (*Tawakkul*) and lack the fundamentals of Unity (*Tawhid*), and those who neither remember Allāh often nor use the various Prophetic supplications and Islamic prayer formulas (*Ruqyah*). In general, the effect of sorcery and magic is more powerful against weak hearts that lean towards the lower desires of this world.

When the heart leans towards this earthly life, sorcery and magic becomes most effective against it, because evil spirits only search for evil in the soul that is prone to submit to their power. Surely, evil in the heart deprives one of divine power that is necessary to provide it with sufficient weapons of defense against these evil spirits. That is why these evil spirits, which seek evil, find the hearts weakened by evil unarmed and prone to submit to evil and this is when sorcery and magic spells are most effective. Allāh knows best.

The Prophet's guidance on vomiting as a remedy

At-Tirmidhi reported that a person narrated that Abu Ad-Dardaa رَضِيَ الله عَنْهُ said, "The Prophet ﷺ once performed ablution after he vomited. I met Thawban in the mosque of Damascus and mentioned what Abu Ad-Dardaa narrated to him and he said, 'True'. I poured water for him (the Prophet ﷺ) then." At-Tirmidhi then commented that this *Hadith* is the most authentic on this subject. [Also, *Ahmad, Al-Hakim, Ibn Al-Jarûd, Ad-Daraqutni, Al-Bayhaqi* and *At-Tahawi*].

Vomiting is one of the five methods used to disgorge septic substances from the body. They are diarrhea, vomiting, cupping, the passing of air or wind and sweating. The Sunnah has mentioned these five types.

As for diarrhea, we mentioned the *Hadith* that states, "Diarrhea is the best of your remedies." We also mentioned the *Hadith* about *Senna*.

We mentioned cupping when we narrated the *Ahadith* about this subject.

As for getting rid of septic gasses and steams, we will elaborate on this subject later on in this book.

As for getting rid of septic substances by sweating, it does not usually involve puncturing of the veins. The body naturally rids itself of these substances through the skin when sweat leaves the body through the open pores.

Vomiting involves throwing up the harmful substances through the upper part of the stomach. An enema and medicines that instigate disgorging artificially through the lower parts of the stomach are of two types, one that occurs naturally and one artificially instigated. The naturally instigated vomit should not be prevented, except when it becomes excessive and becomes unsafe. In this case one should take the medicines that stops vomiting. The second type of vomiting is used for medicinal purposes, in the proper time and under proper conditions.

There are ten reasons for vomiting, the first, excessive amounts of bile that float in the stomach and seek an exit out of the body.

Second, excessive amounts of phlegm in the stomach that also seek a way out of the body.

Third, when the stomach is weak and unable to completely digest the food and the partially digested food seeks an exit out of the body.

Fourth, vomiting occurs when a harmful substance enters the stomach and causes a disruption in the digestion process.

Fifth, when one eats excessive amounts of food or drink, more than the stomach can bear. In this case, the stomach will not be able to tolerate these excessive amounts of nourishment and will seek to throw them out.

Sixth, vomiting occurs when the food or drink consumed is not suitable for the stomach, which then throws them out.

Seventh, when the stomach suffers from a condition that spoils the food and drink which then seeks an exit.

Eighth, nausea might also cause vomiting.

Ninth, depression, sadness and anguish cause disregard for the needs of the body and its necessities of food, including the need to mature and digest the food. The stomach gets rid of this undigested food. Also, vomiting may occur under the pressure of various physiological conditions, because the body and the psyche both effect each other profoundly.

Tenth, one might feel nauseous and then vomit upon seeing other people vomit.

Once, a doctor informed me that he had a nephew who was good at applying Ku'hl (antimony, a black powder used for the eyes) and when his nephew would apply Ku'hl to a person who was suffering form conjunctivitis, he himself would later catch conjunctivitis. When this was repeated several times, his nephew stopped this profession. I asked the doctor about the cause of his nephew's condition and he said that his nephew's body reacted to the condition of the men he was treating by catching the same ailment they suffered from. He also said that he knows of a man who saw a benign growth, an-abscess, on someone's body and that he started to scratch the same part on his body. Later on, he also had a growth in the same area.

I say that this proves that the psyche affects the body in such a way that when certain powers in the body are idle, it suddenly becomes active without a reason.*

Vomiting is suitable as a remedy in hot weather and hot climates

In hot areas and hot weather, certain harmful substances are light and thus prone to float, and this is why vomiting becomes a proficient way to discard these mixtures. On the other hand, certain harmful substances in cold areas and in cold weather become thicker and are harder to extract from above. In this case, getting rid of these harmful mixtures is better done by diarrhea.

Getting rid of harmful mixtures is done by pulling them from the farthest exit or by extracting them from the nearest exit. For instance, there are various mixtures that are not stable and seek to either ascend or descend. If the mixture tends to ascend, then discarding it from below is better. If the mixture tends to descend, then pulling it from above is better. When the mixture becomes stable, then discarding it from the nearest exit is better.

---

* **Editor's note**: Time has proven the author's theory to be correct but the above examples to be suspect.

When the mixture starts to harm the upper organs, it should be pulled down through the lower parts, and vise versa. When these mixtures become stable, they should be discarded from the nearest exit.

This is why the Prophet ﷺ had cupping sometimes in his arm vein, sometimes in his head and sometimes on the top of his foot, so that the spoiled blood is discarded from the nearest possible exit.

Vomiting cleanses the stomach from harmful substances

Vomiting strengthens the stomach, sharpens the sight, relieves headaches, ulcers, and infections in the kidneys and the prostate. Vomiting also relieves and soothes chronic illnesses, such as leprosy, dropsy, partial paralysis, or trembling.

A healthy person should instigate vomiting once or twice a month each time vomiting two times, so that the second vomit rids the body of the substances that remained after the first one. Excessive vomiting harms the stomach and weakens its protective layers. It also harms the teeth, the sight and hearing along with causing headaches. Also, those suffering from swelling in the throat, weak chests, those who have small windpipes, or those who find it difficult to vomit intentionally or those prone to spitting up blood should not vomit intentionally.

Those who have the bad habit of filling their stomachs with food and then instigate vomit will find that this method accelerates old age and leads to many harmful diseases, along with making vomiting habitual.

Also, instigating vomiting while suffering from dehydration, weak or defective intestines, senility, or general weakness in the body is dangerous for the health. The best time to instigate vomit is during summer and spring, not winter or autumn. When vomiting intentionally, one should cover his eyes, wash the face with cold water when finished and should then drink apple juice with some mastic and rosewater if possible. Vomit should be expelled through the mouth or pulled from below in the form of diarrhea. Hippocrates said, "Vomit during the summer should be (naturally) expelled from above more than by using medicine, while in winter it should be pulled from below using medications."

The Prophet's guidance on seeking the best doctors

Imam Malik narrated in his Muwatta that Zaid bin Aslam said:

« أن رجلًا في زَمَن رسول الله صلى الله عليه وسلم جُرح، فَاحْتَقَن الدَّمُ. وإن
الرجلَ دعا رجُلَيْن من بني أَنْمار، فنَظَرا إليه. فزَعَم أنَّ رسولَ الله صلى الله
عليه وسلم، قال لهما : أيُّكما أطَبُّ؟ فقالا : أوَفي الطِّبِّ خيرٌ يا رسولَ الله ؟
فقال : أنزَل الدواءَ الذي أنزل الدَّاءَ »

*"During the time of the Prophet ﷺ, a man was injured and the
blood was congested in the wound. The man then called two
doctors from Bani Anmar to examine him. The man then claimed
that the Messenger of Allāh ﷺ asked them, 'Who is the best
doctor among you?' They asked, 'Is there preferability in the
medicine, O Messenger of Allāh?' He said, 'The One Who has
sent down the disease also sent down the cure.'"*

This *Hadith* indicates that Muslims should seek the best authority in
each and every matter and field, because such expertise will ensure that
the job is done with excellence. For instance, those inquiring about a
matter of religion should seek the most knowledgeable scholar to answer
their questions. Further, those who are unsure about the direction of the
prayer should imitate the most knowledgeable person available. This is
the way Allāh has created His slaves. For instance, those traveling on
land or sea should seek the best guides because their hearts will feel
safer following their lead and in their presence. The religion, the mind
and the way Allāh created mankind all emphasize this fact mentioned in
the *Hadith*.

The Prophet's statement:

« أنزلَ الدَّواءَ الذي أنزَل الداءَ »

"He Who has sent down the disease also sent down the cure."

Like this has been mentioned in several other Ahadith. For example,
Hilal bin Yasaf said:

« دخل رسولُ الله صلى الله عليه وسلم على مريض يَعودُه، فقال : أرسِلُوا

الى طبيب فقال قائلٌ : وأنتَ تقولُ ذلك يارسول الله ؟! قال : نعم ؛ إن الله عز

وجل لم يُنزِلْ داء، إلَّا أنزَلَ له دواءً »

*"The Messenger of Allāh once visited a sick man and said, 'Send
for a doctor.' A man said, 'Do you say that, O Messenger of Allāh
ﷺ ?' He said, 'Yes. Allāh has not sent down a disease but also
sent down a cure for it."* (Ahmad)

In the *Sahihain* it is also narrated that the Prophet ﷺ said:

« مَا أنزَل اللهُ مِن دَاءٍ، إلا أنزَل له شِفاءً »

*"Allāh has not sent down a disease except that He sent down its
cure."*

There is a conflict of opinion on the meaning of sending down the
disease and the cure. Some people say that sending the cure down
means the slaves become aware of it. This opinion is not valid, although
Allāh has informed us about the fact that for every disease there is a cure
still the Prophet ﷺ said:

« عَلِمَهُ مَن عَلِمِه، وَجَهِلَه مَن جَهِله »

*"Those who know it are aware of it, and those who do not know
it are ignorant of it."*

Some people say that the Prophet's statement indicates that Allāh has
created these cures on the earth, like another *Hadith*, "Allāh does not
create a disease but would create its cure." Although this opinion is
better than the first one, it is still not valid because "sending down" is
more precise and specific than creating.

Another group says that the statement means that Allāh sends down
the cure with the angels who are responsible for the affairs of mankind
including the diseases and their cures. Indeed, the angels are responsible
for the daily affairs of this world, especially the affairs of mankind from the
time he or she is a fetus until they die. This opinion that the angels are
sent down with the cure is more plausible.

Other people say that the majority of the medicine comes down with
the rain, as the rain causes the growth of the vegetation and food,
meaning the various sources for cure. Also, rain washes down various
minerals from the mountaintops which are used in remedies. Also,

various types of fruits, plants and even spring water are used in cures and remedies. This opinion is better than the previous three opinions, but Allāh knows best.

This is the perfect wisdom of Allāh, that He tests His slaves with the disease and yet helps them find the cure. He also tests His slaves with sins, but helps them erase these sins by repenting to Him, by performing good deeds and by their enduring different calamities and disasters. Allāh also tests His slaves with evil, yet helps His slaves with angels. Allāh also tests His slaves with desires, but has allowed them to satisfy their desires by taking from the good, pure substances that are also desirable. Allāh has not tested His slaves with anything but would also provide them with what helps them sustain themselves against that trial and test. The difference between the slaves of Allāh in this state is in their knowing and acquiring such aids. Allāh is sought for help regarding each and every matter.

The Prophet's guidance on requiring compensation from those unqualified to practice medicine

Abu Dāwud, An-Nasa'ī and Ibn Mājah said that the Messenger of Allāh ﷺ said:

« من تطبَّبَ – ولم يُعلَم منه الطِّبُّ قَبْلَ ذلك فهو ضَامن »

"Those who practice Tibb, but are not knowledgeable in this profession are responsible for their actions." [Also Al-*Hakim* narrated this *Hadith*].

There are three types of benefits in this *Hadith*: linguistic, religious and medicinal.

Linguistically, *Tibb* entails preparing a thing. It also entails excellence and thus entails other than the profession of doctors. A person might be called *Tabib* (Usually means doctor) when they are proficient in anything. Also, a proficiency might be called *Tibb* sometimes even magic.

In the *Sahih* it is narrated that 'Āishah رَضِيَ الله عَنْها said, "When the Jews worked magic on the Messenger of Allāh ﷺ, two angels sat next to him one at his head and the other at his feet, one of them asked, 'What is the matter with the man?' The other angel said, 'He is *Matbub* (touched by magic).' The first angel asked, 'Who did Tibb (sorcery) on him?' The second angel said, 'Such and such Jewish fellow.' "

Abu 'Ubaid رَضِيَ الله عَنْهُ said that those touched by magic are called *Matbub*, touched by magic. Also, the medicine is called *Tibb*.

The word Tabib describes a knowledgeable person including doctors.

The religious benefit from this *Hadith* requires the ignorant doctor to pay for his mistakes, because he has practiced a profession although he was unqualified in it and then caused harm to the people, whom he in fact has cheated and deceived. Therefore, unqualified doctors are held responsible for any health risks they cause, according to the consensus of the scholars.

Al-Khattabi said, "There is no difference concerning the ruling that when one treats a sick person and causes him harm that he is financially responsible for his acts. Those who indulge in a profession that they are not proficient in are aggressors. Therefore, when their actions lead to harm, the aggressors ought to pay for their action, financially not physically since the sick person actually allows such ignorant people to treat him. "

There are five types of doctors: a proficient doctor who gives the profession its due right and who acts responsibly. When such a person treats a sick person, an act that is allowed both by the religion and the sick person, and then commits a mistake he is not liable for this mistake. For instance, when a doctor who is proficient in his job performs circumcision for a boy under favorable circumstances, but the organ suffers some type of damage, the doctor will not be liable for this mistake. Also, if a swelling was cupped by a proficient person in the proper time and manner, but a certain damage occurred, the doctor is not liable for that mistake.

The second type is an ignorant doctor who treats a sick person and causes him harm. If the sick person had knowledge beforehand that this doctor was ignorant and yet allowed him to treat him, then there is no compensation required in this case. This ruling does not contradict the *Hadith* we mentioned in the beginning of the chapter. The wording of the *Hadith* indicates that those who have to pay for their mistakes have cheated the sick person and caused the illusion that they were proficient doctors.

If the sick person thinks that a certain person is a proficient doctor and thus allows him to treat him, the ignorant doctor is required to compensate the sick person for whatever damage he might cause. Also, when such a so-called doctor prescribes a medicine for the sick person who takes the medicine thinking that the doctor prescribed the medicine to him with knowledge, and if the medicine causes any harm, compensation would be required in this case. The *Hadith* is clear in its indication regarding this type.

The third type is a proficient doctor who was given permission to treat a person but made a mistake and caused harm to a healthy organ (meaning not the organ he was treating), then in this case compensation is required because it is an aggression by mistake. Does this person pay the compensation from his own money or from the Muslim Treasury? There are two opinions on this subject. If the doctor is not Muslim, compensation is paid from his own money and if the doctor is Muslim there is a difference of opinion as we mentioned earlier.

The fourth type is the proficient doctor who prescribes the wrong medicine for the sick person who dies as a consequence. There are two opinions on this subject, one of them requires the compensation from the Muslim Treasury while the other requires it from the doctor's resources. Both of these opinions were attributed to Imam Ahmad.

The fifth type is a proficient doctor who amputated an organ form an insane person or a child without permission, or who circumcised a boy without his parent's permission and the organ was harmed. Some scholars say that the doctor is required to pay compensation in this case because he was not given permission to operate. However, if the guardian or the parent allows the doctor to operate then the doctor is not required to pay for his mistake.

It is possible that the doctor who operates without permission may not have to pay compensation because he intended to do good and is therefore not liable for the damage he causes. The *Hadith* in the beginning of this chapter entails such medicinal professions as remedy prescription, applying Ku'hl, physicians, performing circumcision, cupping and incisions, splintering broken bones, cauterization and administering injections, veterinarians, and so forth. It is a recent practice to restrict the word doctor to mean a specific part of the profession.

The proficient doctor takes the following steps when treating any type of disease.

1. First diagnose the type of disease.

2. Search for the cause behind the disease.

3. Examine the sick person to decide if his body is able to fend off the disease or if it is weaker than the disease. If the patient is strong enough to resist the disease, the doctor should not prescribe medicine.

4. Examine the patient and his mood and condition.

5. Examine the changes in the state of the patient.

6. Examine the sick person's age,

7. Examine his habits and what he is accustomed to,

8. Remember seasonal effects.

9. Consider the sick person's place of origin.

10. Consider the atmospheric conditions at the time he caught the disease.

11. Search for the correct and suitable medicine.

12. Examine the effectiveness of the medicine and the correct dosage.

13. The doctor not only intends to cure the ailment, but also to prevent what is even more serious. For instance, if curing a certain disease leads the way to an even more serious disease, the doctor allows the current illness to remain and tries to make it milder. For instance, the orifice of the veins, which is treated by incision or cutting, might aggravate other acute ailments.

14. Choosing and prescribing the simplest medicine for treatment is warranted. For instance, the doctor does not prescribe medicine unless he investigates his options of food and diet. Also, the doctor should not prescribe multiple or complex medications until he investigates his options regarding simpler medications. It is a sign that the doctor is truly professional that he prescribes food when he can substitute it for medicine, and simple rather than complex medications.

15. The doctor examines if the illness is treatable or not. If the doctor finds out that he is unable to treat the disease, let him preserve his energy and reputation and avoid falling prey to his own greed so that he pretends to cure the incurable.

If the illness is curable, the doctor examines if it can be totally cured, or at least made milder. If the doctor discovers that he cannot cure the diseases or decrease its intensity, he should examine the ways to stop it from being aggravated. In this case, the medication should be administered for that purpose, to increase the body strength and stop the disease from increasing.

16. The doctor should not revert to excreting the septic substances before they become stable and mature.

17. The doctor should also be knowledgeable of the sicknesses of the heart and soul and the methods of treating such ailments. This, indeed, is a major aspect of medicinal science, for the effect of the heart's moods and feelings is apparent in the physical body. This is why we state that if a medical doctor is also proficient in the ills of the hearts, he will be the

prefect doctor. On the other hand, the doctor who does not have knowledge of the ills of the heart while knowledgeable in the ills of the body, he will be only half of a doctor. He is not a doctor who does not examine the righteousness of the sick person's heart and encourages him to strengthen his soul and body by performing righteous, good deeds, such as charity and being interested in drawing closer to Allāh and acquiring the good of the Hereafter. Rather, he is a fake doctor. In fact, the best cures are in performing righteous good deeds, charity, remembering Allāh, supplicating to Him, seeking His help, invoking Him and repenting to Him. Such good deeds have a truly profound effect in curing illnesses, more so than the usual medications, providing that the ailing person has faith in such divine remedies.

18. Being lenient and forbearing with the sick person, just as one is easy going and lenient with a child.

19. The doctor should use the various types of medicinal and spiritual cures, along with using his imagination.

20. The doctor should make his treatment revolve around the six major principles, which are the cornerstone of his profession. First, the doctor should preserve the health. Second he should try and bring back the lost health. Third, the doctor should cure the disease. Fourth, at least lessen the intensity of the disease. Fifth, the doctor should ignore the lesser evil and treat the bigger evil. Sixth, the doctor should ignore the lesser good to acquire the greater good. The science of medicine revolves around these six basics, and the doctor who does not rely on them is not a doctor. Allāh knows best.

The sick person passes through four stages:

1. The beginning. 2. The intense stage. 3. fading 4. the end of the illness.

Since the sick person passes through four stages the doctor has to examine each of these stages carefully and treat them in the proper manner. For instance, if the doctor feels the body needs to remove and excrete harmful substances, if they are mature, he should do so. If this is not possible in the beginning of the ailment, especially if the disease has already progressed, or because the body is weak, the weather is cold, or by mistake, the doctor should not resort to excretion in these cases. If the doctor ignores this warning, the body will be busy dealing with the medication and will not concentrate on resisting the disease. This is similar to requiring a soldier who is busy defending his post to do something else. Rather, the doctor's concern should be concentrated on preserving the strength of the body as much as possible at this stage.

When the disease has stopped progressing, the doctor should then use excretion and treating the causes of the disease. It is even better when the disease has started to subside and end. This case is similar to an enemy whose strength has started to depart and his ammunition nears its end, so capturing him in this case becomes easier. When the enemy starts to give flight, it is even easier to capture him. It is a fact that the strength of the enemy will be at a maximum in the beginning of his aggression. This is the exact case with medicine as regards the ailing body.

The skilled doctor uses the easiest treatment and cure first, then the more difficult or powerful medications. Therefore, the doctor moves from the less powerful to the more powerful, unless he fears that the strength of the body will be drained if he does not use the most powerful medicine first. Also, the skilled doctor does not keep using the same medications in a way that will allow the body to get used to the medicine and thus it looses its effectiveness. We also mentioned that the doctor should first consider prescribing a diet before using medications. If the doctor is unsure about the nature of the disease, he should not prescribe medication before being sure of the correctness of his diagnosis. There is no harm if the doctor administers a medication that does not cause side effects or negative repercussions.

When several diseases attack the body, the doctor starts with the medicine that satisfies three condition: treating the disease that might lead to curing the other diseases, such as when confronted with a swelling and an ulcer, he starts with the swelling.

The second condition, the doctor starts with the disease that has caused the other. For example, if the doctor is confronted with an embolism (the obstruction of an artery by an embolus, usually a piece of clotted blood which breaks away from one part of the circulatory system and travels to another) and septic-related fever, he starts with the cause of the first disease.

Third, when one of the two diseases is more serious than the other disease, then the doctor should start with the acute ailment. Yet, the doctor should also examine the progress of the other disease.

Also, when a disease and a symptomatic ailment both attack the body, the doctor starts with the disease, unless the symptomatic condition is stronger, such as in the case of painful constipation. The doctor first treats the pain then treats the embolism. If the doctor can substitute excretion or extraction (of the septic substances) with hunger, fasting, sleep, then he should do so.

The Prophet's guidance on preventing contagious diseases and enforcing quarantine

Muslim narrated that Jabir bin 'Abdullāh said:

« إنه كان في وَفْد ثَقِيف رجلٌ مجذومٌ، فأرسل إليه النبي صلى الله عليه وسلم: ارجِعْ فقَدْ بايَعْناك» .

"Thaqif's delegation included a man with leprosy. The Prophet ﷺ sent to him, 'Go back, for we have accepted your pledge of allegiance." [Ibn Majah, Ahmad, Ibn Khuzaymah and Ibn Jarir].

Al-Bukhari narrated that the Prophet ﷺ said:

« لا تُدِيموا النَّظَرَ إلى المَجْذومِين » .

"Do not keep looking at the person afflicted by leprosy." [Ahmad, At-Tayalisi, At-Tabarani and Al-Bayhaqi].

Further, in the *Sahihain* it is narrated that the Prophet ﷺ said:

« لا يُورِدَنَّ مُمْرِضٌ على مُصِحٍّ» .

"A healthy man should not be brought near a sick person." [Abu Dāwud, Ahmad, Ibn Mājah, Ahmad and Al-Bayhaqi]

Leprosy is an especially harmful disease that occurs due to the accumulation of black bile in the entire body, altering the condition or temperament and shape of the organs. In the final stages, leprosy might cause such bad corrosion that the affected limbs would start to fall off and disintegrate. Leprosy is also called the diseases of the lion, for three reasons. First, this disease usually attacks lions (or wild beasts). Second, because this disease causes the face to frown, like the lion's face. The third, leprosy is contagious and will devour its victim just as the lion devours its prey.

Leprosy is a contagious disease, and those who come near the person afflicted with leprosy will be bothered by the foul odor, just like those suffering from tuberculosis.

The Prophet, who was full of mercy and pity for his nation, commanded them not to expose themselves to what might bring harm to their bodies and hearts. There is no doubt that certain bodies are disease prone and are easily affected by the surrounding environment, and as we have stated, leprosy is a contagious disease. Sometimes, someone's fear of the disease might actually help the disease attack the body, because fear prepares the organs of the body for the possibility of catching the disease. Sometimes, when one even smells the foul odor emitted by persons inflicted by certain diseases, they in turn catch the same disease, if their body is susceptible to catch the disease. Some people stated that the *Ahadith* we mentioned in this chapter are overruled by some other *Ahadith*. They brought as evidence what the Prophet ﷺ said: "There is no contagion nor evil omen." [*Al-Bukhari, Muslim* and *Abu Dawud*].*

We should state that there is no contradiction between the authentic *Ahadith*. When there is an appearance of contradiction, one of the *Ahadith* might not be an authentic *Hadith*, sometimes, the narrators of *Ahadith* might have made mistakes, although they are truthful themselves. Or, one of the seemingly contradicted *Ahadith* might be overruling the other. Further, there are no two authentic *Ahadith* that are direct in meaning which contradict each other in every respect. Allāh forbids that his truthful Messenger should ever contradict himself, and therefore, everything the Prophet ﷺ uttered is the ultimate truth, no doubt. Problems and errors sometime arise from the narrators of the *Hadith*, the shortcoming in comprehending the true meaning of some *Ahadith* or the inability to distinguish between authentic and forged *Ahadith*.

Ibn Qutaibah said in his book, *Ikhtilaf Al-Hadith*, while talking about the enemies of *Hadith*, They say, "These are *Ahadith* that contradict each other. You narrated that the Prophet said, 'There is neither contagiousness nor evil omen.' And that the Prophet ﷺ was told, 'Wet

---

* **Editor's note**: There is no contagion based on superstition, which was rampant in the pre-Islamic times.

mange attacks the camel's lip and then the camels catch leprosy,' and that he said, 'What has transferred the ailment to the first camel?' You also narrated, 'No healthy person should be brought near a sick person, and avoid the one with leprosy just as you avoid the lion.' You also reported that a man with leprosy came to give his allegiance to the Prophet ﷺ on Islam and that he said to him that his pledge is accepted, ordering him to return without meeting him. He also said, 'Evil omen is in three things: the woman, the animal and the house,' and all these statements contradict each other."

Abu Muhammad (Ibn Qutaibah) then commented, "We say that there is no contradiction, because each statement has its own meaning and timeframe. When the *Hadith* is used in its proper context, the appearance of contradiction will not be substantiated. There are two types of contagion, one of them is leprosy like contagion. For instance, when the odor of the person afflicted with leprosy is felt by those who talk and sit near to the leper for a long time, they might fall victim to the same disease. Such is the case with the wife of the person with leprosy who remains under the same roof with him and thus catches the disease. Also, the children of the person afflicted with leprosy might catch the disease later on in their life (hereditary). Such is the case with those suffering from tuberculosis, hectic fever and mange. The doctors order that those suffering from tuberculosis and leprosy should be avoided, not because they fear that such cases are contagious but because the bad odor that emits from such people might affect the healthy persons when exposed to it for a long time. The doctors are the farthest people from believing in evil or good omens. The same argument is true in the case with the Nuqbah, which is a wet type of leprosy or mange that attacks camels. When the infected camel mixes or mingles with other healthy camels, the infection will be transferred through the water [open sores] or the mucus that the camel produces. This is the meaning that the Prophet ﷺ intended when he said:

'No sick person should be brought near a healthy person.'

He disliked that the sick people associated with healthy people, so that the healthy are not exposed to any substances or rashes that the body of the sick person produces. The second type of contagion, is the plague, for instance, that appears in a land and the person thus seeks to flee that land for fear of catching the disease. The Prophet ﷺ said, 'If it (the Plague) appears in a land where you are residing, do not depart that land. If it appears in a land, do not enter it.' The Prophet ﷺ ordered the people not to depart the land afflicted by the plague, as they might be thinking that by fleeing they would be avoiding Allāh's appointed destiny. Also, the Prophet ﷺ ordered the people not to enter a land afflicted by the plague, for remaining in the healthy land brings calmness to their hearts and tranquility in their livelihood. Also, this type includes the husband who suffers an affliction and attributes it to the bad omen of his wife or the house as is common. This is the type that the Prophet ﷺ meant when he said, "There is neither contagion...' "

Some other people said the Prophet ﷺ only recommended that leprosy patients be avoided and that it is still allowed to eat with them, as the Prophet himself did.

Some other people said that these *Ahadith* contain specific commands for different types of people. For instance, some people have such a strong faith and reliance on Allāh that the strength of their faith would save them from contagious diseases, just as the natural powers that exist in the body sometimes fend off the harm of the disease. Some people, on the other hand, do not have a strong faith, so the Prophet ﷺ commanded them to be cautious. The Prophet ﷺ implemented his own commands in both cases, so that the strong imitate his acts, depending on their trust in Allāh. On the other hand, the weak would imitate the Prophet ﷺ (when he avoided leprous patients, for instance) to be cautions. Both ways are correct, but one is suitable for those who have strong faith while the other is suitable for those who have weak faith. Consequently, both groups of the believers will have their own method that is suitable for their own situation. As another example, the Prophet ﷺ has used fire for medicinal purposes, cauterization. Yet, he praised whoever refrains from using cauterization and mentioned avoiding it with the good deeds of shunning the bad omen and having total dependence on Allāh. There are many other examples on this subject. The Prophet's method is always very gentle, and those who comprehend it in the correct manner will get rid of many suspicions that the authentic *Sunnah* contradicts itself.

Some other people stated that ordering the people to run away from the one with leprosy prevents the transfer of the disease by mingling with the sick or by smelling their odor when such mingling and associations are extensive. As for short visitations with such people for a good purpose, there is no harm in it and catching the disease will not be plausible during these brief contacts. The Prophet ﷺ prohibited long exposures to sick people to preserve health and allowed brief contacts that would not cause harm. Therefore, where is the contradiction here?

Another group of people said it is plausible that the person who suffered from leprosy with whom the Prophet ﷺ sat and ate was suffering from mild leprosy. There are several types of leprosy that vary in their seriousness and the degree of their contagion. In such cases, it is possible to mingle with some people suffering from mild leprosy that has not progressed and avoid catching the disease. When the illness is unable to progress in the sick person's body, it will be even less able to attack another person's body.

Another group of people said that the people before Islam believed that diseases themselves are contagious, without referring this matter to the power and will of Allāh in the beginning and the end. The Prophet refuted their belief and ate with a person with leprosy to prove that Allāh is the One Who causes the disease to come and Who brings about the cure. The Prophet also prohibited the Muslims from mingling with the sick to teach them that sickness and diseases are made by Allāh to have a certain effect on people. The prohibition affirms these effects while his action teaches us that such effects are totally controlled by Allāh, and that if He wills, these effects will not have any power. Also, if He wills, these effects will cause the harm that He has decided and willed.

Finally, some other people say that these Ahadith might be overruled by other Ahadith, and that in case we are unable to produce the latter Hadith that overrules the previous Hadith, we should refrain from discussing this matter further.*

---

* **Editor's note**: In pre-Islamic times called "the days of ignorance" contagion was attributed to an evil wife, an evil location, etc. These practices were stopped by the Prophet ﷺ as he stopped all such practices based on superstition and ignorance. His guidance on how to deal with lepers, those with tuberculosis, the plague and the general principals of not letting the healthy intermingle with the sick are all proofs of his Divine guidance.

The Prophet's guidance on prohibiting using what Allāh has forbidden for medicinal purposes

Abu Dāwud narrated that Abu Ad-Dardaa رَضِيَ اللهُ عَنْهُ said that the Messenger of Allāh ﷺ said:

« إن الله أنزل الداءَ والدَّواءَ، وجعل لكلِّ داءٍ دواءً. فتداوَوْا ولا تداوَوْا بِالمُحَرَّم »

"Allāh has sent down the disease and the cure and has created a cure for every disease. Seek the cure, but do not use what has been prohibited for medicinal purposes." [At-Tabarani].

Al-Bukhari also narrated that Ibn Mas'ud رَضِيَ اللهُ عَنْهُ said:

« إن الله لم يَجْعَلْ شِفاءَكم فيما حُرِّم عَلَيكم »

"Verily Allah has not made your cure in that which has been forbidden for you".

Also in the *Sunan* [*Abu Dāwud* and *At-Tirmidhī*] it is narrated that Abu Hurairah رَضِيَ اللهُ عَنْهُ said:

"The Messenger of Allāh ﷺ has disallowed using impure (prohibited) substances for medicinal purposes."

Also, Imam Muslim narrated that Tariq Ibn Suwayd Al-Ju'fi said that he asked the Prophet ﷺ about alcohol and that he has disallowed it or hated that he makes it. He said, "I only make it for medicinal purposes." The Prophet ﷺ said:

"It is not a cure. Rather, it is a disease."

Also in the *Sunan* it is narrated that the Prophet ﷺ was asked about Al-Khamr [alcohol] for medicinal purposes. The Prophet ﷺ said:

« إنَّ ذلِك ليس بِشِفَاءٍ، ولكِنَّه داءٌ »

"Verily that is not a cure, rather it is a disease.." [Abu Dawood and At-Tirmidhi].

Also, Muslim narrated that Tariq bin Suwayd Al-Hadhrami said, "I said, 'O Messenger of Allāh ﷺ! There are some vines in our land that we squeeze (for alcohol) and that we drink from.' He said, 'Do not do it.' So I went back to him and said, 'We use it for medicinal purposes.' He said:

« إنه ليس بدواءٍ، ولكنه داءٌ »

"It is not a cure. Rather, it is a disease."' [Abu Dāwud and At-Tirmidhi].*

An-Nasa'ī narrated that a doctor mentioned using frogs to make medicine and the Prophet ﷺ prohibited killing the frog for that purpose. [Abu Dāwud, Ahmad and Al-Hakim]

Using what Allāh has prohibited in medicines is an evil act according to the religion and the mind. As for the religion, we mentioned several Ahadith on this subject.

As for the mind, Allāh has prohibited whatever substances He has prohibited because they are impure. Further, Allāh has never disallowed a good, beneficial matter for the Muslims, as He has decided in the case of the Children of Israel:

﴿ فَبِظُلْمٍ مِّنَ ٱلَّذِينَ هَادُواْ حَرَّمْنَا عَلَيْهِمْ طَيِّبَٰتٍ أُحِلَّتْ لَهُمْ وَبِصَدِّهِمْ عَن سَبِيلِ ٱللَّهِ كَثِيرًا ﴾

"For the wrong-doing of the Jews, we made unlawful for them certain good foods which had been lawful for them, and for their hindering many from Allah's Way".

Allāh has prohibited some matters and substances because of the harm that they carry and to save His slaves from such harm. It is not suitable that the slaves seek these harmful substances for medicinal purposes. Even if such substances appear to have an affect on the disease, they bring about a more serious illness in the heart because they are impure and unclean. In this case, the sick person who uses what Allāh has disallowed for medicinal purposes might be able to remove the physical illness but would cause himself a more serious disease in the heart.

Further, the Muslims are required to avoid what Allāh has disallowed, while using them in medicine means that one will not avoid them, as the religion requires. This is the opposite of what the prohibitions seek to achieve.

---

* **Editor's note**: The Prophet ﷺ described Alcoholism, as a disease, over one thousand four hundred years ago.

Also, what Allāh has prohibited is a disease as the religion states by the tongue of the Messenger. Therefore, Muslims are not allowed to use it as a medicine.

Furthermore, prohibited substances affect the heart and soul and make them impure, since the various substances that the body consumes affect the body. When a substance causes an evil outcome in the body, the nature of the body will acquire this evil temperament. What about if the substance is impure and evil itself? In this case, when the substance is impure, the body becomes impure, as well. This is why Allāh has prohibited the impure types of foods, drinks and clothes because of the evil effects that such substances have on the body and soul.

Also, allowing using prohibited substances for medicinal purposes will later on encourage taking these substances to satisfy desire and the lust, especially when the heart likes such substances. This is especially the case when the heart thinks that such substances cure the illnesses of the body, thus making them even more desirable and likable. The religion, on the other hand, has closed the door to consuming or using prohibited substances. There is a contradiction if the religion closes the door to using prohibited substances on one hand and opens the door to using them in other instances on the other hand.

Also, prohibited substances that people might use in medicine carry more types of harm than the harm that they might remove. For instance, the mother of all evil substances, alcohol, which Allāh has not made a cure or a remedy, is very harmful to the brain, which controls the body, according to the doctors and many scholars of Fiqh (Islamic Jurisprudence). Hippocrates, for example, said while discussing serious illnesses, "Alcohol has a serious harmful effect on the brain, because it reaches the brain quickly along with some other harmful substances that the body contains, thus causing harm to the brain." The author of *Al-Kamil* also said, "Drinking [alcohol] brings harm to the brain and the nervous system."

There are two other types of disallowed medicines, one that the heart does not like, such as snake meat and poisons. Such substances are heavy on the heart and the stomach [let alone being dangerous] and are thus a disease not a cure. There are also some other medicines that are not disliked themselves, such as some drinks that pregnant women take.

These substances carry more harm than benefit, and consequently, the mind and the religion corroborate on disliking them.

There is another wisdom behind disallowing taking prohibited substances as medicine. That is that a condition that the medicine works is one's belief that it would work and bring the cure by Allāh's blessing. Indeed, whatever is beneficial is also blessed, and the more benefit it carries, the more blessing it will bring about. Also, what the people consider the most blessed is the substance that they think carries the most benefit. The Muslim, on the other hand, believes that what Allāh has disallowed is not beneficial or blessed. Consequently, he will not have a good idea about the disallowed substance and his system will not accept it. Rather, the stronger the slave's faith is, the more he hates the disallowed substances and believes that it is impure. In this case, if the slave takes such a substance it will indeed be a disease not a cure for him, unless he believes that it is pure and thus his dislike for it subsides. Therefore, the believer will not accept the disallowed substance and will consider it a disease, otherwise he will be contradicting the Faith.

The Prophet's guidance on treating and removing lice from the head

In the *Sahihain* it is narrated that Ka'b bin 'Ujrah said, "I was suffering from lice and I was carried to the Messenger of Allāh ﷺ while lice were falling off on my face, the Prophet ﷺ said:

« ما كنتُ أُرى الجَهْدَ قد بَلغ بكَ ما أَرَىٰ فأمَرَه: أن يَحلِقَ رأسَه، وأن يُطْعِمَ فَرَقًا بَيْن ستةٍ، أو يُهديَ شاةً، أو يَصُومَ ثلاثةَ أيام »

"I did not realize that your trouble had reached the condition that I see (you in). The Prophet ﷺ then ordered him to have his head shaved and either fast three days or feed six poor persons or slaughter one sheep as a sacrifice." [Also, narrated by Ahmad] *

Lice appear on the head and body for two reasons, external and internal. The external cause occurs due to uncleanness and impure substances that the skin might carry. The internal reason is caused by rotted substances that the body expels through the skin and then rots due to the wetness in the skin's pores. The lice appear then (and feed on these rotted substances). Many times, lice appear after one suffers from various illnesses and diseases, because in this case cleanliness is ignored. Also, children are the typical victims of lice because they usually play in and deal with wet things and because of their careless nature. This is why the Prophet ﷺ ordered that the heads of the sons of Ja'far be shaved, as shaving is one the best cures for lice because it exposes the skin to the sun and allows the harmful moistures under the skin to evaporate. Then, the head should be anointed with the cures that prevent lice from reproducing and kill them.

Shaving occurs for three reasons, as a legal ritual, as an act of innovation and polytheism, and as a cure. The first type is performed during *Hajj and Umrah*. The second type occurs for other than Allāh,

---

* **Editor's note** : The Prophet ﷺ ordered Ka'b to fast, feed poor persons, or slaughter a sheep as an expiation for shaving his head while in Ihram (ritual state of one performing Hajj). The fact that Ka'b was performing Hajj was not made clear by the author. Shaving the head in itself does not require such expiations outside of Hajj. AW.

such as when the students have their heads shaved for their masters sake saying, 'I shaved my head for such and such person's sake'. This is similar to one's saying, "I bowed down for such and such person."

Shaving the head is an act of humility and worship, and this is why it is a ritual that completes the *Hajj* acts. Imam Shafi'î even considers shaving the head a cornerstone of *Hajj* since it entails lowering the sides of the head in humility before the Lord and since it is also an honored act of worship. Furthermore, when the Arabs wanted to humiliate a captured warrior and then set him free, they would first shave his head. Later on, the teachers of false guidance and evil who seek to acquire the rights of lordship for themselves and whose ministry concentrates on polytheism and innovations came along. Such evil teachers wanted their students to perform the acts of worship for their sake. Consequently, they encouraged their students to shave their heads for their sake, just as they lured them to prostrate before them, calling this act by other than its true name and claiming that it is not prostrating, but merely lowering the head before the teacher. By Allāh! What is prostrating for the sake of Allāh, if it is not lowering the head before Him? The evil teachers also lured their students to vow to them, repent to them and swear by their names! This is taking such teachers as gods beside Allāh. Allāh said:

﴿ مَا كَانَ لِبَشَرٍ أَن يُؤْتِيَهُ ٱللَّهُ ٱلْكِتَـٰبَ وَٱلْحُكْمَ وَٱلنُّبُوَّةَ ثُمَّ يَقُولَ لِلنَّاسِ كُونُوا۟ عِبَادًا لِّى مِن دُونِ ٱللَّهِ وَلَـٰكِن كُونُوا۟ رَبَّـٰنِيِّـۧنَ بِمَا كُنتُمْ تُعَلِّمُونَ ٱلْكِتَـٰبَ وَبِمَا كُنتُمْ تَدْرُسُونَ ۝ وَلَا يَأْمُرَكُمْ أَن تَتَّخِذُوا۟ ٱلْمَلَـٰٓئِكَةَ وَٱلنَّبِيِّـۧنَ أَرْبَابًا أَيَأْمُرُكُم بِٱلْكُفْرِ بَعْدَ إِذْ أَنتُم مُّسْلِمُونَ ۝ ﴾

"It is not (possible) for any human being to whom Allāh has given the Book and Al-Hukm (the knowledge and understanding of the laws of religion) and Prophethood to say to the people: "Be my worshippers rather than Allāh's." On the contrary (he would say): "Be you Rabbaniyyin (learned men of religion who practise what they know and also preach others), because you are teaching the Book, and you are studying it. "Nor would he order you to take angels and Prophets for lords (gods) Would he order you to disbelieve after you have submitted to Allāh's Will?" (3:79,80)

The prayer is the highest act of worship. Yet the teachers of false guidance, the so-called scholars and tyrants have divided the acts of prayer between themselves. For instance, the teachers of false guidance chose the highest act in the prayer, prostrating, for themselves. Some so-called scholars have also acquired bowing down for themselves. When they meet each other, some of them bow down before the others just as one does while praying to Allāh! As for the tyrants, they acquired standing up for themselves! Free and slave men stand up before the tyrants while the tyrants are sitting down.

The Messenger of Allāh ﷺ has prohibited these three acts for other than Allāh. Therefore, committing these prohibited acts is a clear violation of the Prophet's commands.

The Prophet ﷺ prohibited prostrating to other than Allāh. He said:

« لا يَنبغي لأحدٍ أن يَسجُدَ لأحد »

"No one should prostrate to any other person."

He also criticized Mu'ath رَضِيَ الله عَنْهُ when he prostrated before him. Since prohibiting prostrating before the creation is clearly indicated in the Prophet's *Sunnah*, then those who allow such acts seek to dispute the rights of Allāh and His Messenger ﷺ. Prostrating is one of the essential acts of worship. When the polytheist allows it to the creation, he will be allowing worshipping other than Allāh. The Prophet ﷺ was once asked, "When one sees his brother, should he bow down for him?" He said, 'No.' He was asked, 'Should he hug and kiss him?' He said, 'No.' He was asked, 'Should he shake his hand?' He said, 'Yes.'

Also, bowing down while greeting someone is a type of worship, just as Allāh said:

﴿ وَٱدْخُلُوا۟ ٱلْبَابَ سُجَّدًا ﴾

"And enter the gate in prostration." (or bowing with humility)
(2:58)

Besides, prostrating and entering through the door is not possible at the same time [the prostration mentioned in the Verse is bowing down]!

The Prophet ﷺ also prohibited standing up for someone just as the non-Muslims used to do. He even disallowed this act during the prayer and commanded the Muslim to imitate the leader in the prayer, that if he sits down while praying due to an illness, they all sit behind him although they are healthy. Otherwise, they will be standing while the Imam is sitting down, although their standing is for Allāh. How about if standing was for other than Allāh?

The ignorant misguided people have associated others with Allāh in the worship, thus prostrating before other than Allāh and bowing down for other than Allāh. They also stand up before the creation just as they do when they are praying. They also swear, vow, shave their heads, sacrifice, perform Tawaf (circumambulation of an object or person), love, fear, and obey other than Allāh, just as they do for Allāh and even more. They equate Allāh, the Lord of the Worlds, Whom they worship, with the creation. These are the enemies of the Messages of the Messengers of Allāh ﷺ who equate Allāh with the creation. They are the ones who will say in the Fire, while arguing with the false deities they were worshipping.

$$ ﴿ تَٱللَّهِ إِن كُنَّا لَفِى ضَلَلٍ مُّبِينٍ ۝ إِذْ نُسَوِّيكُم بِرَبِّ ٱلْعَٰلَمِينَ ۝ ﴾ $$

"By Allāh, we were truly, in a manifest error, When We hold you (false gods) as equals (in worship) with the Lord of the Al-'Ālamin (mankind, jinn and all that exists); (26:97,98)

They are also the people, whom Allāh described, when He said:

$$ ﴿ وَمِنَ ٱلنَّاسِ مَن يَتَّخِذُ مِن دُونِ ٱللَّهِ أَندَادًا يُحِبُّونَهُمْ كَحُبِّ ٱللَّهِ وَٱلَّذِينَ ءَامَنُوٓا۟ أَشَدُّ حُبًّا لِّلَّهِ ﴾ $$

"And of mankind are some who take (for worship) others besides Allāh as rivals (to Allāh). They love them as they love Allāh. But those who believe, love Allāh more (then anything else)." (2:165)

All these are among the acts of Shirk (polytheism, associating others with Allāh in worship) that Allāh never forgives.

Part III

The Prophet's Guidance on using
Divine *Ruqyah*
(Islamic Prayer) Formulas and
Natural Medications

The Prophet's guidance on treating those touched by the evil eye

Imam Muslim [and *Ahmad, Ibn Hibban, Al-Hakim* and *At-Tabarani*] narrated that Ibn 'Abbās رَضِيَ الله عَنْهما said, The Messenger of Allāh ﷺ said:

« الْعَيْنُ حَقٌّ؛ وَلَوْ كَانَ شَيْءٌ سَابِقَ الْقَدَرِ لَسَبَقَتْهُ الْعَيْنُ »

"The evil eye is true, and if there is anything that would precede Predestination, it would be the evil eye."

Also, Muslim narrated that Anas رَضِيَ الله عَنْهُ said:

« أَنَّ النَّبِيَّ صلى الله عليه وسلم رخص في الرُّقْيَةِ مِنَ الْحُمَةِ وَالْعَيْنِ وَالنَّمْلَةِ »

*"The Prophet ﷺ has allowed using Islamic prayer formulas *(Ruqyah, divine remedy) against fever, the evil eye and sores."*

Also, in the *Sahihain* it is narrated that Abu Hurairah رَضِيَ الله عَنْهُ said that the Messenger of Allāh ﷺ said, "The evil eye is true." [*Abu Dāwud, Ibn Mājah* and *Ahmad*].

Abu Dāwud reported that 'Āishah رَضِيَ الله عَنْها said:

« كَانَ يُؤْمَرُ الْعَائِنُ فَيَتَوَضَّأُ، ثم يغتسل منه الْمَعِينُ »

"The person who touched others with the evil eye was commanded to perform ablution and the person whom he touched by the evil eye would wash with that water." [Al-*Bukhari, Muslim, An-Nasai'i, Ibn Mājah, Abu Na'im* and Al-*Isma'ili*].

Further, 'Āishah رَضِيَ الله عَنْها narrated, as the *Sahihain* reported:

« أَمَرَنِي النَّبِيُّ صلى الله عليه وسلم، أَوْ أَمَرَ أَنْ نَسْتَرْقِيَ من العين »

"The Prophet ﷺ commanded me, or commanded, that we should use Islamic prayer formulas from the evil eye."

In addition, At-Tirmidhi narrated that Asmā' Bint Umays رَضِيَ الله عَنْها

---

* **Editor's note**: Ruqyah in Arabic literally means incantation and they were used in pre-Islamic times for various purposes. After Islam the Prophet stopped their use and substituted prayers and supplications from the Qur'ān and those that he used in praying to Allāh.

said, "I said, O Messenger of Allāh ﷺ! The children of Ja'far are usually touched by the evil eye. Should I perform an Islamic prayer formula for them?' He said:

« نعم، فلو كان شيءٌ يسبقُ القضاءَ، لسَبَقَتْه العينُ »

"Yes. If there is anything that precedes Predestination, it would be the evil eye." [An-Nasai'ī and Ahmad].

Also, Imam Mālik narrated that 'Amir bin Rabi'ah once saw Sahl bin Hunaif take a bath and said, "By Allāh! I have never seen the skin of a virgin that is softer than what I have just seen." Sahl fell to the ground. The Prophet ﷺ then came to 'Amir while angry and said to him:

« عَلامَ يَقْتُلُ أحدكم أخاه؟ أَلَّا بَرَّكْتَ؛ اغْتسِل لَه »

"Why would one of you kill his own brother? Why have you not said Tabrik [Baraka Allāh, (بارك الله - may Alla·h bless it)]? Take a bath for it."

'Amir then washed his face, hands, elbows, knees, feet and a part of his garment in a pot for what he had done and then poured the used water on Sahl. Soon after, Sahl started moving about with the people. [*An-Nasai'ī, Ibn Mājah, Ahmad, Al-Hakim* and *Ibn Hibban*].

Malik also narrated:

« إن العَيْنَ حقٌّ؛ توضَّأ لهُ »

"The evil eye is true, so perform ablution for it."

Another *Hadith* narrated by Abdul Razzaq reads:

« العَين حَقٌّ؛ ولو كان شيءٌ سابقَ القَدَرِ: لَسَبَقتْه العين؛ فإذا اسْتُغْسِل أحدُكم فليغتسِلْ »

"The evil eye is true, and if there is anything that precedes Predestination, it would be the evil eye. When one is touched by the evil eye, he should take a bath for it."

At-Tirmidhi said:

"The person who touched others with the evil eye should be commanded to submerge his hand in a pot of water and then wash his mouth, then spit the water back into the pot. He should then wash his face in the pot, then submerges his left hand it and

pour some water on the right knee above the pot, and then submerges his right hand and pour water on his left knee. He should then wash his garment inside the pot and the water should not be spilled on the ground. Rather, it should be poured on top of the person whom he touched by the evil eye from behind all at once."

There are two types of the evil eye, human and Jinn related. Umm Salamah رَضِيَ الله عَنْها said that the Prophet ﷺ once saw a young girl, who had a certain expression on her face and said:

« اسْتَرْقُوا لها ، فإنَّ بها النَّظْرَةَ »

"Seek an Islamic prayer formula for her because she is touched by the evil eye." [Al-Bukhari, Muslim, Al-'Hakim, Abu Na'im, Al-Isma'ili and At-Tabarani]

Abu Sa'id also narrated that:

« إنّ النبيَّ صلى الله عليه وسلم كانَ يتعوَّذ من الجَانِّ، ومن عَيْنِ الإنسَانِ »

The Prophet ﷺ used to seek refuge from the Jinn and the evil eye of mankind." [At-Tirmidhi and An-Nasai'i]

Some people who do not have sound comprehension or correct sight and hearing have rejected the fact that the evil eye causes harm, claiming that this is a superstitious, untrue belief. These people are indeed among the most ignorant people who have the least sound comprehension and the thickest minds. They are the farthest from acquiring knowledge of the soul and the heart and the effect of each on the natural world.

The best minds in every nation do not dispute the fact that the evil eye is true, although they differ on its causes and true effects. Some people say that when people who touch others by the evil eye feel evilness in their hearts, then their eyes transform the evil thoughts into harmful rays just like the type of snake that looks at its prey and causes it to perish.

Another group says that it is possible that invisible powers emit from the person who touches others with the evil eye and then enters the body of the person whom they touched and harms them.

However, other people say that Allāh creates the harm on the person touched by the evil eye without any rays that emit from the eye of the person who touched him. Yet, this is the method of those who deny the existence of the various spiritual powers that exist in this world. Allāh has created special powers in some of the creation that have profound effects on other creations. For instance, the soul has such a profound effect on the body that no one can deny. Also, have you not noticed how the face of a shy person turns red if his sight falls on what is not suitable for him, and turns yellow when he looks at someone he fears? You can also witness the effect of the evil eye has on people and the weakness it causes in their bodies.

The evil eye is actually the effect exerted by the soul on the victim. Souls vary in their essence, powers, characteristics and qualities. Therefore, the soul of an envious person can harm a victim profoundly, and this is why Allāh has commanded His Messenger to seek refuge with Him from the evil eye.

The harmful effect of an envious person on the envied person cannot be denied, except by those who are far away from reality. It is a fact that an evil envious soul touches the envied person in such an evil manner that it causes them harm. Similarly, the poisonous viper gets so enraged and evil when it meets the enemy that it has a special effect on the victim, sometimes leading to aborting the fetus or causing blindness. The Prophet ﷺ described the short tailed viper and the striped viper as having the ability that they can affect sight and abort pregnancy. Some types of snakes have a negative effect on people by their mere sight, because of the viciousness of such creatures and the effect of this viciousness on people.

These effects that we mentioned are not restricted to physical contact, as some of those who have little knowledge in the natural world and the religion think. Rather, these effects could be caused by physical contact, sight, the soul directing its power to the victim, through imagination and evil omens, and so forth.

The envious person might be blind, yet when something is described to him or her, his envious soul affects the described object and harms it even though the blind person cannot see it. Allāh said to His Prophet ﷺ:

$$ \text{﴾ وَإِن يَكَادُ ٱلَّذِينَ كَفَرُوا لَيُزْلِقُونَكَ بِأَبْصَٰرِهِمْ لَمَّا سَمِعُوا ٱلذِّكْرَ ﴿} $$

"And verily, those who disbelieve would almost make you slip with

*their eyes (through hatred) when they hear the Reminder (the
Qur'ān) ..." (69:51)*

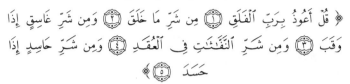

Say: "I seek refuge with (Allāh), the Lord of the daybreak, From
the evil of what He has created, And from the evil of the
darkening (night) as it comes with its darkness; (or the moon as
it sets or goes away), And from the evil of those who practise
witchcraft when they blow in the knots, And from the evil of the
envier when he envies." (113:1-5)

Every person who touches others by the evil eye is an envious
person, but not vise versa. Since envy includes the evil eye in its general
meaning, seeking refuge from it includes seeking refuge from the evil eye
also.

The evil eye includes throwing arrows of envy that depart the envious
heart and soul in the direction of the envied person, sometimes falling on
its target. If the envied person is unarmed and unprepared, the evil eye
will cause him harm. If the envied person is prepared and armed, the
arrows might turn back on the one who threw them. This is similar to
what actually occurs when one shoots real arrows. The resemblance is
that this occurs through the soul while the arrows are shot in the
material world. The evil eye starts when the envious person likes
something then follows it with his evil thoughts and desires and then the
evil eye touches the envied object.

Sometimes a person might even touch his own self with the evil eye,
which is one of the worst types of envy. Sometimes one might touch
others with the evil eye just by his envious nature. Some of our scholars
say that such envious people should be imprisoned and should be given
what they need of sustenance until they die.

The Prophetic medicine for treating sorcery (the evil eye) was of several types

Abu Dāwud narrated that Sahl ibn Hunaif said:

« مَرَرْنا بِسَيْلٍ، فدخلتُ فا غتسلتُ فيه، فخرجتُ مَحمومًا . فَنُمِيَ ذلك إلى
رسول الله صلى الله عليه وسلم، فَقَالَ: مُرُوا أبا ثابت يَتعوَّذُ... لا رُقيةَ إلا
في نَفْسٍ أوحُمَةٍ أَوْ لَدْغَة »

*"We came by a water fall and I went in it and took a bath, but
when I finished I came down with a fever. When the Messenger
of Allāh ﷺ was informed, he said, 'Command Abu Ath-Thabit to
seek refuge (with Allāh for Sahl) with an Islamic prayer formula.' I
said, 'O my master! Does an Islamic prayer formula bring about
benefit?' He said, 'There is no Islamic prayer formula except to
fend off an evil eye and against fever and a (snake or a scorpion)
bite.'" [Also, Al-Hakim narrated this Hadith].*

There are several types of Islamic prayer formulas, such as reciting the
first chapter in the Qur'ān, the Mu'awwithatan (chapters 113 and 114 of
the Qur'ān) and Ayat Al-Kursi (2:255).

Also, there are several types of Prophetic Islamic prayer formulas. For
instance, one might recite:

« أعوذ بِكَلِمات الله التَّامّاتِ من شر ما خَلَق »

*"I seek refuge with Allāh's Prefect Words from the evil of what
He has created."*

Also, one could recite:

«أعُوذ بِكَلِمات الله التَّامَّةِ، من كُلِّ شيطانٍ وهَامَّةٍ، ومن كل عَينٍ لامَّةٍ »

*"I seek refuge with Allāh's Prefect Words from every devil and evil
soul and from every evil eye."*

Also, one might recite,

«أعوذ بِكَلِماتِ الله التَّامّاتِ الَّتِي لا يُجَاوِزُهُنَّ بَرٌّ ولا فاجِرٌ، من شر ما خَلَق
وذَرَأَوبرَأ، و من شرِّ ما ينزِل منَ السَّماء، ومِنْ شرِّ ما يَعْرُجُ فيها، ومن شر
ماذَرَأ في الأرضِ، ومن شرِّ ما يخرُجُ منها، ومن شرِّ فِتَن اللَّيلِ والنَّهارِ، ومن
شر طَوَارِقِ اللَّيلِ والنهار، إلا طارِقًا يَطرُق بخير يا رَحْمانُ »

*"I seek refuge with Allāh's Prefect Words, which no righteous or
evil soul could ever encompass (or supercede), from the evil of
what He has created, made and started; from the evil of whatever*

*descends from the sky and whatever ascends to it; from the evil of
what He has created on the earth and what comes out of it; from
the evil of the trials of the night and the day; and from what
comes by at night or during the day, except whoever comes with
a righteous matter. O Merciful One!"*

Also, this includes the supplication:

«أعوذ بكلمات الله التامَّةِ من غَضَبه وعِقابه وَمِن شرّ عِبَادِه ومِنْ هَمَزاتِ
الشياطينِ و أنْ يَحضُرُونِ »

*"I seek refuge with Allāh's Perfect Words from His anger and
torment, from the evil of His slaves and from the whispers of the
devils or that they might attend me."*

Also, one might say the following supplication:

اللّهم إني أعوذ بوَجْهِك الكريم وكَلِماتك التَّامَّات، من شَرِّما أنْتَ آخِذٌ
بناصِيَتِهِ، اللّهُمَّ أنت تَكْشِفُ المأثَمَ والمَغْرَمَ، اللّهُمَّ إنه لا يُهزم جُنْدُك، ولا
يُخلَفُ وَعْدُك ؛ سُبحانَك وبحَمْدِك»

*"O Allāh! I seek refuge with Your Most Honorable Face and Your
Prefect Words from the evil of every creation that is only in your
grasp (or control). O Allāh! You expel the sins and loss. O Allāh!
Your soldiers will never be defeated nor will Your Promise ever be
broken. All praise and glorification is due to You."*

Also, one might supplicate:

« أعوذ بوجهِ الله العظيم الّذي لا شيءَ أعظَمُ منه، وبكَلِماته التَّامَات الّتي لا
يجاوِزْهنَّ برٌ ولا فاجرٌ، وبأسْماءِ الله الحُسْنَىٰ - ما علمت منها وما لم أعلم -
من شرِّ ما خلَقَ وذرأَ وبرأ، ومن شرِّ كل ذِي شرٍّ لَا أُطيق شرَّه، ومن شرِّ كل
ذي شرٍّ أنْتَ آخِذٌ بِنَاصيته ؛ إن رَبِّي علىٰ صراطٍ مُسْتقيم »

*"I seek refuge with Allāh's Most Exalted Face which is greater
than everything else. And with His Perfect Words that no
righteous or evil being could ever overcome; and with Allāh's Most
Prefect Names, those which I know and those which I have no
knowledge of, from the evil of what He has created, shaped and
made. From the evil of every creation that I cannot overcome and*

*from the evil of every evil creation that only You control (or grasp
its forelock). Certainly, my Lord is on a Straight Path."*

Also, the Prophetic Islamic prayer formulas include:

« اللّهم أنت ربِّي لا إله إلّا أنت، عَلَيك توكّلتُ، وأنت رَبُّ العَرْش العظيم؛
ما شاء الله كانَ، وما لَمْ يشأْ لم يكُنْ؛ لا حول ولا قُوَّةَ إلا بالله؛ أعلم أنَّ الله
على كُلِّ شيءٍ قديرٌ، وأنّ الله قد أحاط بِكُلِّ شيء علمًا، وأحصى كلَّ شَيْء
عَدَدًا. اللّهم إني أعوذ بك من شرِّ نفسي وشِر الشيطان وشرْكِه، ومن شر كل
دابَّةٍ أنت آخِذٌ بناصِيَتِها؛ إن ربي علّى صِراط مستقيم »

*"O Allāh! You Are my Lord, there is no deity worthy of worship
except You. I depend on You (for every thing). You are the Lord of
the Mighty Throne. What Allāh wills, occurs, and what He does
not will to happen, will never exist. There is no power or strength
except with Allāh. I know that Allāh is Able to do everything, that
His Knowledge has encompassed everything and that He has kept
count of everything. O Allāh! I seek refuge with You from the evil
within myself, from the evil and the Shirk (polytheism) of Satan,
and from the evil of every creation that only You grasp its
forelock. Surely, my Lord is on the Straight Path."*

Or, one might recite the following supplication,

« تَحَصَّنْتُ باللهِ الَّذي لا إله إلا هُو إلهي وإله كل شيء، واعتصَمْتُ بربي وربِّ
كل شيء، وتَوَكَّلْتُ على الْحَيِّ الذي لا يموت، واستَدْفَعْتُ الشَّرَّ بِلَا حولَ ولا
قوةَ إلَّا بالله؛ حسبيَ الله ونعمَ الوكيلُ، حسبيَ الرَّبُّ من العِباد، حسبيَ الخالقُ
من الَمَخْلوق، حسبيَ الرازِق من المَرْزوق، حسبي اللهُ هو حَسْبِيَ، حسبيَ
الذي بيده ملكوتُ كل شيء وهو يُجِيرُ ولا يجارُ عليه؛ حسبي الله وكَفَىٰ سمع
الله لِمنْ دَعا، وليس وراءَ الله مَرْمَىٰ؛ حسبيَ الله لا إلٰهَ إلا هو، عليه توكَّلت،
وهو رب العَرْش العظيم »

*"I seek refuge with Allāh, other than Whom there is no god. He
is my God and the God of everything. I seek refuge with my Lord
and the Lord of everything. I depend on the Ever-Living Who never
dies. I seek to fend off the evil with: no power or strength except*

from Allāh.' Allāh is enough of a supporter for me, and indeed, what an Excellent Helper. Allāh is enough for me from the slaves. The Creator is enough for me from the creation. The Sustainer is enough for me from the sustained. Allāh is indeed enough for me. He Who owns everything, Who grants refuge while no one can ever grant refuge against Him is indeed sufficient for me. Allāh is sufficient for me. Allāh's hearing who ever supplicates to Him is also sufficient for me. There is no goal to reach greater than Allāh. Allāh, other than Whom there is no god, is sufficient for me, I depend on Him (for each and everything), and He is the Lord of the Mighty Throne."

Those who try these different types of supplication and Islamic prayer formulas will surely understand their great value and benefit, and consequently, will recognize the great need for them. These supplications will shield one from the effects of the evil eye and will fend off its harm if the evil eye touched them, but according to the degree of Faith, strength of soul, degree of reliance (on Allāh) and strength of heart of whoever recites them. These supplications are types of weapons, and their effectiveness depends on the skill of whoever uses them.

If the person fears that he might touch other people by the evil eye, let him fend off its harm by saying:

« اللَّهُمَّ بَارِكْ عَلَيْهِ »

"O Allāh! Bless him."

The Prophet ﷺ commanded 'Amir bin Rabi'ah,

« أَلَّا بَرَّكْتَ »

"Why did you not say Tabrik [Baraka Allāh, (may Allāh bless it)] for him?"

Further, saying *"Mā shā' Allāh* (what Allāh has willed), *Lā Quwwata illā Billah* (There is no power except from Allāh)" also helps fend off the evil eye. Hisham bin 'Urwah narrated that his father used to say, "What Allāh wills will certainly come to pass, there is no power except from Allāh," upon seeing something that he likes and upon entering one of his gardens.

Also, Jibril once said an Islamic prayer formula for the Prophet ﷺ,

which Muslim narrated in his *Sahih*:

« بِاسْمِ اللهِ أَرْقِيكَ، مِنْ كُلِّ دَاءٍ يُؤْذِيكَ؛ مِنْ شَرِّ كُلِّ نَفْسٍ أَوْ عَيْنِ حَاسِدٍ اللهُ

يَشْفِيكَ؛ بِسْمِ اللهِ أَرْقِيكَ »

*"In the Name of Allāh I say Islamic prayer formulas for your
benefit, from every illness that might harm you and from the evil
of every evil soul or envious person's eye. Allāh will cure you, in
the Name of Allāh I say Islamic prayer formulas for your benefit."
[At-Tirmidhi and An-Nasai'ī]*

Some of our rightly guided ancestors stated that there is no harm if
some *Ayat* (Verse) from the Qur'ān were written in ink and then washed
with water and that the sick person drinks that water. Mujahid issued a
statement to that effect, and so did Abu Qilabah. It was also reported
that Ibn 'Abbās once commanded that two verses from the Qur'ān to be
written for a woman who had hard pregnancies and that the Verses
were then washed with water and she was to drink the water. Also,
Ayûb said, "I saw Abu Qilabah write some Verses from the Qur'ān,
wash it with water and then give the water to a person who was
suffering from some type of illness to drink it."

Also, the person who touches other people with the evil eye should
be commanded to wash his limbs and the end of his garments, or his
sexual organ according to one opinion, from the right side. He then
pours the water on the head of the person whom he touched with the
evil eye from behind him without notice. This is a type of cure that the
doctors cannot produce with their medicine. Also, those who reject such
type of Islamic prayer formulas would never benefit from it because they
do not believe that the Islamic prayer formulas carry any benefit.

Since the doctors cannot explain many natural occurrences in the
world, why would the hypocrites among them reject such powers and
effects that the religion produces? Added to this is the fact that washing
up with the water has a real benefit, experience testifies to its usefulness.
Similarly, the anger will be washed away from the heart if one places his
hand on the angry person's chest. This is similar to confronting a man
who is carrying a lit torch that he wants to throw at you, but you keep
pouring water on it while it is still in his hand until you extinguish it. This
is why the Prophet ﷺ commanded the person who touches people by

the evil eye to ask Allāh to bless whatever he has envied, so that the evil thoughts that he feels go away and are replaced by the supplication, which is a type of good charity. The cure should be compatible to the disease so that it has an affect on it. It is possible that when one touches others by the evil eye that a certain power appears on the end of his garment, or his sexual organ as we stated, and that it is then transferred to the affected person or object. When it is washed by water, the evil power will be removed. Yet again, and as we have stated, this matter has a lot to do with evil spirits, which will be stopped from producing harm if washed by water. Also, it might be that washing with water serves to cool the heart and thus cures the person who was about to touch others with the evil eye. Sometimes, when a poisonous insect bites someone and then the insect is killed, the bitten person feels a little relief afterwards. This might occur because the bitten person feels joy that the insect was killed and this feeling of elation helps to cure the poison faster. In short, when the person who touches others with the evil eye is washed, the evil that he thought of or felt will be washed away with the water.

If someone asks, "If washing with the water helps the aggressor, then what about the victim of the evil eye?"

We say that pouring the water on victims of the evil eye also helps cool the effect of the evil eye on the victim just as it extinguished the veiled thoughts from the aggressor's heart. Water, which is used to cool burning iron rods, is also often used as a medicine with which the doctors would concur. It is natural that the same water used to extinguish the evil eye is used to rid the victim of the evil eye of its effect.

Therefore, comparing the Prophetic medicine to regular medicine that doctors use is just like comparing the doctor's medicine to folk medicines. Rather, the comparison is even less appropriate, for the difference between the Prophets and the doctors is profoundly greater than the difference between the doctors and those who are not qualified to practice medicine. You should have discovered by now the brotherly relation between religion and wisdom, and that they never contradict each other. Allāh guides whom He wills to the straight path and opens the doors of success to those who knock on such doors. He Alone is the Source of all bounties and irrefutable proofs.

Fighting the evil eye is more likely to be successful if one conceals his blessings from the people.

For instance, Al-Baghawi narrated that once Uthman رَضِيَ اللهُ عَنْهُ saw a handsome boy and commanded, "Blacken his cleft chin so that the evil eye does not touch him."

Al-Khattabi also narrated in *Gharib Al-Hadith,* "It was narrated that Uthman رَضِيَ اللهُ عَنْهُ once saw a handsome boy and that he said, 'Hide his cleft chin with black color.'" Uthman رَضِيَ اللهُ عَنْهُ wanted to hide the cleft chin of the handsome boy using black color so that he was not touched by the evil eye.

Another Islamic prayer formula that helps ward off the evil eye was related by Abu 'Abdullāh Al-Tayya'hi he was once traveling for *Hajj* or Jihad using a good animal. There was a man in the caravan who would never look at something but would bring it to its demise. Abu 'Abdullāh was then told, 'Preserve your camel from this man's eye.' He said, 'My camel cannot be touched by harm.' The person who touched with the evil eye was informed of Abu 'Abdullāh's response and he waited for a chance when Abu 'Abdullāh was not present and looked at the camel which soon fell on its feet! When Abu 'Abdullāh came and was told that the person had touched it with the evil eye and that his camel was suffering, as was evident, he said, 'Show me the man.' When he came by him he said, 'In the Name of Allāh a restraint that restrains, a hard rock and a blazing star: I ask that the evil eye returns to the person who started it and on the most dear people to him (meaning the envious person himself)"

Allâh said:

$$\text{﴿ فَٱرْجِعِ ٱلْبَصَرَ هَلْ تَرَىٰ مِن فُطُورٍ ۝ ثُمَّ ٱرْجِعِ ٱلْبَصَرَ كَرَّتَيْنِ يَنقَلِبْ إِلَيْكَ ٱلْبَصَرُ خَاسِئًا وَهُوَ حَسِيرٌ ۝ ﴾}$$

Then look again: "Can you see any rifts?" Then look again and yet again, your sight will return to you in a state of humiliation and worn out." (67:3,4)

Then, the person known for the evil eye lost his sight and the camel was cured.*

The Prophet's guidance on treating sickness in general with Islamic prayer formulas

Muslim narrated that Abu Sa'id Al-Khudri رَضِيَ اللهُ عَنْهُ said that Jibril عليه السلام came to the Prophet ﷺ and said to him:

« يا محمد، اشْتَكَيْتَ ؟ قال . نعم . فقال جبريل عليه السلام : باسم الله أَرقِيكَ، من كل داءٍ يُؤذِيكَ، ومن شرِّ كل نفْسٍ أو عينٍ حاسدٍ الله يَشفيك ؛ باسم الله أرقيكَ»

"O Muhammad ﷺ, are you complaining from an illness?" He said,

---

* **Editor's note**: The problem of the manifestation of evil through human beings is still a very perplexing problem. School boys who gun down there classmates for the most insignificant reasons, serial killers, child abusers, snuff movies (movies where they actually kill a person on film), pornography etc. are common examples that we all have learned to live with. As Muslims we know that there is a force of evil whose main purpose is to destroy the children of Adam (Human beings). We are also told that this force of evil can whisper in the breasts of mankind. Without this knowledge we would have to assume that the source of all evil thoughts is the thinker. We, as Muslims, are told to seek refuge in Allāh from these thoughts and to reject them. Without this knowledge we would have to reconcile our evil thoughts with our perceptions of our own character and how others perceive us. This conflict in our perceptions could produce a destructive form of confusion. Without the Islamic knowledge available we would have to rationalize the evil, by hiding it, attributing it to another outside force, or assuming it is a part of ourselves (our dark side). The final result of our investigation is that we find the only beneficiary of all of these activities is the force of evil itself. As any good investigator knows, the perpetrator of any crime is almost always the one who benefits the most. The perpetrator of the evils we mentioned above (serial killers etc.) leave the human beings associated with it defective and psychologically deformed while the forces of evil are strengthened. Evil entices us to join it with the lure of material benefits, power, or the satisfying of desires, but in the end it only uses us to gain its goal of the destruction of human beings. Throughout the ages these forces of evil have committed themselves to use deception as their most powerful technique, while we are debating their possible existence they are achieving their goals. They recruit those of mankind (with or without their awareness as suits the purpose of evil) who are useful to them and who can serve their purposes giving them limited knowledge and powers to serve them. The power of the evil eye is, as it is named, based on evil. However evil will use the form most suited to its survival at any one given time without exposing itself as the source.

"Yes." Jibril then said, "In the Name of Allāh I say Islamic prayer formulas for your benefit, from every illness that might harm you and from the evil of every evil soul or envious evil eye. Allāh will cure you, in the Name of Allāh I say Islamic prayer formulas for your benefit."

If someone asks, "What do you say about the Hadith that Abu Dāwud narrated:

« لَا رُقْيَةَ إِلَّا مِنْ عَيْنٍ أَوْ حُمَةٍ »

"There is no Islamic prayer formula except for an evil eye or fever."

To answer this question we say that the Hadith does not deny that the Islamic prayer formulas can be used in other instances. Rather, the *Hadith* only states that the Islamic prayer formulas work best for the evil eye and fever of all kinds. What further attests to this fact is that the *Hadith* itself narrated that Sahl ibn Hunaif asked the Prophet ﷺ when he was touched by the evil eye, "Do the Islamic prayer formulas bring about benefit?" The Prophet ﷺ then answered:

« لَا رُقْيَةَ إِلَّا مِنْ عَيْنٍ أَوْ حُمَةٍ »

"There is no Islamic prayer formula (that works better) than in the cases of evil eye and the fever."

Also, the various *Ahadith* in general allow Islamic prayer formulas. For instance, Muslim narrated that the Prophet ﷺ allowed using Islamic prayer formulas in the cases of the evil eye, fever and *Namlah* (ant's bite or sores).

The Prophet's guidance on treating one bitten (by an animal) by reciting Al-Fātihah

In the *Sahihain* [also *At-Tirmidhi, Ibn Mājah* and *Ahmad*] it is narrated that Abu Sa'id Al-Khudri said, "Some of the Companions of the Prophet ﷺ went on a journey till they reached some of the Arab tribes (at night). They asked the latter to treat them as their guests but they refused. The chief of that tribe was then bitten by a snake (or stung by a scorpion) and they tried their best to cure him but in vain. Some of them said (to the others), 'Nothing has benefited him, will you go to the people who resided here at night, it may be that some of them might possess something (as treatment).' They went to the group of the companions (of the Prophet ﷺ) and said, 'Our chief has been bitten by a snake (or stung by a scorpion) and we have tried everything but he has not benefited. Have you got anything (useful)?' One of them replied, 'Yes, by Allāh! I can recite an Islamic prayer formula, but as you have refused to accept us as your guests, I will not recite the Islamic prayer formula for you unless you fix for us some wages for it.' They agreed to pay them a flock of sheep. One of them then recited (The chapter *Al-Fātihah*): 'All the praises are for the Lord of the Worlds' and puffed over the chief who became alright as if he was released from a chain, and got up and started walking, showing no signs of sickness. They paid them what they agreed to pay. Some of them (i.e., the Companions) then suggested to divide their earnings among themselves, but the one who performed the recitation said, 'Do not divide them till we go to the Prophet ﷺ and narrate the whole story to him, and wait for his order.' So, they went to Allāh's Messenger ﷺ and narrated the story. Allāh's Messenger asked:

« وما يُدْريك أنها رُقْيَةٌ »

"How did you come to know that the chapter Al-Fātihah could be recited as an Islamic prayer formula?"

Then he added:

« قد أَصَبْتم؛ اقتسِمُوا واضرِبُوا لي معكم سَهْمًا »

"You have done the right thing. Divide (what you have earned) and assign a share for me as well."

It is a well-known fact that certain types of speech have a profound effect and benefit that experience testifies to. So how about the Words of the Lord of the Worlds that are as preferred to the creation's speech as Allāh is preferred above His creation? Allāh's Words contain the ultimate cure, the perfect immunity, correct guidance and an encompassing mercy, that if it was revealed to a mountain, it would turn to dust in appreciation of Allāh's Glory. Allāh said:

﴿ وَنُنَزِّلُ مِنَ ٱلْقُرْءَانِ مَا هُوَ شِفَآءٌ وَرَحْمَةٌ لِّلْمُؤْمِنِينَ ﴾

"And We send down of the Qur'ān that which is a healing and a mercy to those who believe (in Islāmic Monotheism and act on

it)" (17:82)

﴿ وَعَدَ اللَّهُ الَّذِينَ ءَامَنُوا وَعَمِلُوا الصَّالِحَاتِ مِنْهُم مَّغْفِرَةً وَأَجْرًا عَظِيمًا ﴾

"Allāh has promised those among them who believe (i.e., all those who follow Islāmic Monotheism, the religion of Prophet Muhammad ﷺ till the Day of Resurrection) and do righteous good deeds, forgiveness and a mighty reward (i.e., Paradise)." (48:29)

What could one think of the opening of the Qur'ān (*Al-Fātihah*, the first chapter) that is not comparable to any Verse or chapter revealed in the Qur'ān, the Torah, the Gospel or the Zabur (that was revealed to Prophet Dawūd عليه السلام). The *Al-Fātihah* contains the general meaning of all the Divine Books sent down by Allāh. It contains Allāh's Names and Attributes, such as Allāh, the *Rabb* (Lord), *Ar-Rahmān* (Most Merciful) and *Ar-Rahīm* (Most Beneficent). It also affirms Resurrection, Allāh's Oneness in Lordship. It also mentions the creation's dependence on Allāh's help and guidance and that He Alone grants such bounties. It also contains the best and most beneficial supplication that the creation needs: being guided to the Straight Path that entails acquiring knowledge of His Names and Attributes, worshipping Him alone, obeying His Commands, refraining from His prohibitions and staying firm on this path until death. It also contains the kinds of creation that are divided into those who have acquired the bounty of knowing the Truth, and who prefer and implement its implications. On the other hand, there are those who have earned Allāh's Anger by avoiding the truth after knowing it and there are those who are led astray from the True Path. These are the camps that the creation is divided into. Also, the *Al-Fātihah* affirms Predestination and the Commandments of the religion, Allāh's Names and Attributes, Resurrection and Prophethood. It also purifies the heart and mentions Allāh's Justice and Generosity. It also refutes all types 'of innovations and evil methods. We mentioned all these virtues for the *Al-Fātihah* in our book that explains it, *Madariju As-Salikin*. Certainly, a chapter that contains all these virtues and benefits deserves to be used as a cure for disease, as well as an antidote for poisonous stings.

Indeed, *Al-Fātihah* is the best cure because it contains sincere servitude to Allāh, praising Him, relating all bounties to Him, seeking His help and support, and invoking Him for all types of advantages, such as the correct guidance that brings about benefit and fends off torment.

It was reported that the part in *Al-Fātihah* that contains the Islamic prayer formula is what Allāh said:

$$﴿ إِيَّاكَ نَعْبُدُ وَإِيَّاكَ نَسْتَعِينُ ﴾$$

"You (Alone) we worship, and You (Alone) we ask for help (for everything)." (1:5)

Indeed, these are mighty powerful words that contain the strongest medicine contained in this chapter. These words entail sincere dependence and reliance on Allāh, seeking refuge and help from Him and showing meekness and need of Him. Consequently, these words contain the best goals to seek, which is worshiping Allāh Alone. Also they contain the best method to acquire these goals, that is, invoking Allāh for His support so that one achieves these goals.

While I was in Makkah, I once fell sick and had no access to a doctor or medicine. So I used to seek a cure in The *Al-Fātihah* by sipping a drink from the well of Zamzam that I recited the *Al-Fātihah* on. I found complete cure in this method and I used to rely on it whenever I felt pain. This cure always helped me.

There is a wonderful secret in using the *Al-Fātihah* as an Islamic prayer formula to treat poisons, and Allāh has created a cure for every disease as we have stated. Venomous beasts have a special effect on their victims with their evil souls. Furthermore, the weapon that the venomous beasts use is the needle that they use to sting and inject the venom into their victims. Likewise, the person who is applying the Islamic prayer formula will have a positive effect on the person receiving the Islamic prayer formula, thus enhancing his chances of a speedy recovery by Allāh's will. In this case, the victim will feel that his strength and resolve are enhanced with the Islamic prayer formula and the divine remedy, similar to the relation that exists between regular medicine and the sick person. Also, the wetness and the air contained in the spit of the person who recites the Islamic prayer formula, that contains the supplication and the remembrance of Allāh, will all enhance the chances of recovery. Since the person who recites the Islamic prayer formula recites it with both his heart and mouth, then adding some of the air and moisture that exists inside his body through the spit will maximize the effectiveness, power and strength of the remedy. Certainly, this mixture of heart and soul used in the divine remedy works just as regular medicine works on the body.

The person who applies the Islamic prayer formula has an advantage over the evil forces (including poisonous snakes etc.,) since he adds words of the Islamic prayer formula and spit to the strength of his inner self to remove the effects of the evil forces and the venom. Also, the more strength of heart the person has, the stronger the Islamic prayer formula he recites becomes. There is another secret behind using spit in the divine remedy, which is also used by the evil forces, just as Allāh said,

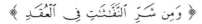

"And from the evil of those who practise witchcrafts when they blow in the knots." (113:4)

The body is greatly affected by what the heart feels and so blowing the air and spitting resembles a way to intensify the effect of what the heart feels and intends. Those who work sorcery tie some knots and blow onto them words of sorcery, which work on the victim although he or she might not be present. In this way, the evil force helps transferring the words of sorcery and their effect to the victim. When the force for good retaliates by using the Islamic prayer formula and then breathing unto the victim, the more powerful of the warring parties wins. War between good and evil forces resemble real war that occurs between people. The spiritual forces essentially use and enlist physical bodies in their wars against each other. Whoever is only concerned about the material world will not feel any of this raging war since he is attached to the environment that he believes in, that is, the material world, and he is far away from the world of spiritual forces and their effect on mankind.

In short, when the good spiritual force is strong enough and feels the effects and the meanings contained in the *Al-Fātihah,* along with the breathing that accompanies reciting it, the Islamic prayer formula will have the intended effect against the evil forces and will thus remove their harmful effect. Allāh knows best.

The Prophet's guidance on treating scorpion stings

The chapter *Al-Ikhlas* contains the essentials of the Faith and the Creed, various aspects of *Tawhid,* and attesting to and affirming Allāh's Oneness that entails denying all types and forms of *shirk* with Him. It also entails affirming that Allāh is the Sustainer, along with asserting every type of perfection for Him. Consequently, the creation seeks Allāh for each and every need. This chapter also denies that Allāh has a parent, an offspring, or an equal, and this is why it equals one third of the Qur'ān. Furthermore, Allāh's Name "*As-Samad* (the Sustainer)" that the chapter contains includes each and every type of perfection. Also, the chapter denies that Allāh has an equal, while Allāh's Name *Al-Āhad* (the One) also denies the existence of a partner with Allāh. These are the three essential cornerstones of Tawhid [Allāh's Oneness in Lordship and worship and in His Names and Attributes].

The *Mu'awwidhātān* (chapters 113 and 114 of the Qur'ān) also includes seeking refuge with Allāh from every type of evil and harm. Seeking refuge from the evil that Allāh has created includes every type of evil that such creations, whether physical or spiritual, can ever produce and cause. Seeking refuge from the night when its sign, (the moon), sets, entails seeking refuge from the evil souls that thrive during the night, as opposed to the light of the day. This is because when the darkness falls and the moon sets, the evil forces come out. Also, seeking refuge from those who tie knots and blow on them includes seeking refuge from the evil of sorcerers and their sorcery. Also, seeking refuge from envious people means seeking refuge from the evil forces that cause harm through the envious people's bodies and sight. The second chapter (114) of the *Mu'awwidhatān* entails seeking refuge from the evil of humans and Jinn. Consequently, the two *Mu'awwidhātn* entail seeking refuge from every type of evil. Therefore, they have a great benefit as a shield against evil before it occurs. This is why the Messenger of Allāh ﷺ advised 'Uqbah bin 'Amir to recite them after every prayer, as At-Tirmidhi has narrated. This advice from the Prophet ﷺ contains a great secret and benefit that helps repulse all types of evil during the time between the prayers. The Prophet ﷺ also described the *Mu'awwidhatān* when he said:

« ما تَعَوَّذَ المُتَعَوِّذون بِمِثْلِهما »

"No one who seeks refuge can ever find a refuge like them."

It was also reported that when the Prophet ﷺ was the victim of sorcery the spell contained eleven knots tied each with a special incantation blown on it, and that whenever Jibril عليه السلام recited a Verse from the *Mu'awwidhatan*, a knot was untied, until all eleven knots were untied. Then, the Prophet ﷺ was cured, as if being released from a restraining chain.

As for using regular medicines to cure scorpion sting, salt has a great value in this regard. The author of *Al-Qanoon* said, "Salt should be used in a bandage with linen seeds to cure the scorpion's sting." Salt helps dissolve the poison, which has a burning pain that needs to be cooled. The cool moisture contained in the linen seed cools the pain, while the salt helps extract and remove the poison. This is one of the best and easiest types of remedies for scorpion stings, which require cooling the pain and extracting the venom. Allāh knows best.

Muslim narrated that Abu Hurairah رَضِيَ الله عَنْهُ said, "A man came to the Prophet ﷺ and said to him, 'O Messenger of Allāh ﷺ! I have suffered greatly from a scorpion that stung me last night." The Prophet ﷺ said:

أما لو قلتَ حين أَمْسَيْتَ: أعوذ بكلماتِ اللهِ التَّامَّاتِ مِن شرِّ ما خلَقَ؛ لم يضُرَّك

"Had you said these words when you went to sleep, 'I seek refuge with Allāh's Perfect Words from the evil of what He has created,' it would not have harmed you." [Ahmad]

Know that the Divine cures help after one catches a disease and also help prevent if from happening. If any type of harm befalls one afterwards, it will not be severe. Natural medicines, on the other hand, only help after the disease attacks. Islamic prayer formulas and the various supplications either prevent the disease from happening or make it milder after it happens, depending on the strength of soul and heart of the sick person. Therefore, the Islamic prayer formulas and supplications are used as preventive measures and also as a cure.

As for prevention, in the *Sahihain* it is narrated that 'Âishah رَضِيَ الله عَنْها said:

« كان رسولُ الله صلى الله عليه وسلم إذا أَوَىٰ إلى فِراشِه : نَفَثَ في كفَّيه بقُلْ
هو الله أحدٌ والمُعَوِّذتين، ثم يمسَحُ بهما وجهَه وما بلغت يدُه من جَسَده »

"Whenever the Messenger of Allāh ﷺ would go to bed, he used to breathe into his hands with

Qul huwa Allahu Ahad (Al- Ikhlas) and the Mu'awwidhatan." He then would wipe his face and whatever he could reach of his body with his hands."

Also, in the *Sahihain* it is narrated that the Prophet ﷺ said:

« مَن قرأ الآيَتَيْن من آخِر سورةِ البَقَرة، في ليلة، كفَتاه»

"Whoever reads the last two Verses from Chapter Al-Baqarah (the second chapter in the Qur'ān), at night, they will be enough for him."

Also, Muslim narrated that the Prophet ﷺ said:

« من نَزَل منزلًا، فقال : أَعُوذ بكلماتِ الله التَّامَّات مِن شرِّ ما خلَق؛ لم يضُرّه
شيء حتى يرتَحِل من منزله ذلك»

"Whoever resided in a place and said, 'I seek refuge with Allāh's Perfect Words from the evil of what He has created,' then nothing will harm him until he departs that place."

Abu Dāwud also narrated that the Messenger of Allāh ﷺ used to say at night when he was traveling:

« يا أرضُ؛ ربِّي وربُّكِ اللهُ؛ أعوذ بالله من شرِّكِ وشرِّ ما فيكِ، وشرِّ ما يدُبُّ
عليكِ؛ أعوذ بالله من أَسَد وأَسْوَدَ، ومن الحيَّة والعَقْرب، ومن ساكن البَلَد،
ومِنْ والدٍ وما وَلَدَ »

O land! My Lord and your Lord is Allah. I seek refuge with Allah from your evil, from the evil of whatever is in you and from the evil of whatever walks on your surface. I seek refuge with Allah from a lion, a despot (or jinn), a snake and a scorpion and from those who reside in this land, and from the begetter (son of Adam) and that which he begot (his progeny)."

As for the second benefit of *Ruqyah*, providing a cure, we mentioned healing the ill person by reciting the Al-Fatihah and also reciting the

Ruqyah to cure scorpion stings.

The Prophet's guidance in treating the Namlah (Sore)

We mentioned the *Hadith* narrated by Anas رَضِيَ الله عَنْهُ in *Sahih Muslim* that the Prophet of Allah ﷺ allowed using the *Ruqyah* from every type of fever, evil eye and *Namlah*. .

Also, Abu Dawood narrated that Ash-Shifaa bint Abdullah said, "The Messenger of Allah came by while I was with Hafsah and said:

« أَلا تُعَلِّمِين هذه رقية النملة كما علّمتيها الكتابة »

"Why do you not teach her (Hafsah, his wife) the Ruqyah from Namlah as you taught her how to write."
An-Namlah, literally, the ant, is called as such because it is a type of swelling that appears on the sides of the body. The Namlah is a known disease and causes a type of sting in the sides that makes one think that an ant is crawling on his side and biting him. There are three types of this disease.

Al-Khallal narrated that Ash-Shifaa bint 'Abdullah used to recite *Ruqyah* from the *Namlah* during the time before Islam. When she emigrated to the Prophet ﷺ in Madinah, after she had given him her pledge of allegiance in Makkah, she said, "O Messenger of Allah! I used to recite the *Ruqyah* from the *Namlah* during the time of *Jahiliyyah* (before Islam) and I want to read it to you." She recited it to him, "In the Name of Allah! May the harm be extracted until it goes back to where it came from without harming anyone. O Allah! Remove the harm, O Lord of the people." She used to recite it on a clean branch of wood seven times, choose a clean place, rub the branch on a clean stone with sour wine vinegar and then anoint the affected area with it. The *Hadith* also asserts the fact that it is legislated to teach women to read and write.

The Prophet's guidance in treating the snake's bite

We mentioned the *Hadith* in which the Prophet ﷺ said,

« لا رُقيةَ إلا في عَيْنٍ أو حمةٍ »

"There is no Ruqyah more beneficial than one recited for the evil eye and fever."

Also, Ibn Majah said that 'Āishah رَضِيَ الله عَنْها narrated, "The Messenger of Allah ﷺ allowed using the *Ruqyah* for the scorpions and the snakes bite." Further, Ibn Shihab Az-Zuhri narrated, "One of the companions of the Messenger of Allāh was stung by a snake. The Prophet ﷺ said, 'Is there a person who could recite *Ruqyah*?' They said, 'O Messenger of Allāh ﷺ ! The children of Al-'Hazm used to recite a *Ruqyah* for snake's bite but abandoned the practice when you prohibited using *Ruqyah*.' He said, 'Summon 'Umarah bin 'Hazm.' When they summoned him, he recited his *Ruqyah* to the Prophet ﷺ who said that there is no objection to it. Hence, the Prophet ﷺ allowed him to use it, and 'Umarah recited the *Ruqyah* on the victim.'" [*Al-Bukhari, Muslim, An-Nasaī and Ahmad*].

The Prophet's guidance in treating an ulcer and various wounds

In the Two *Sahih*sit is narrated that 'Āishah رَضِيَ الله عَنْها said:

«كان رسول الله صلى الله عليه وسلم، إذا اشتَكَى الإنسانُ أو كانت به قَرْحةٌ
أو جُرْحٌ، قال بإصبعه هكذا وقَالَ: باسم الله تُرْبةُ أَرْضِنا، بِرِيقةِ بَعْضِنا؛
لِيُشْفى سَقِيمُنا، بإذنِ رِبّنا »

"Whenever a person would complain from an ulcer (or a canker), or a wound, the Messenger of Allāh ﷺ would put his finger in the soil (on the ground after inserting it in his mouth, then raise it), saying, 'In the Name of Allah: with the soil of our earth moistered with the saliva of some of us, let our sick be cured, with our Lord's permission.'"

This is an easy, beneficial cure for the various ulcers and fresh wounds, especially when there is no available medicine. The sand, which is cold and dry and is available on all parts of the world, dries out the moisture that accumulates around the ulcer or wound. This moisture prevents quick healing by natural means, especially in warm areas. Most ulcers and wounds are also accompanied by a hot fever, which, when added to the irritant of warm weather, would only intensify the pain of those who are especially sensitive to heat. Since pure sand is cold and dry, more cooling than even the most effective medications for this purpose, the coolness of the sand will effectively pacify the warmth caused by the wound, especially when the sand is washed and dried. Pure sand also helps dry out most harmful moistures and wetness, because it is a strong drying agent against the wetness that prevents quick healing, as we stated. Further, pure sand helps cool the hotness in the ailing organ, which will strengthen its power of resistance (immunity) and thus end the pain by Allāh's Leave.

The *Hadith* indicates that one should place some saliva on his index finger then place it on pure sand, some of which will stick on to his finger. The finger should then be placed on the affected organ or the wound, and then one recites the supplication mentioned in the *Hadith*. This practice joins the blessings of mentioning Allah's Name, relating all matters to Him and trusting in Him, adding both the cure and the supplication that will make the remedy even more effective.

There are two opinions regarding the Prophet's statement, "The sand of our land", if whether it entails the sand of the entire earth or just the sand of Madinah. There is no doubt that some types of sand are more effective remedies for various ailments than sand from other areas. Galinus said, "In Alexandria, I saw many people who suffer from sever dropsy and an ailing spleen use the sand of Egypt as ointment on their legs, thighs, hands, backs and ribs, and they used to benefit from this remedy." He also said, "Hence, this ointment (muddy sand) could help cure Putrid and limp tumors." He continued, "I know of many people, whose bodies have swollen due to excessive bleeding, who benefited from remedy using mud. I also know of others who used it to cure terminal illnesses that attacked various organs, and the terminal ailments were eradicated." Another author said, "Sand that is imported from the area of Kannus – known as the island of Mastic – is an effective cleanser and causes the flesh to grow in and around ulcers, thus effectively eradicating them."

Since various types of sand have a healing effect, what about the sand of the best and most blessed area on the face of the earth, especially when mixed with the Prophet's saliva? Added to these blessings is the supplication that the Prophet recited and in which he mentioned the Lord's Name and related all matters to Him. We mentioned that the Ruqyah increases in effectiveness according to the strength of faith of the person who is reciting it and the response of the ill person to the

Ruqyah. No sane, honorable Muslim doctor can deny this fact. However, if any of these qualities is absent, let such a person say whatever falsehood he wishes!

The Prophet's guidance on treating pain in general with Islamic prayer formulas

Muslim [*Ibn Ma'jah, Ahmad* and *At-Tabarani*] narrated in his *Sahih* that 'Uthman bin Abu Al-'Âs complained to the Prophet ﷺ from a pain in his body that he suffered from ever since he became a Muslim. The Prophet ﷺ said:

« ضَعْ يدكَ على الَّذي تَأَلَّمُ من جسدك، وقل: بِاسم الله ثلاثًا؛ وقل سَبْعَ مراتٍ: أعوذُ بعزةِ الله وقُدْرته، من شر ما أَجِدُ وأحاذرُ »

Place your hand on the affected area in your body and say, 'In the Name of Allāh,' thrice. Then say, 'I seek refuge with Allāh's Might and Power from the evil of what I am suffering from, and because of which I have become wary',seven times."

The remedy mentioned here entails reciting Allāh's Name, relating all matters to Him and seeking refuge with His Might and Power from the pain, and will surely eradicate the pain. Also, repeating the supplication contained in the remedy frequently will make it even more effective and successful just as the case when the medication is frequently administered until the disease is fully eradicated.

In the *Sahihain* it is narrated that the Prophet ﷺ used to visit some of his family members (who were ill) and would touch them with his right hand, saying:

« اللهم ربَّ النَّاس، أَذْهب البأس واشفِ أنتَ الشَّافي، لا شِفاءَ إلَّا شفاؤُك، شفاءً لا يُغادِر سَقَمًا »

"O Allāh, the Lord of mankind! Do away with the complaint and bring about the cure. You Alone bring the cure, and there is no cure except Your cure, a cure that does not leave illnesses."

The last Islamic prayer formula includes begging Allāh by His Perfect Lordship and Mercy to bring about the cure. The Islamic prayer formula also affirms that Allāh is the only One Who brings the cure and that there is no cure except the cure that He brings about. The Islamic prayer formula includes begging Allāh by His Oneness, Kindness and Lordship.

The Prophet's guidance on treating shock from disasters and calamities

Allāh said:

﴿ وَبَشِّرِ ٱلصَّـٰبِرِينَ ۝ ٱلَّذِينَ إِذَآ أَصَـٰبَتْهُم مُّصِيبَةٌ قَالُوٓا۟ إِنَّا لِلَّهِ وَإِنَّآ إِلَيْهِ رَٰجِعُونَ ۝ أُو۟لَـٰٓئِكَ عَلَيْهِمْ صَلَوَٰتٌ مِّن رَّبِّهِمْ وَرَحْمَةٌ وَأُو۟لَـٰٓئِكَ هُمُ ٱلْمُهْتَدُونَ ۝ ﴾

"... but give glad tidings to As-Sābirûn (the patient). Who, when afflicted with calamity, say: 'Truly, to Allāh we belong and truly, to Him we shall return. They are those on whom are the Salawāt (i.e. who are blessed and will be forgiven) from their Lord, and (they are those who) receive His Mercy, and it is they who are the guided ones." (2:155,157)

In the Musnad (by Imam Ahmad) it is narrated that the Prophet ﷺ said:

« ما مِن أحد تُصِيبه مُصِيبةٌ فيقول: إنا للّه وإنا إليه راجِعُون، اللّهم ! أُجُرني في مُصِيبَتي، وأخلِف لي خَيْرًا منها – إلّا آجَرَه الله في مُصِيبته، وأخلف له خيرًا منها »

"No person suffers a calamity and then says, 'Truly! To Allāh we belong and truly, to Him we shall return. O Allāh! Reward me for the calamity that has befallen me and replace it with what is better.' Except that Allāh will reward him for his calamity and will replace it with what is better than whatever he lost."

The words that are contained in the Hadith are a truly effective and are a beneficial cure for those afflicted by disasters or calamities. These words contain two major aspects that if the slaves of Allāh acquire knowledge of them, they will relieve them from the shock of the disaster. First, the slave of Allāh, his family and wealth are Allāh's exclusive property that Allāh has loaned to the slave. When Allāh takes back some of what he has loaned the slave, He is the Owner who takes back what belongs to Him. Further, whatever Allāh gives the slave is preceded and followed by periods of non-existence, and the slave only takes temporary possession of them when they come into existence. Also, the slaves of Allāh neither create whatever they own, and they are not its true owners, nor are they capable of protecting such possessions and property. Therefore, the slaves are only hired agents who do what they are commanded, since they are not the real owners.

The slaves return is to Allāh, the True Lord, and consequently, they will have to sooner or later depart this life and leave it behind. The slaves will return to Allāh just as He created them the first time: dispossessed, without a wife or a family or wealth or tribe. Only the good and bad deeds will the slaves have then. If this is the case with whatever Allāh gives the slaves, its beginning and end, then why should the slaves be proud of whatever they have or get sad if they loose them? When the slaves remember their beginning and end, this thought will help them discard sadness and depression for their loss.

Also, sadness and depression will be relieved when the slaves realize that they have neither the power to avoid whatever has befallen them, nor to bring about what was not destined for them. Allāh said:

$$\text{﴿ مَآ أَصَابَ مِن مُّصِيبَةٍ فِى ٱلْأَرْضِ وَلَا فِىٓ أَنفُسِكُمْ إِلَّا فِى كِتَـٰبٍ مِّن قَبْلِ أَن نَّبْرَأَهَآ}$$
$$\text{إِنَّ ذَٰلِكَ عَلَى ٱللَّهِ يَسِيرٌ ۝ لِّكَيْلَا تَأْسَوْا۟ عَلَىٰ مَا فَاتَكُمْ وَلَا تَفْرَحُوا۟ بِمَآ ءَاتَىٰكُمْ}$$
$$\text{وَٱللَّهُ لَا يُحِبُّ كُلَّ مُخْتَالٍ فَخُورٍ ۝ ﴾}$$

"No calamity befalls on the earth or in yourselves but it is inscribed in the Book of Decrees (Al-Lauh Al-Mahfūz) before We bring it into existence. Verily, that is easy for Allāh. In order that you may not grieve at the things over that you fail to get, nor rejoice over that which has been given to you. And Allāh likes not prideful boasters." (57:22,23)

Also, the anguish caused by the calamity will be relieved when the slaves think deeply about what Allāh has bestowed on them as compared to what they have lost. They will find that whatever they still have of Allāh's bounty is much larger, especially since Allāh has promised them what is even better than whatever they have lost, providing that they are patient with the calamity. If Allāh wills, He could make the calamity even larger and more severe.

The shock of calamities could also be soothed by observing other people around him and realizing that wherever one looks he sees a disaster to his right and to his left. If someone searches the entire world, he will see that all of mankind is suffering some type of calamity: either losing a loved one, or from a disaster. He will also realize that the joys of this world are just daydreams or passing shadows, and that even if this earthly life brings a little joy, it also brings many tears, and if it brings a comfort for one day, it can bring about a long term disaster. Further, if this life brings some joy, it can prevent further joy from coming for a long time. In addition, no place of residence will be filled with any type of good, but could soon be filled with lessons and losses. Finally, if this life brings happiness for a day, it can be hiding the evil of the days to come.

Ibn Mas'ud رَضِيَ اللهُ عَنْهُ said, "Every joy will be followed by sadness, and no house is filled with joy but will soon be filled with anguish."

Also,Ibn Sirin said, "There is not a laugh but a cry to succeed it."

Further, Hind bint An-Nu'man said, "One time, we were some of the most mighty people enjoying the most respected authority. Soon after, when the sun went down, we became the fewest people. It is Allāh's promise that He will not fill a house with joy but it will soon be filled with lessons (or sadness)."

Once, a man asked Hind to tell him her story and she said, "One morning, we woke up while none among the Arabs but seeks us in eagerness. When the night fell, all the Arabs felt pity for us."

Further, her sister Hurqah once cried, at a time when they were mighty. When she was asked about why she cried and if someone had bothered her, she said, "No. I saw that my family was enjoying comforts and remembered that no house is filled with joy but would one day be filled with grief."

Furthermore, Ishaq bin Tallhah said, "I came by her (Hurqah) one day and said to her, 'What do you know about the lessons from the stories of the kings?' She said, "What we enjoy today is better than what we enjoyed yesterday. We read in the books that no people of a house would enjoy a bounty, but would later on be tested with a trial. Also, time would never show a people a joyous day but would be hiding another day that they would hate."

Curing the shock of disasters and calamities also comes through knowing that sadness and grief will not avert the calamity but will intensify it.

Also, curing grief and anguish comes through knowing that missing the rewards for being patient and content, such as mercy and correct guidance that Allāh has promised in return for being patient, is much larger than the calamity itself.

A part of the cure also comes through knowing that grief brings comfort to the heart of the enemy, grief to the friends, anger to the Lord, joy to the devil, destruction to the reward and weakness to the heart. On the other hand, when one observes patience and satisfaction, he will expel the devil and defeat his plots, will please the Lord, bring joy to the friends and sadness to the enemy. In this case, the person would say words of condolence to his friends instead of they to him. This, indeed, is the sought after perfection and firmness, unlike striking the cheeks, uttering foul words and being dissatisfied with what Allāh has decided.

Curing grief after disaster strikes also comes through knowing that being patient and content would lead to a type of joy, tranquility and comfort that is much greater than what had been lost because of the disaster. In this case, it will be enough of a reward for the patient slave that he will acquire a house of praise that will be built for him in Paradise as a reward for praising his Lord and referring all matters to Him. Let one think about the bigger disaster the one that he had suffered or to lose the rewards that he would have gained in the Residence of Eternity [for being patient].

At-Tirmidhi related from the Prophet ﷺ that he said, "On the Day of Resurrection some people would wish that their skins were sliced with scissors in the life of this world because of the reward that they witness the people who endured disasters would receive for being patient."

Some of the followers of the people of Al-Madinah once said, "If it was not for the calamities of this life, we would be bankrupt of rewards on the Day of Resurrection."

Also, curing anguish and grief entails feeling content in the heart seeking Allāh's rewards, for everything can be replaced, except for Allāh's

Pleasure. The cure also entails knowing that the calamity's effect on one is all what he will gain of it. Those who are content with the calamity will gain contentment, while those who are enraged, will only gain rage. The calamity will affect one as much as he allows it. One should then choose between the best of rewards or the most evil consequences. If one feels rage and disbelief, he will be written in the record of the destroyed ones. If one feels grief and abandons an obligation or commits a prohibition, he will be written in the record of those who neglect their duty. If the calamity caused one to complain and be impatient, he will be written with those who commit injustices against themselves. If one rejects Allāh's decision and questions His wisdom, he will have knocked on the door that leads to hypocrisy or will have entered through it. If one is patient and firm for Allāh's sake, he will be written among the patient ones. If one feels content, he will be written among the content believers. If one praises and thanks Allāh, he will be written with the thankful slaves and will be gathered under the flag of those who praise Allāh. If the calamity directed one to feel eager to meet his Lord, he will be written among the sincere persons in their love for Allāh.

Ahmad and At-Tirmidhi related that the Prophet ﷺ said:

« إنّ الله إذا أَحَبَّ قومًا ابتلَاهم؛ فمن رَضِي فله الرِّضَا، ومن سخِط فله السَّخَطُ »

"When Allāh loves a people, He tests them with trials. If they are content, then they will achieve contentment. Those who get enraged, will only reap rage."

Curing grief also entails knowing that no matter how much grief one feels he will sooner or later be forced to forego the matter. And then, he will not be rewarded for this forced patience.

A wise man once said, "In the first day when a calamity strikes, the wise person behaves just like the ignorant person behaves days later. Those who do not observe an honorable patience, will soon be forced to forget just as the animals do."

Also in the Sahih it is related that the Prophet ﷺ said:

« الصَّبْرُ عِندَ الصَّدْمة الأُولَىٰ »

"Verily, patience is at the stroke of the calamity."

Further, Al-Ash'ath bin Qays said, "Observe patience with Faith and await the reward from Allāh Alone. Otherwise, you will be forced to forget just as the animals do."

Among the cures of grief is that the person should know that the most useful remedies for his case are his agreeing with his Lord and God in what He has chosen for him, for the secret that love contains is that those who love agree with the loved one. Those who claim to love then disagree with what the loved one likes and seek what he dislikes will anger the loved one and will be testifying to the untruthfulness of their claimed love.

Abu Ad-Dardā' once said, "When Allāh decides a matter, He likes that His decision is accepted." Also, 'Imran bin Al-Husain used to say when he was ill, "The most beloved to Him is also the most beloved to me." Abu Al-Aliyah also said similar words. This remedy only works for those who have sincere love for Allāh and is not suitable for just any one.

Also, curing grief includes comparing what is more joyous, beloved and enduring: being content with the calamity or the joy of receiving Allāh's reward. When one realizes and acquires the superior option, he should thank Allāh for His guidance. If one chooses the lesser of the two, let him know that the affliction that his mind, heart and religion have suffered is more than the affliction he suffered through the disaster.

Curing grief also requires knowing that He Who has tested the slave with the affliction is the Most Wise, the Most Merciful, and that He did not test him with the affliction to destroy, punish or overwhelm him. Rather, the affliction is merely a test of his patience, contentment with Allāh and faith. Also Allāh wants to hear the slave's pleas, supplications, and humility before Him, seeking refuge with Him, his heart's humbleness before Him and his explaining his grievances to Him.

Shaikh Abdul Qadir said, "My son! The affliction was not meant to destroy you. Rather, it was meant as a test of your patience and faith. My son! Fate is a lion, and lions do not eat carrion." The affliction is just like the bellows for the believer that rids him of impurities. The believer will either end up being pure gold or pure evil! When the bellows do not benefit the slave in this life, he will be faced with the mightiest bellows, hell. The slave should thus know that his being tested with the bellows of this life is better for him that being tested with the bellows of the next life! Also, the slave has no other choice but to be tested with one of the two bellows, so let him appreciate Allāh's bounty on him by testing him with the bellows of this world.

Curing grief also entails knowing that if it were not for the afflictions of this life, the slave would become arrogant, proud and hard-hearted, which would ultimately cause his destruction. It is the mercy of the Most Merciful that He tests the slave with afflictions sometimes so that these afflictions act as a prevention against evil manners, thus preserving the health of one's slavery to Allāh. Also they extract spoiled substances from his system. All praise is to He Who sends down mercy with afflictions, and Who tests the slaves with the bounties He grants.

If it was not for the fact that Allāh treats His slaves with the remedies of afflictions and trials, they would be arrogant and would commit injustices and aggression. When Allāh decides to do good for a certain slave, He tests him with pain and affliction, according to the degree of his faith. This is how Allāh rids the slaves of destructive ailments (sins and lusts), until the slave is purified and correctly guided, and Allāh qualifies him to the highest degree in this world: being His slave. He will also qualify him for the best rewards in the Life Hereafter: *Gazing at Allāh and residing close to Him.*

Curing grief also entails knowing that the bitterness of this life is itself the sweetness of the Life Hereafter, as Allāh will turn it to sweetness later on. Also the sweetness of this life is itself the bitterness of the Life Hereafter. Moving away from a short-lived bitterness to acquire an eternal sweetness is surely better than vise versa.

If one does not comprehend these facts, let them remember the words of the truthful one,

« حُفَّتِ الجَنَّةُ بِالمَكَارِهِ، وحُفَّتِ النَّارُ بِالشَّهَواتِ »

"Paradise is surrounded with joys while the Fire is surrounded with lusts."

Therefore, bring yourself to what Allāh has prepared for His loyal supporters - those who obey Him - of eternal joy, everlasting happiness and ultimate success. Also consider and remember the torment, everlasting sadness and the humiliation that Allāh has prepared for the evil and wasteful slaves. Then choose which of the two destinations you deserve and seek,

$$ ﴿ كُلٌّ يَعْمَلُ عَلَى شَاكِلَتِهِ ﴾ $$

"Each one does according to Shakilatihi (i.e., his way or his religion or his intentions)." (17:84)

Every person seeks what is suitable for him and what he deserves. Do not think that the cures mentioned herewith are over-explained, for the utter need of them by both the doctor and the sick required explaining them in detail. Allāh knows best.

The Prophet's guidance on treating sadness, grief, and depression

In the *Sahihain* it is narrated that the Messenger of Allāh ﷺ said:

« لا إله إلَّا الله العظيمُ الحَلِيمُ، لا إله إلَّا الله إلَّا ربُّ العَرْش العظيم، لا إله إلا الله رَبُّ السَّموات السبع وربُّ الأرْض، ربُّ العَرْش الكَرِيم»

"There is no deity worthy of worship except Allāh, the Most Great, the Most Forbearing. There is no deity worthy of worship except Allāh, the Lord of the Mighty Throne. There is no deity worthy of worship except Allāh, the Lord of the seven heavens, the Lord of the earth and the Lord of the Honorable Throne."

Also, Abu Dawūd narrated in his *Sunan* that Abu Bakrah related from the Prophet ﷺ that he said:

« دَعَواتُ المَكْروب: اللّهم رَحْمَتَكَ أرجُو؛ فلا تَكِلْني إلى نَفْسي طَرْفة عَيْن، وأصْلِح لي شأْني كُلَّه؛ لا إله إلا أنتَ »

"This is the supplication of those afflicted by distress, 'O Allāh! I seek Your Mercy. Do not make me reliant on my own self for an instant, and lead all my affairs to success, there is no deity except You."

Also, Abu Dāwud narrated that Asmaa Bint 'Umays رَضِيَ الله عَنها said that the Allāh's Messenger ﷺ said to her:

« ألا أعلِّمُكِ كَلِمات [تَقُولِينَهُنَّ] عند الكَرْب – أو في الكرب -: اللهُ ربي لا أُشْرِك به شيئًا»

*"Should I teach you some words that you should recite when in
distress, 'Allāh, is my Lord with Whom I associate nothing and no
one."*

Imam Ahmad narrated that Ibn Mas'ud said that the Prophet ﷺ said:

« ما أصاب عَبْدًا هَمٌّ ولا حُزْنٌ - فقال: اللهم إني عبدُكَ ابنُ عبدكَ ابنُ
أمتِكَ، ناصِيَتي بيدكَ، مَاضٍ فيَّ حُكمُك، عَدْلٌ فيَّ قضاؤُك؛ أسألك بكل
اسم هولك، سمَّيت به نَفْسَك، أو أنْزَلْتَه في كتابِكَ، أو عَلَّمْتَه أَحَدًا مِن
خَلْقِك، أو استأْثَرْتَ به في عِلْم الغَيْبِ عِنْدَك؛ أنْ تَجْعَلَ القُرآنَ العَظيمَ ربيعَ
قَلْبِي، ونُورُ صَدْرِي، وجِلاءَ حُزْني، وذهابَ همِّي . إلا أذهبَ الله حُزْنه
وهَمَّه، وأبدله مكَانه فَرَحًا»

*"Whenever a sadness or grief strikes a slave and the slave then
says, 'O Allāh! I am Your slave, the son of Your slave, the son of
Your female slave. My forelock is in Your grasp. Your decision
about me will certainly come to pass. Your judgment on me is
certainly just. I ask You by every Name that is Yours and which
You call Yourself by, whether You revealed it in Your Book, taught
it to some of Your creation or kept in the Knowledge of the
Unseen that You have. Make the Noble Qur'ān the spring of my
heart, the light of my chest, the eliminator of may sadness and
the end of my grief. Then, Allāh will remove his sadness and
depression and will replace them with joy."*

Also, At-Tirmidhi narrated that Sa'd bin Abu Waqqas related from the
Messenger of Allāh ﷺ that he said:

« دعوةُ ذِي النُّون إذ دعَا ربَّه وَهُو في بَطْن الحُوت »

*"The supplication of Thu An-Nun (Jonah) which he supplicated to
the Lord while in the belly of the whale."*

﴿ لَّآ إِلَهَ إِلَّآ أَنتَ سُبْحَنَكَ إِنِّى كُنتُ مِنَ ٱلظَّلِمِينَ ﴾

*"Lā ilāhā illā Anta [none has the right to be worshipped but You
(O Allāh)], Glorified (and Exalted) be You [above all that (evil)
they associate with You]! Truly, I have been of the wrongdoers."*
(21:87)

« لم يَدْعُ بها رجلٌ مسلمٌ في شيءٍ قطُّ، إلا اسْتُجِيبَ له»

"No Muslim man would supplicate with it concerning a matter
but would be positively answered by Allāh."

Imam Ahmad also narrated in the *Musnad*,

« أنَّ النَّبي صلى الله عليه وسلم، كان إذا أمرٌ حَزَبه أمْر: فَزِع إلَى الصَّلاة »

"Whenever the Prophet ﷺ would be concerned about a matter, he
would turn to prayer."

Furthermore, Allāh said:

$$﴿ وَٱسْتَعِينُوا۟ بِٱلصَّبْرِ وَٱلصَّلَوٰةِ ﴾$$

"And seek help in patience and As-Salāt (the prayer)." (2:45)

In the *Sunan* it is also narrated, "Revert to Jihad, because it is among
the doors of Paradise with which Allāh drives away sadness and
depression from the hearts."

Ibn 'Abbās رَضِيَ الله عَنْهما was also reported to have related from the
Prophet ﷺ that he said:

« مَن كَثُرَت هُمومُه وغُمُومُه: فلْيُكْثِرْ من قَوْل لا حَوْلَ ولا قوةَ إلّا بالله »

"Whenever sadness and grief intensify on someone, let him often
repeat, 'There is neither power nor strength except from Allāh.'"

In the *Sahihain* it is also narrated that this supplication is a treasure of
Paradise, while At-Tirmidhi narrated that it is a door of Paradise.

These cures that we mentioned are of fifteen types. If they are not
sufficient to remove sadness, depression and grief, then the sickness has
become chronic and needs to be completely removed and dissipated.

The first cure, affirming Allāh's Oneness in His Lordship. The second,
affirming Allāh's Oneness in the worship. The third cure, the belief in the
creed of *Tawhid* (There is no true god but Allāh and Mohammed is His
Messenger). The fourth, praising Allāh for not dealing with His slave with
injustice and for not punishing him without a reason. The fifth, the slave's
affirming that it is he who has committed the injustice. The sixth, pleading
to Allāh by the most beloved methods to Him, by His Names,
Attributes, such as Al-'Hay (The Ever Living), Al-Qayyum (Who Sustains
everything and everyone). The seventh, depending and relying on Allāh

Alone for everything. The eighth, the slave affirms that his hope is only in Allāh. The ninth, acquiring true dependence on Allāh and relating all matters to Him, while admitting that the slave's forelock is in His Hands Alone and that He does with it whatever He will. Also, admitting that Allāh's decision on the slave will certainly come to pass and that His judgment is certainly just.

The tenth, the slave's heart should enjoy the gardens of the Qur'ān and should make the Qur'ān just like the spring of pure water to the animals. Also, the slave should use the light of the Qur'ān to shatter the darkness of desires and lusts. The Qur'ān should be one's companion when no one else is present; the comfort that relieves every type of calamity and the cure that discards every illness that attacks the slave's heart. In short, the Qur'ān should be the remover of sadness and the end of depression and grief. The eleventh, turning to *Istighfar*, seeking forgiveness from Allāh. Twelfth, repenting to Allāh. Thirteenth, performing *Jihad* in Allāh's cause. Fourteenth, performing prayer. Fifteenth, relating all power and strength to He Who grasps them in His Hands.

How divine remedies affect diseases

Allāh has created the son of Adam and his body's organs and designated a state of perfection that each organ could attain and achieve. Consequently, when the organ looses its perfection, it feels pain. Allāh has also designated a state of perfection for the heart, the leader of the organs. When the heart looses its perfection, it will fall down with various ills and sicknesses, such as sadness, grief and anguish.

Furthermore, when the eye looses what it was created for, sight; when the ear looses what it was created for, hearing; and when the tongue looses what it was created for, speech; then these organs will have lost their perfection.

The heart was created to acquire knowledge of its Creator and to love Him, worship Him Alone, be content with Him, to be joyous loving Him and to feel satisfied with Him. The heart was also created to rely on Allāh, to love for His Sake, hate for His Sake, to be loyal for His Sake, to be enemies of His enemies for His Sake and to remember Him always. The heart was created to love Him more than anyone or anything else, to have Hope in Him rather than anyone or anything else and to revere Him more than anything or anyone else. There is no joy, happiness, delight or sweetness except by acquiring such qualities, which are just like food, good health and life for the heart. When the heart looses its food, health and life, then sadness, grief and affliction will attack it from all sides and will remain with it.

The worst diseases that attack the heart are *Shirk* (polytheism, making partners with Allāh), sins, and forgetfulness, ignoring what Allāh likes and is pleased with, abandoning relating all matters to Him and not depending on Him for everything. Diseases of the heart also include relying on other than Allāh, rejecting His decisions and doubting and ignoring His warnings and promises.

When one thinks about the diseases of the heart, he will find that the reasons that we mentioned are the only ones behind these ills. Consequently, the only effective remedies for these ills are their opposites and antidotes that the Prophetic remedies contain. We stated before that the disease is removed by its opposite and that health is preserved by using what it is accustomed to which is included in the Prophetic remedies.

Tawhid opens the door to all types of good, happiness, joy, elation and enjoyment for the slave. Also, repenting to Allāh extracts all types of harmful, sinful causes of the heart's ailment. Further, *Tawhid* is the diet of the heart against bad substances, for it closes the doors of evil. The doors of happiness and all types of good will be opened with *Tawhid*, while repentance and seeking forgiveness will close the doors of evil.

Doctors of old said, "Whoever seeks to acquire good health for the body should consume less amounts of food and drink. Whoever seeks the well being of his heart, let him abandon sin." Also, Thābit bin Qurrath said, "The body's well being requires consuming less food, the soul's comfort is in committing less sins and the consolation of the tongue is in uttering less speech."

Sins are just like poison to the heart - if they do not destroy it, they will weaken it. Then when the heart is weaker, it will become less efficient in fighting disease.

The biggest of the heart's ills occur by satisfying its lusts and desires, while ignoring them constitutes its biggest cure. We should also mention that originally, ignorance and injustice were created in the self. Because the self is ignorant, it thinks that its cure is in following its desire, although this path leads it to its destruction and demise. And because the self is unjust, it does not accept the prescription of the sincere doctor. Consequently, when the self is prescribed the ailment instead of the cure, it accepts it while refusing to take the cure when it is prescribed. And because the self prefers the illness rather than the cure, which it tries to avoid, many other illnesses and diseases will break out and by then the doctor will not be able to diagnose them and consequently, the cure will not be available. The biggest calamity of all this is that the self absolves itself of guilt and blames Fate and its Lord, inwardly in the beginning and then explicitly later on!*

---

* **Editor's note**: In Arabic the word *Ruh* means soul and the word *Nafs* means self. There is sometimes confusion about these words. Generally it is understood the *Ruh*, soul, is created pure without sin and becomes affected by how we live our individual lives and we will be judged by the condition it is in on the Day of Judgement. The *Nafs* on the other hand is considered to be our instinctual animal qualities (self) that must=

When the ailing person reaches this stage, there is no hope of curing him, unless the Mercy of the Lord rushes to his aid and Allāh allows him to start a new life while providing him with the required sustenance. This is why the *Hadith* that Ibn 'Abbās رَضِيَ اللهُ عَنْهُما has narrated about the supplication during the time of distress contained Unity *(Tawhid)* of Allāh in Lordship and worship, glorifying Him and mentioning His being Most Forbearing. These two Attributes (Glory and Forbearing) are necessary to add perfection to the Attributes of Ability, Mercy, Kindness and Forgiveness. Also, the same *Hadith* described Allāh's Lordship above the upper and lower worlds and above the Throne, which is the ceiling and the mightiest of all creation. Affirming Perfect Lordship to Allāh requires worshiping Him alone in Unity *(Tawhid)*, and loving, fearing, hoping, glorifying and obeying Him Alone. Also, affirming Allāh's Perfect Glory requires affirming and attributing every type of perfection to Him and denying every type of shortcoming and being equated with the creation. In addition, Allāh's being Most-Forbearing necessitates affirming the perfection of His Mercy and Kindness towards His creation.

When the heart has access to these facts, it will seek to acquire the qualities of loving Allāh and glorifying Him in *Tawhid*. Then, the heart will acquire and enjoy such elation and delight that will allow it to overcome the feelings of affliction, sadness and grief. It is a fact that whenever the sick person hears of what brings happiness and joy to his heart, the body will be more effective in resisting the ailment.

Furthermore, when one compares the depressing feelings while in anguish to the wonderful meanings contained in the supplication while distressed, he will find that these words are perfectly suitable to deliver the heart from its depression and substitute it with the elation that accompanies happiness and joy. Only those who have had access to such feelings and whose hearts are filled with the light of the truth that comes with these feelings will give this subject matter its due consideration.

The Prophet's statement:

=be trained or at least restrained by the laws of Islam. Satan (the force of evil) appeals to our *Nafs* (self) and tries to encourage it to commit sins. This in turn causes negative damage to the soul, which we are responsible for.

$$\text{« يا حَيُّ يا قَيُّومُ بِرَحمتِكِ أَسْتَغِيثُ »}$$

"O the Ever-Living, the Self Subsisting! I urgently seek Your Mercy."

It has a special kind of effect in removing the grief.

Allāh's Living is an attribute that includes every type of perfect quality, while the attribute "The Self Subsisting" entails Allāh's perfect Actions. That is why Al-Hayy (The Ever Living), Al- Qayyum (The Self Subsisting) are included in Allāh's Mightiest Name, which if He is called by it, He will answer and if He is begged by it, He will give.

Furthermore, Perfect Life is the opposite of sickness and shortcomings since the residents of Paradise do not die, they do not feel any sadness, depression or any type of ailment. When life has an end, it indicates the existence of shortcomings in actions and in ability to sustain. Being ever-living is thus suited to being ever-sustaining. The Ever-Living does not have any shortcoming in His being. The Self Subsisting Al-Qayyum, is Able to do everything He wills. This is why asking Allāh by His Names Al-Hayy, The Ever-Living, Al-Qayyum, the Self Subsisting has profound effects on removing what is the opposite of life and Ability.

Related to this, the Prophet ﷺ used to ask Allāh by His Lordship of Jibril, Michael and Israfil عليهم السلام to guide him to that which the people had differed in concerning the truth, by His Will, for the heart lives by correct guidance. The three angels mentioned in the supplication are responsible for the elements and necessities of life. For instance, Jibril عليه السلام is responsible for delivering the revelation with which the heart lives. Michael is responsible for the sustenance, which is the life of the body. Israfil عليهم السلام is responsible for blowing the Horn, which signals the resurrection of the souls and their being returned to their bodies. Asking Allāh by His Lordship of these three angels, who are responsible for all types of life, has a special effect in acquiring what one seeks and longs for.

Therefore, invoking Allāh's Name Al-Qayyum has a special effect in answering supplications and ending afflictions. The Sunan and Abu Hatim in his Sahih narrated that the Prophet ﷺ said: "Allāh's Greatest Name is in these two Verses."

$$\text{﴿ وَإِلَٰهُكُمْ إِلَٰهٌ وَاحِدٌ لَّا إِلَٰهَ إِلَّا هُوَ ٱلرَّحْمَٰنُ ٱلرَّحِيمُ ﴾}$$

*"And your Ilāh (God) is One Ilāh (God - Allāh), Lā ilāha illa Huwa
(there is none who has the right to be worshipped but He), the
Most Gracious, the Most Merciful." (2:163)*

And:

﴿الٓمٓ ۞ اللَّهُ لَآ إِلَٰهَ إِلَّا هُوَ ٱلْحَىُّ ٱلْقَيُّومُ ۞﴾

*"Alif Lam Meem. Allāh! Lā ilāha illa Huwa (none has the right to
be worshipped but He), Al-Hayyul-Qayyum (the Ever Living, the
One Who sustains and protects all that exists)." (3:1-2)*

At-Tirmidhi commented that this is an authentic *Hadith*.

In the *Sunan* and the *Sahih* of Ibn Hibban it is also narrated that Anas
رَضِيَ الله عَنْهُ said, "A man once supplicated, 'O Allāh! I ask You by Your
owning the praise, there is no deity worthy of worship except You, the
Mannan (Munificent), Who created the heaven and the earth. O Owner
of the praise and Honor. 'O Hayy, Qayyum.'"

The Prophet ﷺ said:

« لَقَد دعا اللهَ باسمِه الأَعْظم: الذي إذا دُعِيَ به أجابَ، وإذا سُئِل به أعطى »

*"He has asked Allāh by His Greatest Name, which if He is called
by it He answers, and if He is asked He gives."*

This is why the Prophet ﷺ used to say when making *Du'ā'*,

« يا حيُّ يا قَيُّوم »

"O Hayy, O Qayyum."

The Prophet's statement:

« اللهم رَحْمَتَك أَرْجُو؛ فلا تكِلْني إلى نَفْسي طرْفةَ عينٍ، وأصلح لي شَأْنِي
كلَّه؛ لا إلٰهَ إلَّا أنت »

*"O Allāh, I seek Your Mercy. Do not make me rely on my own
self for an instant, and lead all my affairs to success. There is no
deity worthy of worship except You."*

This supplication entails invoking Allāh, Who grasps all good in His
Hands. It also includes depending on Allāh Alone, relating all matters to
Him Alone and pleading to Him to lead the slave's matters to success. It

also includes asking Him not to allow the slave to rely on his own self, and invoking Him by mentioning His Oneness. All these have a special effect in removing grief. Such is the case with the Prophet's statement:

« اللهُ رَبِّي لا أُشرِكُ به شيئًا »

"Allāh is my Lord, I associate none with Him."

As for the *Hadith* that Ibn Mas'ud narrated:

« اللهم إني عَبدُك [وَ] ابنُ عَبدِك »

"O Allāh, I am Your slave, the son of Your slave..."

It contains what no one book can explain of divine knowledge and the secrets of the slavery to Allāh. The *Hadith* includes attesting to the slavery of the person and the slavery of his father and mother to Allāh, that the forelock of the slave is in the Hands of Allāh and that He does what He will with the slave. The slave cannot bring about benefit, harm, life, death or resurrection without Allāh. When the slave's forelock is in someone else's hand, the slave does not own anything regarding himself. Rather, he is a prisoner in the grasp, power and authority of his owner.

The Prophet ﷺ also stated that:

« ماضٍ فيَّ حُكْمُكَ، عَدْلٌ فيَّ قضاؤُكَ »

"Your decision on me will certainly come to pass, and Your judgment on me is certainly just."

This portion of the *Hadith* contains two major aspects of Unity (*Tawhid*). First, the *Hadith* affirms Predestination and that Allāh's decisions will certainly come to pass on His slaves and that the slave can neither escape them nor fend them off.

Allāh's decisions are certainly just and thus do not contain any injustice in them for His slave. Rather, Allāh's decisions always conform to justice and kindness. Also, injustice is a shortcoming that constitutes a need of some sort, an ignorance or abuse. Such behavior can never occur by He Who has encompassing knowledge of everything, Who does not need anything or anyone, while everything and everyone stand in need of Him, and Who is the Most Just Disposer of affairs. No part of Allāh's decisions can ever be empty of Wisdom and Perfection, just as none of it can ever escape His Power and Will. Allāh's Wisdom is encompassing, just as His Power and Will are, and this is the reason why the Prophet Hūd السلام عليه said when his people wanted to scare him with their idols:

$$ \text{﴿ إِنِّى أُشْهِدُ ٱللَّهَ وَٱشْهَدُوٓا۟ أَنِّى بَرِىٓءٌ مِّمَّا تُشْرِكُونَ ۞ مِن دُونِهِۦ فَكِيدُونِى جَمِيعًا ثُمَّ لَا تُنظِرُونِ ۞ إِنِّى تَوَكَّلْتُ عَلَى ٱللَّهِ رَبِّى وَرَبِّكُم مَّا مِن دَآبَّةٍ إِلَّا هُوَ ءَاخِذٌۢ بِنَاصِيَتِهَآ إِنَّ رَبِّى عَلَىٰ صِرَٰطٍ مُّسْتَقِيمٍ ۞ ﴾} $$

"I call Allāh to witness and bear you witness that I am free from that which you ascribe as partners in worship, With Him (Allāh). So plot against me, all of you, and give me no respite I put my trust in Allāh, my Lord and your Lord! There is not a moving (living) creature but He has the grasp of its forelock. Verily, my Lord is on the Straight Path (the truth)." (11:54-56)

This Âyah indicates that although Allāh owns the forelock of His slaves and does what He wills regarding their affairs, He is on the Straight Path, meaning He never decides anything regarding them that is not full of wisdom, justice, kindness and mercy. The Prophet's statement:

$$ \text{« ماضٍ فِيَّ حُكْمُكَ »} $$

"Your Decision regarding me will certainly come to pass,"

It is similar to what Allāh said:

$$ \text{﴿ مَّا مِن دَآبَّةٍ إِلَّا هُوَ ءَاخِذٌۢ بِنَاصِيَتِهَآ ﴾} $$

"There is not a moving (living) creature but He has the grasp of its forelock." (11:55)

Also, the Prophet's statement:

$$ \text{« عَدْلٌ فِيَّ قَضَاؤُكَ »} $$

"Your judgment on me is certainly just,"

It is also similar to what Allāh said:

$$ \text{﴿ إِنَّ رَبِّى عَلَىٰ صِرَٰطٍ مُّسْتَقِيمٍ ﴾} $$

"Verily, my Lord is on the Straight Path (the truth)." (11:55)

Then, the Prophet ﷺ begged Allāh by the Names that He has called Himself with, those which the slaves know and those which they do not know, such as the Names that He has kept with Him and did not allow any angel or Messenger to have access to. This type of supplication is one of the best and dearest to Allāh, along with being the most beneficial in achieving what one seeks and longs for.

The Prophet ﷺ then asked Allāh to make the Qur'ān in his heart just like a spring is to the animals. He also asked Allāh to make the Qur'ān a remedy for his sadness and grief, so that it works just as medicine works when it removes an ailment, allowing the body to regain its health and youth. He also asked Allāh to make the Qur'ān the remover that clears rust and impurities from the heart. This remedy, when the ailing person uses it with a sincere heart, will certainly remove the ailment and will replace it with complete recovery, health and energy.

As for the supplication that Zhin An-Nun (Jonah) has made, it contains an affirmation of Tawhid (Unity) and praises Allāh's perfection. Also, it contains the slave's affirming his own injustice and the sins that he has committed, making the supplication an especially effective remedy for sadness, grief and anguish. It is also a very effective means of approach to Allāh that ensures deliverance of what one seeks. Tawhid (Unity) and praising Allāh include affirming all types of perfection for Allāh and denying every type of shortcoming from approaching Him. One's affirming his injustices indicates the slave's faith in the religion and belief in reward and punishment. It also leads the slave to being humble and to repent to Allāh, asking Him to forgive his faults and affirming his slavery and meekness to Allāh. There are four matters that the slave would be begging Allāh with in this supplication: Tawhid (Unity), praising Allāh, affirming one's slavery to him and admitting one's mistakes.

As for the Hadith narrated by Abu Umamah,

$$ \text{« اللّٰهُمَّ؛ إِنِّي أَعُوذُ بِكَ مِنَ الهَمِّ وَالحزَنَ »} $$

"O Allāh! I seek refuge with You from sadness and anguish,"

It contains seeking refuge with Allāh from eight matters. There are four pairs of things that are related: grief and anguish, inability and laziness, cowardice and miserliness, and preponderance of debts and dominance of men. When a hated matter reaches the heart, it will be either a current concern, which will cause sadness, or it will be an anticipated matter of concern and anguish, which might affect the slave's important interests.

When one does not attain his vital interests, it will be because he is unable or unwilling to seek such interests. When one does not bring about benefit to others and to himself, it will be because he is either a coward or miserly and unwilling to spend from his money. When one falls under domination, it will be because of his being indebted, or because he is overwhelmed by other people unjustly. The *Hadith* includes seeking refuge from all types of evil.

Seeking forgiveness has a profound effect on repelling grief, anguish, sadness and depression. This is a fact agreed upon by those of wisdom of every nation. This is because sins and errors bring about grief, anguish, fear, sadness, distress, and ailments of the heart. After a while, those who are used to committing evil and sins will get bored with them. Then, they will commit these errors to drive away the depression and loneliness that they feel. Since these are the effects of sins and errors on the hearts, then the only remedy for this condition includes seeking forgiveness and repenting (to Allāh).

As for the prayer, it has a profound effect on bringing relief and comfort to the heart, along with strengthening it and bringing about joy and elation to it. The prayer is the connection of the heart and soul with Allāh and brings about feelings of joy by drawing closer to Him, remembering Him, feeling happy by speaking to Him, standing before Him, and using one's entire body and strength in implementing one's slavery to Him. The prayer also entails giving each organ and limb its due right of its slavery, while freeing the heart from remembering the creation, dealing with it or talking of it. The attention of the heart and limbs will thus be concentrated on the Lord and Creator, along with being free from the irritation caused by his enemy (Satan) while in prayer. This is why the prayer is one of the best types of medicines, remedies, and nutrition and is only suitable for healthy hearts. As for ailing hearts, they are just like ailing bodies, not fit for normal good foods.

The prayer is one of the best methods to acquire the good of this life and the life hereafter while fending off the harm of this and the next life. It also discourages people from falling into sin, cures diseases of the heart, fends off the ailments of the body, brings light to the heart and the face and elevates the energy of the limbs and the soul. It also brings about sustenance, fends off injustice, helps the oppressed, dissipates the lusts of the hearts, preserves one's bounty, fends off torment, brings about mercy, relieves calamity and helps against many ailments that attack the internal organs.

Ibn Mājah narrated in his *Sunan* that Abu Hurairah رَضِيَ اللهُ عَنْهُ said, "The Messenger of Allāh ﷺ saw me while I was asleep suffering from a pain in the stomach. He said to me:

$$ \text{« يا أَبا هريرة؛ أَشِكْمْ دَرْدْ ؟ قال قُلتُ : نَعْم يا رسولَ الله . قال : قُم فصلٍّ ؛} $$

$$ \text{فإن في الصلاة شِفاءً»} $$

" 'O Abu Hurairah! Does your stomach bother you (he said it in Persian)?' I said, 'Yes, O Messenger of Allāh (ﷺ)!' He said, 'Stand up and pray, because the prayer is a cure.'"

It was also reported that these words are not the Prophet's words but Abu Hurairah رَضِيَ اللهُ عَنْهُ said them to Mujahid.

When the hypocrite doctor's heart is not pleased with all these facts, we talk to him in medical terms. We say to him that the prayer is an exercise for the body and soul, as it entails various movements and positions, such as standing up, bowing down, prostrating, sitting on the ground, moving between these positions during which most of one's joints are used. Also, most of the internal organs are exercised in the prayer, such as the stomach, the intestines and the rest of the body organs that are responsible for food and digestion. Who can deny that these acts and movements strengthen the body, especially when the soul is strengthened and relieved during the prayer? In this case, the body will be strengthened and the pain will subside.

The disease of hypocrisy and rejecting what the Messengers were sent with and preferring atheism has no cure except for Fire. Allāh said:

$$ \text{﴿ نَارًا تَلَظَّى ۝ لَا يَصْلَىٰهَآ إِلَّا ٱلْأَشْقَى ۝ ٱلَّذِى كَذَّبَ وَتَوَلَّىٰ ۝ ﴾} $$

"Blazing Fire (Hell). None shall enter it save the most wretched. Who denies and turns away." (92:14-16)

As for the effect of Jihad on repelling sadness and grief, it is well established, when the heart is forced to tolerate evil succeeding and becoming dominant and apparent, its sadness, depression, fear and distress increases. But when the soul performs Jihad for Allāh's sake, Allāh will turn that sadness and grief into happiness and strength. Allāh said:

﴿قَٰتِلُوهُمْ يُعَذِّبْهُمُ ٱللَّهُ بِأَيْدِيكُمْ وَيُخْزِهِمْ وَيَنصُرْكُمْ عَلَيْهِمْ وَيَشْفِ صُدُورَ قَوْمٍ
مُّؤْمِنِينَ ۝ وَيُذْهِبْ غَيْظَ قُلُوبِهِمْ وَيَتُوبُ ٱللَّهُ عَلَىٰ مَن يَشَآءُ وَٱللَّهُ عَلِيمٌ
حَكِيمٌ ۝﴾

*"Fight against them so that Allāh will punish them by your hands
and disgrace them and give you victory over them and heal the
breasts of a believing people, And remove the anger of their
(believers') hearts. Allāh accepts the repentance of whom He
wills. Allāh is All-Knowing, All-Wise." (9:14,15)*

No act is more capable of removing the heart's grief, sadness and
anguish more than *Jihad*.

As for the effect of saying "there is no deity worthy of worship except
Allāh" in removing depression, it is a fact because these words include
referring all matters, power and strength to Allāh Alone. They also
include submitting all matters to Allāh, not denying Him any supremacy
over any matter and referring the Ability to make any changes in this and
the higher worlds to Allāh Alone. Nothing can super-cede these words
in this regard.

It was said that there is no angel who descends from or ascends to
the heaven without uttering the words, "there is no power or strength
except from Allāh". Finally, these words have an especially profound
effect in repelling the devil.

The Prophet's guidance on curing fear and insomnia

At-Tirmidhi narrated in his *Sunan* that Khalid once complained to the
Prophet ﷺ that he does not sleep well at night. The Prophet ﷺ said:

« إِذَا أَوَيْتَ إِلَى فِرَاشِكَ، فَقُلْ : اللَّهُمَّ رَبَّ السَّمَوَاتِ السَّبْعِ وَمَا أَظَلَّتْ، وَرَبَّ
الْأَرَضِينَ وَمَا أَقَلَّتْ، وَرَبَّ الشَّيَاطِينِ وَمَا أَضَلَّتْ؛ كُنْ لِي جَارًا مِنْ شَرِّ خَلْقِكَ
كُلِّهِمْ جَمِيعًا : أَنْ يَفْرُطَ عَلَيَّ أَحَدٌ مِنْهُمْ، أَوْ يَبْغِيَ عَلَيَّ؛ عَزَّ جَارُكَ و وَجَلَّ
ثَنَاؤُكَ، وَلَا إِلَهَ غَيْرُكَ »

*"When you go to bed say, 'O Allāh! The Lord of the seven
heavens and what is under them, the Lord of the earths and what*

they carry, and the Lord of the devils and whoever they misguide!
Be my supporter against the evil of all of Your creation, preventing
any of them to cause me any harm or injustice. Mighty indeed are
those whom You support, honorable indeed is Your praise, and
there is no deity worthy of worship except You.'"

Also, At-Tirmidhi narrated that the Messenger of Allāh ﷺ used to
teach his companions these words when they face any fear,

« أَعوذُ بِكَلِمات اللهِ التّامَّةِ من غَضَبه وعِقابه وشرِّ عباده، ومن هَمَزاتِ

الشَّياطينِ؛ وأعوذُ بك رَبِّ أن يَحضُرُونِ »

"I seek refuge with Allāh's perfect Words from His anger and
torment, and from the evil of His slaves and the whisperings of
the devils. I seek refuge with You, my Lord from their presence.'"

Ibn Umar رَضِيَ الله عَنْهما used to teach these words to his children and
would even write them for those who were not able to memorize
them. There is no doubt that such words are suitable and effective in
removing and repelling all types of harm.

The Prophet's guidance on treating burns

Burns are usually caused by fire, which is the substance from which
the devil was created, and this is why the devil finds it befitting his nature
and the evil that he seeks to achieve. Therefore, the devil helps the fire
cause harm. The fire usually seeks domination and devastation. These
two matters, domination and devastation, are the guidance of the devil
that he calls to and with which he leads mankind to destruction. The fire
and the devil both seek domination and affliction, while Allāh's Pride
always intervenes by extinguishing these evils and the acts of the devil.

This is why praising Allāh that He is the Great has a profound effect
on extinguishing the fire, for Allāh's Greatness overwhelms anything and
everything. When the Muslim praises Allāh's Greatness, this supplication
will cause the fire and the efforts of the devil to fade away and thus the
fire will be extinguished, Allāh willing. We have used this method before
and found it to be true.

The Prophet's guidance on staying healthy

Preserving one's good health requires the help of wetness that resists heat. The wetness resists heat while the heat helps mature various substances and rids the body of its wastes. Otherwise, without wetness, the excessive heat would harm the body and would not allow its organs to function normally, while excessive dryness allows the heat to burn the body and make it dry. Each one of the two conditions, wetness and heat, thus needs the other to sustain and allow the body to function. Further, since the heat feeds on wetness, it preserves the moisture from rotting and decomposing. When one of these two conditions is more dominant than the other, the constitution of the body will be altered and changed.

As we have stated, heat decomposes wetness, compelling the body to seek to replace the lost moisture with food and drink, which also provides the body with sustenance. When moisture is present in excessive amounts, the heat is not able to decompose the excess wetness and thus the moisture decomposes and rots, causing harm to the body. In this case, various ailments attack the body, as much as the body and the various organs are susceptible to accept these ailments. All these facts are taken from what Allāh said:

$$﴿ وَكُلُواْ وَاشْرَبُواْ وَلَا تُسْرِفُواْ ﴾$$

"And eat and drink but waste not by extravagance..." (7:31)

Allāh directs the slaves to consume what helps the body of food and drink and to replace lost energy. The amount [of food and drink] that should be consumed should not exceed what the body has lost plus what the body needs to function properly. Otherwise, the excess food will be an extravagance that brings about ailments and will not preserve the health, and such is the case when one eats excessively or does not consume sufficient amounts.

Therefore, the few words that Allāh stated hold the key to staying healthy. There is no doubt that the body is always going through the process of decomposing and producing waste. The more the decomposition occurs, the less the heat will be effective, since decomposition feeds on moistures (which in turn feeds the inner heat). When the heat is weak, the digestion efficiency decreases until the moisture dissipates. Thus, the heat will be extinguished and consequently, the term (life span) that the slave was allowed in this life will come to an end.

The goal behind the person seeking a cure for himself and for others is to preserve the body until everyone reaches their final destination (death), not because preserving the necessary moistures and heat will keep the youth and health forever, for this goal is not attainable in this life. The goal that the doctor seeks to achieve entails preserving the existent wetness from what might spoil it and to preserve body-heat from what might weaken its power. The doctor thus preserves the balance between the two powers or conditions in the body, just as Allāh has created the heaven and earth with justice and perfect balance. In fact, the entire creation thrives on and by justice and balance.

Those who study the guidance of the Prophet ﷺ will find it the best guidance with which the health of the body can and will be preserved. Preserving good health depends on eating and drinking sensibly and on utilizing one's clothes, place of residence, the air, sleep, being awake, mobility, idleness, sex, extracting the excess material of the body and keeping whatever is necessary and important in the best form and shape. When these aspects are satisfied in the manner that is suitable for the body, the area, age and custom, the person is more likely to have good health and well being until it is his time to die.

Good health is one of the best bounties that Allāh bestows on mankind and also one of His best rewards. In fact, good heath is the best earthly bounty of all, and those who have been bestowed with sound comprehension should strive to preserve their health and protect it against what might oppose or alter it.

Al-Bukhari narrated in his *Sahih* that the Messenger of Allāh ﷺ said:

« نِعمَتَانِ مغبُونٌ فيهما كَثِير من النَّاس : الصِّحَّةُ والفَرَاغُ »

"Two bounties regarding which many people cheat themselves, health and free time."

Further, At-Tirmidhi narrated that 'Abdullāh bin Mihsan Al-Ansari رَضِيَ

عَنْهُ اللهِ said, The Messenger of Allāh ﷺ said:

« مَنْ أَصْبَحَ مُعَافًى فِي جَسَدِهِ، آمِنًا فِي سِرْبِهِ، عِنْدَهُ قُوتُ يَوْمِهِ، فَكَأَنَّما حِيزَتْ لَهُ الدُّنْيا »

" 'He who reaches the morning while health in his body, safe in his residence and having his day's sustenance, will be as if the entire life of this world was granted to him."

Also, At-Tirmidhi related from Abu Hurairah رَضِيَ اللهِ عَنْهُ that the Prophet ﷺ said:

« أُوَّلُ مَا يُسْأَلُ عَنْهُ العَبْدُ يَوْمَ القِيَامَةِ مِنَ النَّعِيمِ؛ أَنْ يُقَالَ لَهُ: أَلَمْ نُصِحَّ لَكَ جِسْمَكَ، وَنُرَوِّكَ مِنَ المَاءِ البَارِدِ »

"The first blessing that the slave will be asked about on the Day of Resurrection will be the saying to him, 'Have We not made your body healthy and drove away your thirst with cold water?' "

This is why some of the *Salaf* (righteous predecessors) stated that the Verse:

﴿ ثُمَّ لَتُسْأَلُنَّ يَوْمَئِذٍ عَنِ ٱلنَّعِيمِ ﴾

"Then on that Day you shall be asked about the delights (you indulged in, this world)." (102:8)

It is referring to health.

In addition, Imam Ahmad narrated that Abu Bakr As-Siddiq said, I heard the Messenger of Allāh ﷺ saying:

«سَلُوا اللهَ الْيَقِينَ والْمُعَافَاةَ، فَما أُوتِيَ أَحَدٌ – بَعْدَ اليَقِينِ – خَيْرًا مِنَ العَافِيَةِ»

"Ask Allāh for certainty and good health, for indeed, no one will have a better possession after certainty of Faith than good health."

The Prophet ﷺ joined the well being of this life and the Next Life. Further, the slave's success cannot be complete in both lives except by joining certainty of faith and well being. Certainty of faith fends off the torments of the Next Life while well being fends off the ailments of this life that might attack the body or the heart.

An-Nasai'ī narrated that Abu Hurairah رَضِيَ اللهِ عَنْهُ related from the

Prophet ﷺ that he said:

« سَلُوا الله العَفْوَ والعافية والمُعَافاةَ، فمَا أُوتِيَ أحد – بعد يقينٍ – خيرًا من مُعَافاة »

"Ask Allāh for forgiveness, well being and health. Indeed, no one acquires a better possession after certainty of faith than good health."

The three matters mentioned in the *Hadith* entail removing the ills of the past with forgiveness, of the present with well being and of the future with immunity (from error and thus from the Torment). Indeed, these words entail the continuity of well being always.

Abdur-Rahman bin Abu Laila said that Abu Ad-Dardaa said, "O Messenger of Allāh ﷺ, it is more beloved to me to acquire good health so that I am thankful for it rather than being tested and I then observe patience. The Messenger of Allāh ﷺ said:

« وَرَسُولُ الله يحِبُّ معك العَافية »

"The Messenger of Allāh ﷺ likes good health just like you."

Further, Ibn Abbâs رَضِيَ الله عَنْهما is reported to have narrated:

"A Bedouin man came to the Messenger of Allāh ﷺ and said to him, 'What should I ask for after I finish the five prayers?' The Prophet ﷺ said, 'Ask Allāh for good health.' The man repeated the question, and the Prophet ﷺ said to him after the third time, 'Ask Allāh for well being in this and the Next Life.'"

If this is how significant health is, we should then mention and study the Prophet's guidance on preserving health and well being, for we will come to realize that his guidance is the most perfect in this regard. With the Prophet's guidance, one attains health of his body and heart and also their very existence, both in this world and in the Next Life. Allāh is sought for all types of help, and our dependence is on Him, and there is neither power nor strength except from Him.

The Prophet ﷺ did not restrict himself to eating one type of food

This would be harmful to one's nature. Also, the body could face weakness and even death if one consumed only one type of food. In addition, when someone is used to only one type of food his body does not accept any other type. Restricting the diet to only one type of food, even if it is the best type, is harmful and dangerous.

The Prophet ﷺ used to eat what his people used to eat in their regular diet, such as meat, fruits, bread, dates, and other types of food that we mentioned.

When one type of food needed to be made milder the Prophet ﷺ would use its opposite, such as neutralizing the hotness of ripe dates with watermelon. If he did not find what neutralized the effect of a type of food, he would eat of it the necessary amount without excessiveness.

When the Prophet ﷺ would not like a food, he would simply refrain from eating it and would not force himself to have it. This is a great aspect of preserving the health. When one eats what he does not have an appetite for, the food's harm will overweigh its benefit.

Abu Hurairah رَضِيَ الله عَنْهُ said, "The Messenger of Allāh ﷺ never criticized a food. If he had an appetite for it, he ate it. Otherwise, he did not eat from it." When the Prophet ﷺ was presented with lizard meat *(Dhabb)* he did not eat from it. He was asked, "Is it disallowed?" He said:

« لا ؛ ولكنْ: لـم يكن بأرضِ قومي؛ فأجِدُني أعَافُه »

"No; But, this food is not among the foods that my people used to eat, and I do not have an appetite for it."

The Prophet ﷺ used eat a regular diet when he was offered a type of food that he was not used to eating and which he had no appetite for, he refrained from eating it. Yet, he did not prevent those who were used to that kind of food and who had an appetite for it from eating it.

The Prophet ﷺ used to like eating meat, especially the arm and the upper parts of the sheep. This is the part that was poisoned and offered to the Prophet ﷺ.

In the *Sahihain* it is narrated that the Prophet ﷺ was once brought some meat and that he was given the arm, which he liked. Furthermore, Abu 'Ubaid narrated that Dhiba'ah bint Az-Zubair said that she slaughtered a sheep in her house. The Messenger of Allāh ﷺ sent to her.

« أَنْ أَطْعِمِينا من شاتِكم. فقالت للرَّسول: ما بقِيَ عندَنا إلَّا الرَّقَبَةُ؛ وإني لأَسْتَحِي أَنْ أُرسِلَ بها إلى رسولِ الله صلى الله عليه وسلم. فرجَع الرسولُ فأخبَرَه، فَقَالَ: ارجِعْ إليها، فقلْ لها: أَرسِلي بها؛ فإنها هاديةُ الشاةِ وأقربُ إلى الخير، وأبعدُها من الأذى »

"Feed us from your sheep." She said to the messenger, 'Only the neck is left, and I feel shy to send it to the Messenger of Allāh ﷺ.' The Prophet's emissary went back to the Prophet ﷺ to tell him what happened. The Messenger said, 'Go back to her and tell her to send it, because the neck is the part that guides the sheep and is closer to the good things and far away from the septic things.'"

There is no doubt that the lightest part of the sheep's meat is the neck, arm and thigh. These parts are also the easiest to digest and the softest on the stomach. The method the Prophet ﷺ observed in this regard satisfies the three basic rules regarding food, which are, the food being beneficial and helpful to the nature, being light on the stomach and not heavy, and being quickly digested. This is the best type of food to consume and consequently, eating a small part of this food is better than consuming a large amount of the other types of food.

The Prophet ﷺ used to like eating sweets and honey. Meat, honey and sweets are the best foods and the most beneficial for the body, liver and various organs. Also, eating these types of food has a profound effect on preserving the health and strength, and that is why only those who already suffering from an ailment would be harmed by consuming them.

The Prophet ﷺ used to eat bread with whatever condiment happened to be available. Sometimes he would eat bread with meat, sometimes with watermelon and sometimes with dates. One time, the Prophet ﷺ placed a dried date on a piece of bread and said that this, the date, is the condiment of that, the bread. Barley bread is cold and dry while dates are hot and wet, so eating both foods together is one of the wisest decisions, especially for those used to this type of food, such as the people of Al-Madinah. Sometimes, the Prophet ﷺ would eat bread with vinegar, saying, 'What a good condiment vinegar is.' This praise for the vinegar came because it was the only available food in the house then, not because vinegar is better than the other types of foods, as some ignorant people think. The Hadith sates that the Prophet ﷺ once came to one of his wives and asked if she had any condiment when they offered him some bread. When she said that they only had vinegar, he said, "What a good condiment vinegar is."

Eating bread with a condiment preserves the health unlike eating only one type of food. Condiments are called as such because when they are added to the bread, the bread tastes better and the food helps preserve the health.

In addition, the Prophet ﷺ used to eat from the fruits that were in season in his land, as this also is one of the best methods of preserving health. Allāh's wisdom decided that every land has its own fruits that are suitable and beneficial to that land when in season. When the people consume these fruits they will help preserve their health and well being and it serves as several medicines. On the other hand, those who refrain from eating the fruits of their area will be among the most ailing persons and the farthest from good health and well being.

The wetness that the various fruits contain represents the favorable heat of the season and the land. The stomach would then be able to bring the fruits to maturity and would fend off their harm, if one does not eat them excessively causing his nature to bear what it cannot bear. Also, one should not spoil the food that his stomach is digesting by eating fruits, nor drink water with it. Fruits should be eaten only after the food in the stomach is digested to prevent constipation. Those who consume fruits in the proper manner, in the proper time and in the proper conditions the fruits act as a cure and a remedy for them.

The Prophet's guidance on the proper way to sit while eating

The Prophet ﷺ said:

« لَا آكُلُ مُتَّكِئًا » وقال « إِنما أَجلِسُ كما يَجلِسُ العبدُ، وآكلُ كما يأكل العبدُ»

*"I do not eat while leaning on my side." He also said, "I only sit
like the slave sits and eat like the slave eats."*

Leaning on the side harms the stomach because it prevents the food from going down the proper channel and reaching the stomach quickly, as it pressures the stomach and does not allow it to be open properly for the food to pass through.

Eating while leaning on something is the practice of the arrogant people and this is why the Prophet ﷺ said that:

« آكُلُ كَما يأكُلُ العَبْد »

"I only eat like the slave eats."

The Prophet ﷺ used to sit on his feet while eating. He used to place his knees on the ground and would place the bottom of his left foot on the upper part of his right foot in humility for the Lord and in respect for the food and for those present. This is the best way to sit for eating, because the organs of the body will all be in their proper position, along with observing good manners.

As we have stated, the best way to eat is sitting up with the organs of the body in their natural position. The worst way of eating is leaning on one's side because the windpipe and the chewing organs will be pressured in this position and squeeze the stomach.

Also, the Prophet ﷺ could have meant that he does not sit while leaning on pillows as the arrogant do and those who want to eat more food. Rather, the Prophet ﷺ used to eat what is barely sufficient just as the slave does.

The Prophet ﷺ used three fingers while eating

This is one of the best methods of eating. Eating with one or two fingers does not help the appetite or provide sufficient amount of food in each bite, and consequently, one would only be able to finish eating after a long time. Also, the organs responsible for handling the food would not be comfortable with the fact that they are getting so little food with each bite, in this case the organs will pass through periods of inactivity while one is still eating! If one eats one or two grains at a time, he will neither enjoy eating or feel comfortable. Eating with five fingers sends to the stomach more food than it can handle in each bite. Death might even occur if one of the organs becomes clogged with excessive food. Also, the organs of the body will be forced to handle large amounts of food and thus the person would neither enjoy eating it nor would their body be comfortable digesting it. Therefore, the best way of eating is by using three fingers as the Prophet ﷺ and those who imitate him do.

The Prophet's guidance on certain combinations of food

The Prophet ﷺ never mixed fish and milk, milk and sour foods or two hot dishes, or two cold dishes, two sticky dishes, two constipating dishes, two laxative dishes, two heavy dishes, two liquid foods or two types of foods that produced the same condition. Also, he did not join between two types of food that caused opposite effects, such as constipating and diarrhea, or easily digested with heavy foods broiled with cooked foods, dry with fresh foods, eggs and milk or meat and milk. Also, he neither ate a food when it is rather hot, nor old food that was heated for him the next day. Further, he did not eat any salty or rotten foods, such as pickles. All these types of foods are harmful and cause the health to change for the worst.

The Prophet ﷺ also used to neutralize the harm of some foods by their opposites, as much as he could. When the food is hot, he neutralizes its effect with a cold food, and when it is dry, he neutralizes it with wet foods, such as eating ripe dates with cucumbers and dried dates with butter. He also used to drink the water of soaked dates to neutralize the effect of heavy foods. Further, the Prophet ﷺ used to eat dinner even if it only consisted of a few dates.

Abu Nu'aym mention that the Prophet ﷺ used to discourage sleeping just after eating food because it will harden the heart. The doctors also advise the people to walk even a few steps after dinner, because sleeping just after dinner is very harmful. Muslim doctors add that one could also pray after eating his dinner, so that the food resides in the bottom of the stomach where it will be easily digested.

The Prophet ﷺ did not drink [water or milk] with his food, because the drink would spoil the food, especially when the water is hot or cold.

It is not preferred that one drinks water after sports activity, when tired, after sexual intercourse, before and after eating food and after eating fruit. Also, it is not preferred that one drinks water after taking a bath and after sleeping. All these activities will harm the health and one should not think about the benefits he might gain from drinking with the food.

The Prophet's guidance on beverages

The Prophet's guidance regarding beverages was also the most beneficial for preserving the health. The Prophet ﷺ used to drink honey with cold water, and this is an especially effective method to preserve the heath that only the best doctors could have knowledge of. Drinking honey on an empty stomach will dissolve phlegm, purify the stomach's protective layers and dissipate its viscidity and excrements while heating it mildly. Honey also helps against the clogs in the stomach, kidney, liver and prostate. Honey is much more profitable to the stomach than any other sweet.

We should state that honey might harm those suffering from bile, because it aggravates it. In this case, the harmful side effect of honey is neutralized when taking it with vinegar, as this method makes the honey very beneficial. In addition, honey is much more beneficial than any other sugar based drink, especially for those who are not used to these types of sweet drinks.

When one drinks sweet drinks that he is not used to, he will not benefit as much as he will benefit from honey, as this is the role that one's customs play. The customs remove foundations and establish foundations..

When the drink is both sweet and cold, it will be most beneficial for the body and one of the best methods to preserve its health and the well being of the soul, strength, liver, and heart. Also, when the drink is both sweet and cold, the body will be eager for it, will benefit from it, nutrition wise, and will quickly digest and transfer it to the other organs of the body.

Cold water is wet, quenches the thirst, preserves the moistures in the body, regenerate the moistures that the body has lost, softens the food and helps transfer it through the veins quickly.

The doctors differed on if water is also nutritional, as some of them said that it is nutritious since the body grows and becomes milder and stronger, especially when it is in need of water. They also said that there are several similarities between man and animals, such as growing and becoming fairer and stronger. The plants also grow and have their own special kind of senses and movements. Since plants feed on water, how can anyone deny that water is nutritious, they asked?

They also say that they do not deny that food provides most of the nutritional intake of the body. They only deny that water is not considered of any nutritional value at all. They also say that the food only provides nourishment because of the watery parts it contains.

They also say that water is the resource of life for animals and plants. There is no doubt, they say, that the substance that is closer to the resource of life will provide more nourishment. How about if the substance is the resource of life itself?

Allāh said:

$$ ﴾ وَجَعَلْنَا مِنَ ٱلْمَآءِ كُلَّ شَيْءٍ حَيٍّ ﴿ $$

"And We have made from water every living thing." (21:30)

They ask, how is it that the resource of life does not provide nutrition to the body?

They also add that the thirsty person would regain his strength and activity when he satisfies his thirst. He will also be able to restrict his food intake and rely on water. However, the thirsty person would not quench his thirst if he eats a large amount of food. They add, "We do not deny that water helps transfer the food to the various parts and organs of the body. We only deny the statement that water does not have any nutritional value at all."

Another group denied that water is nutritional saying that water alone does not sustain life, or help the body grow, or restore the moisture that the body has lost through heat. However, their opponents do not deny these facts. They only say every substance provides nutrition in a different way compatible to its nature. For instance, good aroma provides a type of nutrition, and this fact makes the nutritional value of the water even more apparent.

In short, when the water is cold and mixed with a sweet substance, such as honey, raisins, dates or sugar, it will be one of the most beneficial substances that enters the body and will indeed preserve health. This is why the best drink to the Prophet ﷺ was cold and sweet. Warm water begets flatulence and is not favorable for the body or the health.

Since water that is kept overnight is more favorable than recently drawn water, the Prophet ﷺ said when he entered a garden of Abu At-Taihan:

« هل من ماءٍ باتَ في شَنِّه ؟ »

"Do you have any water that was kept in its skin overnight?"

He was brought some of that water and he drank from it. [*Abu Dāwud, bin Mājah* and *Ahmad*]. This *Hadith* was collected by Al-Bukhari, who narrated that the Prophet ﷺ said:

« إن كان عندَكم ماءٌ باتَ في شَنِّه، وإلّا كَرِعْنَا »

"If you have some water still in its skin (then bring me some).
Otherwise we will sip (from the well).."

Water that is not freshly drawn is similar to yeasty dough, while freshly drawn water is similar to the dough that does not contain yeast. When water is soaked overnight, its earthly and sandy pollutants will rest on the bottom. It was mentioned the Prophet ﷺ liked kept water, as 'Aishah رَضِيَ الله عَنْها said:

« كان رسول الله صلى الله عليه وسلم يُستَقَى له المَاءُ العَذْبُ من بئرِ السُّقْيا »

"Fresh water was being brought to the Messenger of Allāh ﷺ
drawn from the well designated for drinking."

The water that is kept in skins, especially leather skins, has a better taste than water kept in clay containers. This is why the Prophet ﷺ asked for the water that was kept in skin containers rather than the other types of containers. When the water is kept in skin containers, it will filter through the pores in the skin [thus making its taste better]. Similarly, the water that is kept in clay containers that allow the water to filter is better than that in the clay containers that do not allow the water to filter. The Prophet ﷺ had the best methods, the most honorable soul and the best guidance in every matter. He has showed his nation the most beneficial methods and means concerning the benefit of their hearts and bodies in this life and the Next Life.

'Aishah رَضِيَ الله عَنْها said that the best type of drink to the Prophet ﷺ was cold and sweet. This statement might indicate that the Prophet's drink contained fresh, sweet water drawn from wells and springs. Her statement might also indicate that he used to drink water that is mixed with honey or soaked dates and raisins. Or, her statement could carry both meanings, which is the correct opinion.

The Prophet's statement:

« إِنْ كَانَ عِنْدَكَ مَاءٌ بَاتَ فِي شَنٍّ، وَإِلَّا كَرِعْنا »

"If you have some water in its skin. Otherwise we will drink from the pool (with the mouth),"

It indicates that it is allowed to drink the water directly from the pool or container with the mouth. Many doctors advise against this method and say that it is harmful for the stomach. It appears that the Prophet ﷺ did so only to demonstrate that it is allowed. Further, drinking with the mouth from the pool is harmful when one lays on his stomach and face, such as drinking from a river or a spring. Drinking with the mouth from an elevated pool of water while sitting up is not different from drinking using the hands.

The Prophet ﷺ guided his nation to drink while sitting down

He specifically commanded his nation not to drink while standing up. He also commanded those who drink while standing to vomit. Yet, he did drink while standing as is correctly reported of him.

Some people said that the Prophet's drinking while standing overrules his command not to drink while standing. Another group said that his drinking while standing only demonstrates that this practice is only disliked not prohibited. Another group said that there is no contradiction between the two *Ahadith*. The Prophet ﷺ drank while standing when he needed to do so, as he came to the well of Zamzam and was given a bucket of water that he drank from while standing.

Drinking while standing begets many ailments and does not quench the thirst, nor will the water settle in the stomach so that the liver transfers it to the rest of the body. In this case, the water will descend quickly to the stomach and will aggravate it, and the water will not be digested properly. However, if one does this occasionally, it will not harm him.

Drinking water in three separate breaths

Muslim narrated that Anas رَضِيَ الله عَنْهُ said that the Messenger of Allāh

🕮 used to sip the water in three separate breaths and would say:

«إنه أَرْوَى وَأَمْرَأُ وَأَبْرَأُ »

"This method quenches the thirst better and is more palatable and sanitary."

This *Hadith* indicates that the Prophet 🕮 used to remove the cup away from his mouth, take a breath and then drink some more. In another *Hadith*, the Prophet 🕮 commanded that one should not breathe in the cup, but should move the cup away from his mouth and breath away from it. This method of drinking is very beneficial for quenching the thirst and more sanitary as the Prophet 🕮 has stated. When the water enters the hot thirsty stomach in intervals, the second sip of water will quench the thirst left by the first, and the third will quench the thirst left by the first two. Also, this method is better suited for the temperature of the stomach, so as not to suddenly invade it with cold substances. Also, when one drinks the water in one breath, it will only partially quench the thirst unlike when he drinks it in separate sips.

This method [that the Prophet 🕮 taught us] gives better results than drinking the water or liquid in one breath, since water might dissipate the instinctive heat or weaken it, thus spoiling the temperament of the stomach and the liver. Water might also beget many other ailments, especially for those who live in warm areas, such as Yemen and Hijaz, and especially during summer. Drinking in one breath is dangerous for such people because their instinctive heat is weak especially during hot weather, as we have stated.

The Prophet's statement, "It quenches the thirst better and is more palatable and sanitary," is similar to what Allāh said:

﴿ فَكُلُوهُ هَنِيئًا مَّرِيئًا ﴾

"And enjoy it without fear of any harm." (4:4)

Also, when one takes the drink in one breath, he might choke on it because of the large amount of the liquid. However, there is no fear from choking when one takes a breath while drinking. Further, when one takes a drink, the hot gases accumulating in his body will ascend from around the liver and the heart because of the cold water or liquid that is descending on the stomach. In this case, the water will come rushing down while the gases are ascending, causing flatulence and sometimes choking the person. One will not enjoy the drink in this case.

Also, when cold water descends suddenly on the liver it will weaken it and cause a decrease in its temperature. However, when one takes the drink in separate sips, the liver will not lose its warmth and thus will not weaken. Similarly, when one pours water on a boiling pot, it will not decrease its temperature significantly.

At-Tirmidhi narrated that the Prophet ﷺ said:

« لا تَشْرَبُوا نَفَسًا واحدًا : كَشُرْب البَعير؛ ولكن : اشرَبُوا مَثْنَى وثُلاثَ؛ وسَمُّوا إذا أنتم شَرِبْتم، واحمَدُوا إذا أنتم فَرَغْتُم »

"Do not drink in one breath just as the camel does. Rather, drink twice and thrice, and mention (Allāh's) Name before drinking and thank (Him) upon finishing."

Mentioning Allāh's Name before drinking and thanking Him upon finishing has a significant effect in benefiting from the drink, enjoying it while fending off its harm. Imam Ahmad said, "When the food has four qualities, it will have become perfect: when Allāh's Name is mentioned before having it, when Allāh is thanked after finishing with it, when there are many hands to eat from it, and when it is from legal, pure sources."

Covering pots and closing water skins

Muslim narrated in his *Sahih* that Jabir bin 'Abdullāh رَضِيَ الله عَنْهُ said, I heard the Messenger of Allāh ﷺ say:

« غَطُّوا الإِناءَ وأوكُوا السِّقاءَ؛ فإِن في السَّنة لِيلةً ينزل فيها وَباءٌ: لا يمُرُّ بإِناءٍ
ليس عليه غِطاءٌ، وسِقاءٍ ليس عليه وِكاءٌ – إلا وقع فيه من ذلك الداءِ »

"Cover the pot and tie the knot of the water skin, for there is a day during the year in which a disease descends and falls in whatever pot that is not covered, or water skin, which is not tied, that it passes by."

This *Hadith* contains a type of divine knowledge that the doctors could never reach on their own. Laith bin Sa'd, one of the narrators of this *Hadith*, said, "Non-Muslims know which day it is, in January, and they try to avoid its harm."

The Prophet ﷺ commanded that the pots be covered, even with a branch, so that one makes covering it a habit. Also, when one covers the pot with a branch, crawling insects will not fall in the food but will pass over it on the branch.

Furthermore, the Prophet ﷺ commanded that we mention Allāh's Name when covering the pot to repel Satan and insects and animals.

Drinking from the mouth of the water skin is not allowed

Al-Bukhari narrated that Ibn 'Abbās رَضِيَ الله عَنْهما said:

« أن رسولَ الله صلى الله عليه وسلم نَهىٰ عن الشُّرْب مِن في السِّقاءِ »

"The Messenger of Allāh ﷺ disallowed drinking from the mouth of the water skin."

There are many benefits in this *Hadith*. For instance, when one drinks from the tip or the mouth of the water skin, he will breathe in it and will give it an offensive odor. Also, water may descend strongly and harm the stomach. In addition, there might be an insect in the water that one is unaware of, and that might harm him if he swallows it. Also, water might be polluted with harmful substances that will enter the person's stomach while he is unaware. Also, drinking from the mouth of the skin fills the stomach with air and thus the water will not have sufficient space.

Drinking from a chipped cup is not allowed

Abu Dāwud narrated in his *Sunan* that Abu Sa'id Al-Khudri رَضِيَ الله عَنْهُ said:

« نهى رسولُ الله صلى الله لله عليه وسلم عن الشُّرْب في ثُلْمةِ القَدَح، وأن يُنْفَخَ
في الشَّراب »

"The Messenger of Allāh ﷺ disallowed drinking from the chipped side of the cup and from breathing in the drink."

This *Hadith* also teaches the Muslim many types of good behavior. For instance, drinking from the chipped side of the cup might cause one to swallow the substances that have accumulated near the chipped side. Also, one might not be able to enjoy his drink when he is drinking from the cup's chipped side. In addition, dirt and fat concentrate near the chipped side and are usually not fully cleaned when rinsed. Also, the chipped side of the cup is the worst and is not beneficial. One of our *Salaf* saw a man once buying inferior goods and said to him, "Do not buy it, do you not know that Allāh has not blessed inferior things?" Also, the chipped side of the cup might cause injury to the mouth.

As for breathing in the cup, it will transfer the foul odor from the person to the drink. This is why the Prophet ﷺ has disallowed breathing or blowing in it. In the *Hadith* that At-Tirmidhi narrated, Ibn 'Abbās رَضِيَ الله عَنْهُما said:

« نهى رسول الله صلى الله عليه وسلم: أن يُتنفَّس في الإناء، أو يُنفخَ فيه »

"The Messenger of Allāh ﷺ prohibited breathing in the pot (or cup) or blowing on it."

If some asks, "What about the *Hadith* in the *Sahihain* in which Anas رَضِيَ الله عَنْهُ narrated:

« إنّ رسولَ الله صلى الله عليه وسلم كان يتنفَّسُ في الإناء ثلاثًا »

"The Messenger of Allāh ﷺ used to take three breaths while drinking" ?

We say that we believe in this *Hadith* and that it does not contradict the *Ahadith* that we mentioned, because it only means that the Prophet ﷺ did not sip the drink in one breath.

The Prophet ﷺ drank milk undiluted or mixed with water

Drinking sweet milk in hot areas is very beneficial in preserving the health and providing moisture for the body and the liver. This is especially the case when the animals that produce the milk have grazed on wormwood, lavender, lavender cotton, and so forth, because their milk is both a food and a medicine.

At-Tirmidhi narrated that the Prophet ﷺ said:

« إذا أَكَلَ أحدُكم طَعامًا، فليقلْ: اللهم، باركْ لنا فيه، وأَطْعِمنا خيرًا منه. وإذا سُقِي لبنًا، فليقل: اللهم، باركْ لنا فيه، وزِدْنا منه. فإنه لَيْس شيٌء يُجزِىءُ منَ الطَّعام والشراب، إلَّا اللَّبَنُ »

"When any of you eats food, let him say, 'O Allāh! Bless it for us and give us what is better than it.' When someone is given milk, let him say, 'O Allāh! Bless it for us and give us more of it.' Certainly, milk is the only food or drink that is sufficient."

Further, Muslim narrated:

« إنَّه صلى الله عليه وسلم كَانَ يُنْتَبَذُ له أولَ الليل، ويشرَبُه – إذا أصبح – يَوْمَه ذلك، والليلة الَّتي تجيءُ، والغَدَ والليلةَ الأُخْرى، والغَدَ إلى العَصْرِ. فإنْ بقِيَ منه شَيْءٌ: سقاهُ الخادِم، أو أمرَ به فَصُبَّ »

"The Messenger of Allāh ﷺ used to be made Nabith (some dates soaked in water) in the beginning of the night and would drink it in the morning of the next day, the next night and the next day, and another night, and the next day until 'Asr. If any of it remained, he would then give it to a servant or would order that it be poured out."

The *Nabith* mentioned in this *Hadith* is some dates that are soaked in water to sweeten the water and it is used both in drinks and foods. The Nabith has a great benefit in strengthening the body and preserving the health. The Prophet ﷺ did not drink the Nabith that is more than three days old fearing that it might have started to decompose and become intoxicating.

The Prophet's guidance regarding clothes

The Prophet's guidance regarding clothes was the best guidance, the most beneficial for the body and the easiest to wear and take off.

The Prophet ﷺ used to wear an outer garment and *Izar* (which covered the body), as these types of clothes are the softest on the body. The Prophet ﷺ also liked to wear shirts, which was preferred by him.

What the Prophet ﷺ used to wear was the most beneficial for the body, as his clothes did not have excessively long or wide sleeves. Rather, the sleeves were to the wrists and would not be longer than the hand, as this would make them harder to wear and to move about easily. Further, the sleeves were not shorter than what we have described, so as not to expose the hands to the cold and heat.

In addition, the Prophet's shirts and garments did not reach the ankles and would usually reach the middle of his legs. Otherwise, if the clothes were longer, they will restrict the movement and make one feel restrained. They were not shorter than what we have described, so as not to expose the thighs to the heat and cold.

The Prophet's turban was not excessively big so that it did not harm the head. It was not very small either, otherwise it would not be sufficient to protect the head from the heat and cold. It was medium in size, and he used to pass a part of it under his chin to protect the neck from the heat and cold and to keep the turban firmly on the head when riding his horse or camel and when in battle.

Many people use some type of braces instead of passing the turban under the chin, although the two methods cannot be compared in terms of benefit or even beauty.

When one thinks about the types of clothes that the Prophet ﷺ used, he will find that they are indeed among the best for the body and health and the farthest from extravagance and difficulty to wear.

Most of the time, the Prophet ﷺ used to wear *Khuffs* (socks) while traveling, because the feet would need such types of foot covering to fend off the effects of the heat and cold. Sometimes, he would use the *Khuffs* when he was not traveling.

The best colors that the Prophet ﷺ used to wear were white and striped garments. He did not wear all red, black or dyed garments.

As for the red garment the Prophet ﷺ was reported to have worn, it was a Yemeni garment that had black, red, and white stripes. We have mentioned this before and stated that some people erred when they thought that the Prophet wore red garments.

The Prophet's guidance concerning one's place of residence

The Prophet ﷺ had knowledge that this life-term was just a transit station in which one resides for the remainder of his earthly life and then moves on to the Next Life. It was not a part of his guidance or the guidance of his companions, and all those who followed and imitated him, to establish and be concerned with building houses, raising them, beautifying them and extending them. Rather, their places of residence were among the best transit stations that could benefit the traveler, fending off the cold, heat, people's eyes, the beasts and even the fear that it might fall down on them because of its considerable weight! Also, their residence were neither shared by wild animals, due to their size, nor did the air and wind buffet them due to their excessive height. They were neither built underground, because this would harm the inhabitants, nor were they very high above the ground. They were on the level of the ground. These are the best types of houses, most beneficial and least cold or hot. They were not so small that the inhabitants would be irritated by their smallness, nor very spacious, for the residents would not be able to benefit from the excess space. Their homes did not contain bathrooms so that they did not bother the people with a stinking odor. The scent in their homes was fresh, as the Prophet used to like good smells and always had a good scent in his house. In fact, the Prophet's sweat was one of the best scents ever smelled, and such was the scent of his body. There is no doubt that this is the description of the best type of home, most suitable for the body and for staying healthy.

The Prophet's guidance concerning sleep

Those who read about the Prophet's guidance concerning being awake and concerning sleep will find that his sleep was the best and most beneficial for the body, the organs and one's strength. He used to sleep in the early part of the night and would wake up in the beginning of the latter part, use *siwak* (natural toothbrush), perform ablution and pray as much as Allāh permitted him. Consequently, the body, the organs and one's strength will acquire their fair share of sleep, rest and physical activity, along with acquiring the complete rewards (from Allāh). This method ensures righteousness of the heart and body in this life and the Next Life.

The Prophet ﷺ did not oversleep or deprive his body of necessary sleep, making his method in this regard the most perfect. He used to sleep when sleep is warranted and would lay on his right side and remember Allāh in supplication until sleep overwhelmed his eyes. Also, his body would not be burdened with overeating or overdrinking. He neither slept on the bare floor, or on high beds. Rather, he had mats made of leaves, used to lean on a pillow and would sometimes place his hand under his cheek.

We will now elaborate on the beneficial and harmful methods of sleep.

Sleep is a condition during which the body's instinctive heat becomes idle, so that the body gets some rest. There are two types of sleep, normal and abnormal. Normal sleep entails resting the inner powers and the senses. When these powers are idle, the body refrains from its usual activity and thus the vapors and wetness that were moving and decomposing while awake would ascend to the brain which is the residence of these powers. The brain then becomes idle, and this is the normal type of sleep.

Abnormal (i.e. heavy) sleep occurs because of an accident or a disease. In this case, the excess wetness will take over the brain in a manner that prevents the person from waking up easily. Or, excessive amounts of vapor and moisture ascend to the brain, just as what happens in the aftermath of overeating and overdrinking, and cause the brain to relax and thus the person goes to sleep.

There are two benefits in sleep: the senses get to rest from the fatigue that overtakes them. In this case, the senses will rest from the tiresome activity that occurs when one is awake. The second benefit is digesting food and leading the various mixtures, conditions or temperaments to maturity (processing bodily wastes). While one is asleep, his instinctive energy or heat concentrates on the digestion process and this is why the body gets cold and needs a cover while one is asleep.

The best type of sleep is for one to sleep on his right side so that the food sits in the stomach comfortably, for the stomach leans to left side as we have stated. One could also lay on his left side a little so that the digestion is made faster because the stomach leans on the liver. One should then turn again on his right side to help the stomach push the food down the stomach and this way one starts and ends his sleep while laying on his right side. Sleeping on the left side regularly harms the heart because the organs of the body will pressure the heart with their weight.

One of the worst types of sleep is on the back, although resting while laying on the back without going to sleep is not harmful.

Sleeping on the stomach is the worst way to sleep. Ahmad and Ibn Mājah narrated that Abu Umamah رَضِيَ اللهُ عَنْهُ said: "The Prophet ﷺ passed by a sleeping man in the mosque who was laying on his face (stomach) and he touched him with his foot, saying.

« قُمْ – أَو اقْعُدْ – فَإِنَّها نَوْمةٌ جهنَّميَّة »

'Sit up, for it is a Hellish sleep."

Hippocrates said in his book, "If an ailing person sleeps on his stomach whereas this was not his usual habit when he is not sick, then he will be either testifying to the weakness in his mind or that he is suffering from a pain in the stomach." Those who explained Hippocrates' book said that he meant to indicate that such a person sleeps on his stomach, which is a bad habit, instead of the good habit, without any apparent reasonable explanation for this act.

Good habits of sleeping help the natural powers of the body to fulfill there tasks and also strengthens the psychological health of the person.

Sleeping during the day is bad for health and causes humid ailments, makes the color pale, ails the spleen, softens the nerves, causes laziness and weakens desire, except during the summer time around noon. The worst type of sleep occurs in the early hours of the day and in the afternoon. Ibn 'Abbās رَضِيَ الله عَنْهما once saw his son sleeping in the early morning and said to him, "Wake up! Do you sleep at the hour during which sustenance is being divided."

It was said that sleeping during the day is of three types: good habit, which entails sleeping around noon; careless habit, which occurs in the early morning and keeps one busy from matters of this and the Next Life; and madness, which occurs after 'Asr (afternoon). This is why some of our Salaf said, "Those who sleep after 'Asr and lose their minds should only blame their own selves."

Sleeping during the early morning prevents sustenance from coming, in that the early morning is the time when the creation goes out to seek their sustenance. Being asleep during this time in which sustenance is being divided causes one to miss out on this chance of gaining sustenance, except when one sleeps for a necessity or a need. This type of sleep is also very harmful for the body because it causes numbness in the senses and spoils the stomach's contents that should be being decomposed through physical activity. Further, sleeping in the early morning hours causes numbness and a general weakness in the body, especially if one goes to sleep before relieving himself (using the toilet), moving about, performing physical activity and before having the stomach busy (by eating some food). This itself is a difficult ailment that even leads to more ailments.

Sleeping under the sun excites otherwise dormant ailments, and such is the case with sleeping while a part of the body is under the sun and a part of the body is under the shade. Abu Dāwud narrated that Abu Hurairah رَضِيَ الله عَنْهُ said that the Messenger of Allāh ﷺ said:

« إِذَا كَانَ أَحدكم فِي الشَّمْسِ، فقلصَ عنه الظِّلُّ - فصار بعضُه فِي الشمس، وبعضُه فِي الظِّلّ - فليقُم »

"If one of you was in the shade and then the shade recedes and exposes a part of the body to the sun while the other part is still under the shade, let him move from that place." [Al-Hakim].

Ibn Mājah and Abu Dāwud also narrated:

«أن رسولَ الله صلى الله عليه وسلم نهى أنْ يقعدَ الرَّجلُ بين الظِّلِّ والشَّمْس»

"The Messenger of Allāh ﷺ disallowed sitting between the shade and the sun."

This *Hadith* indicates that it is not allowed for one to sleep while partially in the shade and partially in the sun.

Further, in the *Sahihain* it is narrated that Al-Bara' bin 'Azib said that the Messenger of Allāh ﷺ said:

« إذا أتيت مَضْجَعَكَ: فتوضأ وُضوءَكَ للصلاة، ثم اضطجعْ على شِقِّكَ الأيمن؛ ثم قل: اللهم؛ إني أسْلمتُ نفسي إليكَ، ووجَّهتُ وجْهي إليكَ، وفوَّضتُ أمري إليكَ وألجأْتُ ظهري إليكَ: رَغْبةً ورَهْبةً إليكَ؛ لا مَلْجأ ولا مَنْجا منك إلَّا إليكَ؛ آمَنتُ بكِتابكَ الذي أنْزلْتَ، ونبيِّكَ الذي أرْسلتَ، واجعلْهنَّ آخر كلامِكَ. فإن مِتَّ مِن ليلتِك: مُتَّ على الفِطْرة »

"Whenever you go to bed perform ablution like that for the prayer, lie on your right side and say, 'O Allāh! I surrender myself to You, turn my face towards You, entrust all my affairs to You and depend upon You for Your Blessings both with hope (in You) and fear of You. There is no fleeing from You, and there is no place of protection and safety except with You O Allāh! I believe in Your Book (the Qur'ān) which You have revealed and in Your Prophet (Muhammad) whom You have sent.' Make these words the last of your speech, because if you die on that very night, you will die on the Fitrah (i.e. or the religion of Islam)."

Also, Al-Bukhari narrated that 'Āishah رَضِيَ الله عَنْها said:

« أن رسول الله صلى الله عليه وسلم كان إذا صلى ركعتي الفجر – يعني: سُنَّتها – اضطجعَ على شِقِّه الأيمن »

"When the Messenger of Allāh ﷺ would pray the two (voluntary) Rak'ah of Dawn, he would lay on his right side."

It was said that the wisdom behind sleeping on the right side of the body is that the person does not oversleep. Since the heart leans towards the left side, then sleeping on the right side prevents the heart from residing in its normal place thus causing the sleeping person to wake up when he feels restless. Sleeping on the left side makes the heart comfortable and thus the person oversleeps and misses out on the affairs of his life and religion.

Since sleeping is similar to death, it is not possible or suitable for the Ever-Living Who does not die. Further, sleeping is not suitable for the residents of Paradise. In addition, while asleep, people need to be protected from every type of harm or affliction, and since only Allāh is Able to fulfill this need, the Prophet ﷺ has taught us to supplicate to Allāh with words of reliance, fear and eagerness before going to sleep. With these words, one invokes Allāh's prefect protection for himself and for his body. The Prophet ﷺ also directed us to remember our faith in Allāh and making such words the last of our speech at night. Since one might die in his sleep, he then will enter Paradise if these words of faith were the last words he uttered in this world.

The Prophet's guidance in this regard has included the benefits of the heart, body and soul while awake and asleep and for this life and the Next Life. Allāh's peace and blessings be on he whose nation has acquired all types of good through him.

The Prophet's statement:

« أَسلَمتُ نفسي إِليكَ »

"I submit myself to You."

This means I surrender myself to You just as the owned slave surrenders his freedom to his master.

Further; turning the face towards Allāh means directing one's full attention to the Lord with sincerity with the intention and while affirming being a slave, humble and obedient to Him. Allāh said:

﴿ فَإِنْ حَاجُّوكَ فَقُلْ أَسْلَمْتُ وَجْهِيَ لِلَّهِ وَمَنِ اتَّبَعَنِ ﴾

"So if they dispute with you (Muhammad ﷺ) say: "I have submitted myself to Allāh (in Islām), and (so have) those who follow me." (3:20)

The face is the most honorable part of the body and the residence of the senses and awareness.

Referring matters to Allāh means submission and contentment in the heart, while being pleased with what Allāh decides and chooses of what He wills and with what He is pleased with. Referring all affairs to Allāh is one of the most honorable parts of slavery to Allāh.

Leaning one's back to Allāh indicates the strength of one's depending on and trust in Him. He who leans his back to a firm foundation will not have fear of falling down.

The heart has two types of strength, seeking, which is also eagerness, and running away, which is also fear. The slave seeks his interest and runs away from whatever might harm him. Therefore, the Prophet ﷺ has joined both powers in this *Hadith* by saying, "With eagerness and fear."

The Prophet ﷺ then praised the Lord by stating that the slave has no refuge or resort from Allāh except Allāh. Allāh is the One Whom the slave seeks refuge with so that He saves him from Himself. In another *Hadith*, the Prophet ﷺ said:

« أعوذ برِضَاك من سَخَطِكَ، وَبِمُعَافَاتِكَ من عُقوبِتِكَ؛ وأعوذُ بك منك »

"I seek refuge with Your Pleasure from Your Anger, and with Your Pardon from Your Torment, and I seek refuge from You with You."

Therefore, Allāh Alone grants refuge to His slave and saves him from His torment, which also occurs by His will. Torment and Favor are both from Allāh Alone. Further, the slave asks Allāh for support against what He has (of Torment and trials) and seeks Him Alone for his safety. He Alone is the Lord of everything and nothing occurs except by His will.

﴿ وَإِن يَمْسَسْكَ ٱللَّهُ بِضُرٍّ فَلَا كَاشِفَ لَهُۥ إِلَّا هُوَ ﴾

"And if Allāh touches you with hurt, there is none who can remove it but He..." (10:107)

And:

﴿ قُلْ مَن ذَا ٱلَّذِى يَعْصِمُكُم مِّنَ ٱللَّهِ إِنْ أَرَادَ بِكُمْ سُوٓءًا أَوْ أَرَادَ بِكُمْ رَحْمَةً ﴾

"Say: 'Who is he who can protect you from Allāh if He intends to harm you, or intends mercy on you?'" (33:17)

The Prophet ﷺ then ended the supplication by affirming faith in Allāh's Book and Messenger, which holds the key to the ultimate safety and success in this life and the Next Life. This is the Prophet's guidance concerning sleep.

The Prophet's guidance on waking

The Prophet ﷺ used to wake up when the rooster crowed and would then praise Allāh, affirm His Greatness and Oneness, supplicate to Him, and he would use siwak (natural toothbrush). He would then perform ablution and stand before his Lord reciting His Speech (the Qur'ān), praising Him and hoping in Him with eagerness and fear. What actions can be more preserving for the health of the heart, body, soul and general strength and that acquires the favors of this life and the Next Life than these actions?

The Prophet's guidance on physical activity

As for the Prophet's guidance while busy and while free, we will mention a part of the Prophet's guidance that will satisfy us that his guidance in this regard was the most perfect.

It is a fact that the body relies on food and drink for its survival. It is also a fact that not all of the food and nourishment is digested when consumed. Rather, a part of it remains, and as time goes by, these substances accumulate in various qualities and quantities in the body. These accumulations harm the body because they cause clogs in different vessels and make the body feel heavy. If one gets rid of these substances by extracting them with medication, the body is harmed because most of these medications are toxic to varying degrees. In fact, the medication extracts the beneficial substances along with the harmful ones. As for the quality of these substances, the body is harmed when they heat up, spoil, become cold or weaken the natural heat and energy from fully maturing the excess substances.

The clogs caused by the residual substances are harmful whether they remain in the body or get extracted. Moving about is one of the best methods to deny these substances the chance to accumulate. Moving heats the organs and dissipates the leftover substances disallowing them from accumulating by the passage of time. The body will also get used to being energetic and light through physical activity and would optimize the intake of food, firm up the joints and strengthen the muscles and the ligaments. Moderate physical activity immunizes the body against most ailments and mood changes, providing the activity is done at the right time and under the proper circumstances.

Physical activity should be practiced after one has digested their food. In addition, moderate physical activity is that which gives the cheeks color and which nourishes the body. As for the activity that causes sweat it is too excessive.

Any organ that is used regularly in a type of physical activity will get stronger, especially during enjoyable sports in which the organ is used. Those who practice sports regularly will strengthen their bodies and those who nourish their memory their memory will get it stronger. Every organ has its own suitable sport or physical activity. For instance, the chest needs recitation, where one should start speaking with a low tone and then increases the volume of his tone. Hearing needs to hear various sounds and voices, gradually from the softer to the louder voices. The tongue needs to speak, and the eye needs to see while the legs need to walk while increasing the pace of walking gradually.

Horse riding, archery, wrestling and running are sports for the whole body. These types of sports dissipate chronic ailments, such as leprosy, dropsy and constipation.

Furthermore, the heart needs a type of sport that entails learning, behaving, and feeling happiness, joy, patience, firmness, courage, forbearing, performing righteous good deeds, and so forth. Patience, love, courage and kindness are among the best types of sports or physical activity for the inner-self. When the heart learns these types of physical activities little by little, these attributes will firmly reside in the heart and will be characteristic of that person.

In short, when you learn the Prophet's guidance in this regard you will realize that it is the most perfect and beneficial and that it preserves good heath and the power of the body. It is also beneficial for the worldly affairs and the Next Life.

In addition, there is no doubt that prayer preserves the health of the body and helps dissolve its excess and residual substances. It also preserves faith and brings happiness for this and the Next Life. Standing up in prayer at night also preserves health. Prayer also helps against acute ailments and energizes the body, heart and soul profoundly. In the *Sahihain* it is narrated that the Prophet ﷺ said:

« يَعقِدُ الشيطانُ على قافِيةِ رأسِ أحدكم – إذا هو نام – ثلاثَ عُقدٍ، يَضربُ

على كل عقدةٍ: عليكَ ليلٌ طويلٌ فارقُدْ. فإنْ هو استيقَظَ، فذكرَ اللهَ انحلَّتْ
عقدةٌ. فإنْ توضأ: انحلَّتْ عُقْدةٌ ثانيةٌ. فإنْ صلَّى: انحلَّتْ عُقْدُهُ كلُّها، فأصبَحَ
نشيطًا طيِّبَ النفْسِ. وإلّا: أصبح خَبيثَ النفسِ كَسْلانَ »

*"Satan ties three knots at the back of the head of any of you if
he is asleep. On every knot he reads and exhales the following
words, 'The night is long, so stay asleep.' When one wakes up
and remembers Allāh, one knot is undone. When one performs
ablution, the second knot is undone. When one prays, the third
knot is undone and one gets up energetic with a good heart in the
morning. Otherwise one gets up lazy and with a mischievous
heart."*

The Islamic commandment of Fasting also preserves the health and is
a type of physical activity for body and soul. No one whose character is
not spoiled could ever deny these facts.

As for Jihad and what it entails of various movements and activities, it
is one of the best preservers of strength, good health, firmness of the
heart and body and extracting unwanted residual substances that
accumulate in the body. Jihad also helps remove sadness, grief, anguish
and depression. Only those who have tasted this cure know these facts.
Hajj and performing the rest of its obligations, horseracing, helping other
people achieve their needs and rights, visiting the sick, following funerals,
walking to the mosque to perform Jumu'ah and congregational prayers,
performing ablution and taking a bath all have similar effects and benefits.

All the acts that we mentioned will help preserve the health and aid
the body towards the healthy passing of liquid and solid wastes. There is
an added benefit in these acts as they help acquire the good of this life
and the Next Life and fend off harm.

Now, we should realize that the Prophet's guidance in all of this is the
best guidance. His guidance is superior regarding the treatment of the
heart and the body, preserving their well being and fending off harm
from them. There is no more proof for those who have been given the
correct guidance than what we have already mentioned. Indeed, all
success comes from Allāh Alone.

The Prophet's guidance concerning sexual activity

His is the most effective guidance, as it preserves the health, completes satisfaction, and acquires the goals that this activity was meant to achieve.

Sexual intercourse is meant to achieve three essential goals: reproduction and the preservation of mankind until the number of souls that Allāh has ordered to come to this world is fulfilled and completed. Second, expelling the water (semen), which would cause harm if it remains inside the body. Third, satisfying sexual desire and enjoying sex and the bounty that it represents. The last essential goal is the only one that will be satisfied in Paradise, because there will be no reproduction in Paradise nor accumulation of sperm that needs to be discarded.

The best doctors state that sex is one of the best methods to preserve good health. Galinus said, "The essence of the sperm consists of heat and air, and it is hot and wet because it is produced from the pure blood that feeds the essential organs."

If this is how significant sperm is, one should realize that it should not be used or spent except to achieve reproduction or to legally rid the body of it when it gets old. When the sperm is congested in the body, it will cause certain ailments, such as obsession, madness, and epilepsy. Discarding it, on the other hand, helps cure many of these ailments. When the sperm is kept in the body for a long time, it becomes spoiled and turns into a toxic material that can cause certain ailments. This is why sometimes sperm is expelled from the body naturally.

Some of our Salaf said, "Man should take care of three things: he should not ignore walking, so that when he needs it one day he is able to do it; he should not refrain from eating, because the intestines will shrink; he should not refrain from sexual activity, because if the well's water is not drawn out, it will drain."

Also, Muhammad bin Zakariyya said, "Whoever ignores sex for a long time, his nerves will weaken, and their flowing will be blocked, and his penis will shrink. I have seen some people who did not have sex claiming to observe some kind of abstinence and their bodies became colder, their movements restricted and unexplainable depression touched them. Further, their appetite and digestive powers also decreased."

Sexual activity helps lower the gaze, repulse lust, allows one the ability to refrain from illegal sexual activity and also achieves these goals for the wife. When one uses his sperm in a legal manner, he will benefit himself and his wife in this life and the Next Life.

This is why the Prophet ﷺ used to fulfill his legal sexual desire, as he used to say:

« حُبِّبَ إليَّ من دنياكم النساءُ والطيبُ »

"I was made to like women and perfume from your world."

Further, the Prophet ﷺ encouraged his nation to marry:

« تزوَّجُوا، فإني مُكاثِرٌ بكم الأممَ »

"Get married, because I will compete by your numbers with the other nations."

Also, Ibn 'Abbās رَضِيَ الله عَنْهما said: "The best of this nation are those who have the largest number of wives (up to four)." * Also, the Prophet ﷺ said:

« إني أتزوَّجُ النِّساءَ، وآكلُ اللحمَ، وأنامُ وأقوم وأصومُ وأُفْطِرُ. فمن رغِبَ
عَنْ سُنَّتي: فليس منِّي »

"I marry women, eat meat, sleep, stand in Qiyam, fast and break my fast. Whoever ignores my Sunnah is not from my people."

Furthermore, he ﷺ said:

« يا معشرَ الشَّبابِ، من استطاعَ منكم الباءة فَلْيتزوَّجْ، فإنه أغضُّ للبَصَرِ،
وأحفظُ للفَرْج. ومن لم يَستطِعْ: فعليه بالصَّوم؛ فإنه له وِجاءٌ »

"O young men! Get married whoever can afford it, because it helps lower the gaze (from looking at what is prohibited) and protects the sexual organ (from illegal sexual activity). Those who cannot afford it should fast because fasting will cure them."

Also, when Jabir رَضِيَ الله عَنْهُ married a matron woman, the Prophet ﷺ said:

---

* **Editor's note:** This narration of Ibn Abbas could also be translated to mean: "Get married, for the best of this (Muslim) nation (i.e. Muhammad) had the largest number of wives." (See Sahih Al- Bukhari, The Book of An-Nikah, 5069.) A.W.

« هَلَّا بِكْرًا تُلَاعِبها وتُلَاعبُكَ »

"Why not have a virgin who fondles you and you fondle her."

Also, Ibn Mājah narrated in his *Sunan* that Ibn 'Abbās رَضِيَ الله عَنْهما related from the Prophet ﷺ that he said:

« لم نَرَ للمُتَحابَّيْنِ مثلَ النِّكاحِ »

*"We do not see a better resort for those who love each other
than marriage."* *

Muslim also narrated in his *Sahih* that Abdullah bin Umar related from the Prophet ﷺ that he said:

« الدُّنيا متاعٌ؛ وخيْرُ متاع الدنيا: المَرْأةُ الصالحةُ »

*"The life of this world is enjoyment, and the best enjoyment in
the life of this world is a righteous wife."*

The Prophet ﷺ used to encourage his nation to marry beautiful virgin women who are also religious. An-Nasai'î narrated that Abu Hurairah رَضِيَ الله عَنْهُ said, The Messenger of Allāh ﷺ was asked, 'Who among women is the best?' He said:

« التي تَسُرُّه إذا نَظَرَ وتُطيعه إذَاأَمَر، ولا تُخالِفُه فيما يَكرهُ في نَفْسِها ومالِه »

*"The one who would please him (her husband) if he looks at her,
obeys him if he commands her and avoids disobeying him in what
he hates concerning herself and his money."*

In the *Sahihain* it is also narrated that the Prophet ﷺ said:

« تُنكَحُ المرأةُ: لمالِها، ولِحَسَبِها، ولِجَمالِها، ولِدِينها . فَاظفَرْ بذاتِ الدِّين؛
تَرِبَتْ يدَاكَ »

*"The woman is married for four reasons: her wealth, position,
beauty and religion. So marry the religious woman, may your hand
be filled with sand (a good expression)."*

The Prophet ﷺ also used to encourage marrying women who bare children and did not like marrying women who cannot bare children.

---

* **Editor's note**: The translator has chosen to translate the word *Nikah* as marriage. However the word Nikah also means sexual intercourse and could be understood as such in this narration (within the legal limitations of Islam). A.W.

Abu Dāwud narrated that Ma'qil bin Yasar said, "A man came to the Prophet ﷺ and said, 'I know of a beautiful, rich woman whom I want to marry, but she does not bare children. Should I marry her?' He said, 'No.' The man came a second time, and the Prophet ﷺ did not allow him. On the third time, the Prophet said:

« تَزَوَّجُوا الوَدُودَ والوَلُودَ؛ فإِني مُكاثِرٌ بكمُ الأُمم »

"Marry the kind woman who bares children, for I will compete concerning your large numbers with to the other nations."

At-Tirmidhi related from the Prophet ﷺ that he said:

« أَرْبَعٌ من سُنَنِ المُرْسَلِين: النكاحُ، والسِّواكُ و التَّعَطُّرُ، والحِنَّاءُ »

"Four are among the tradition of the Prophets: marriage, using siwak (natural toothbrush), wearing perfume and dyeing with Henna."

The husband should first fondle his wife before having sex with her, by kissing her and sucking her tongue sometimes. The Messenger of Allāh ﷺ used to do the same with his wives. Abu Dāwud narrated in his *Sunan*:

« إنه صلى الله عليه وسلم كان يقبِّلُ عائشة ويمَصُّ لِسَانَها »

"The Prophet ﷺ used to kiss 'Āishah رَضِيَ الله عَنْها *and suck her tongue."*

Also, Jabir bin 'Abdullah narrated:

« نَهَىٰ رسولُ الله صلى الله عليه وسلم عن المُواقَعةِ قبلَ المُلاعَبةِ»

"The Messenger of Allāh ﷺ did not allow sexual intercourse before fondling (the wife)."

Sometimes, the Prophet ﷺ would sleep with all of his wives in one night and would only take one bath afterwards. Sometimes, the Prophet ﷺ would take a bath after sleeping with each of his wives. Muslim narrated in his *Sahih* that Anas رَضِيَ الله عَنْهُ said, "The Prophet ﷺ would sometimes sleep with all of his wives and take one bath afterwards." Also, Abu Dāwud narrated in his *Sunan* that Abu Rafi' the Prophet's servant, said, "The Messenger of Allāh ﷺ once slept with all of his wives and took a bath after each time. I said, 'O Messenger of Allāh ﷺ, why not take only one bath afterwards?' He said,

« هذا أَزْكَىٰ و أَطْهَرُ وأطيبُ »

"This is more pure, cleaner, and better."

It is allowed for those having sexual intercourse to have sex for a second time after they perform ablution. Muslim narrated in his *Sahih* that Abu Sa'id Al-Khudri said that the Messenger of Allāh ﷺ said:

« إذا أتى أحدُكم أهلَه، ثم أراد أن يعُود: فلْيَتَوَضّأ »

"When one of you sleeps with his wife and then wants to repeat, let him perform ablution."

Taking a bath or ablution after sex refreshes the energy and the strength and cleans whatever has remained during sex (semen, for example). It is also an act of purity and cleanness. The inner heat will also get back to its normal level of activity after it had been excited during sex. Also, taking a bath satisfies what Allāh prefers of cleanliness and discards its opposite (impurity), which Allāh hates. Thus, taking a bath after sex is one of the best acts that preserves ones health and strength.

Sex is best after your food has been digested

At that time the bodies' inner coldness, hotness, dryness and wetness are moderate. Sex is harmful when the stomach is full more than it is empty. Such is the case when the body feels excessive wetness, as compared to dryness, and heat as compared to coldness. Also, one should have sex when the desire is ignited and thus the body is naturally ready to have sex, not because one just thought about it.

One should not ignite his sexual appetite when it is not naturally excited and should not force himself to have sex. Also, when one feels that his sexual appetite is ignited, he should have sex to satisfy it. One should avoid having sex with an old woman, the very young who are not ready yet for sex or do not desire it, an ailing woman, a woman who isn't comely or a hated woman. Having sex in such cases will weaken the strength and the sexual drive.

Some doctors made an error when they stated that having sex with a matron women is better for the health than with a virgin. This statement defies what the best minds have stated and goes against the nature of mankind in general. When one marries a virgin, his heart will be fully dedicated to her and will be filled with her love. Also, he will not divide the type of love he reserves for her with any other women (who he marries later on). This is why the Prophet ﷺ said to Jabir رَضِيَ اللّٰه عَنْهُ :

« هَلَّا تَزَوَّجْتَ بِكْرًا ! »

"Why did you not marry a virgin?"

The women of Paradise, the *Houris*, have not been touched by any person before their future, believing husbands in Paradise, a bounty from Allāh that makes them more appealing. In addition, 'Āishah رَضِيَ اللّٰه عَنْها once said to the Prophet ﷺ.

« أرأيت لو مررتَ بِشَجَرة قد أُرْتِعَ فيها ؛ وشجرةٍ لم يُرْتَعْ فيها ؛ ففي أيِّهما كنت تُرتِع بعيرك ؟ قال: في التي لم يُرْتع فيها »

"If you pass by a tree that has been grazed on and a tree that is still untouched, which one would you allow your camel to graze on?" He said, "The tree that is still untouched by grazing."

She meant that he did not marry a virgin woman except her.

Having sex with a woman that one loves will not weaken the body and will expel the semen more effectively. Having sex with a woman that one does not like will weaken his strength and will not expel sufficient amounts of the semen congested in the body.

Having sex with a woman who is having her period is not allowed in the religion and by the nature of things, as it is very harmful and all doctors warn against it.

Furthermore, we should state that the best sexual position is for the man to get on top of his wife after having fondled and kissed her. This is why the woman is sometimes called "*Firash* (mat, or bed)". The Prophet once said,

« الوَلَد للفراش »

"The son belongs to the Firash.*"*

This (a sexual position that we mentioned above) is a part of man's being responsible for the woman, as Allāh said:

﴿ الرِّجَالُ قَوَّٰمُونَ عَلَى النِّسَآءِ ﴾

"Men are the protectors and maintainers of women." (4:34)

Also, Allāh said:

$$ ﴿ هُنَّ لِبَاسٌ لَّكُمْ وَأَنتُمْ لِبَاسٌ لَّهُنَّ ﴾ $$

"They (women) are *Libās* [i.e. body cover, or screen, or Sakan, (i.e., you enjoy the pleasure of living with her) for you, and you (men) are Libās for them." (2:187)

The favored sexual position that we mentioned is taken from the beautiful description the *Ayah* gave for the wife and her husband of being the garment or the cover for each other.

The worst sexual position is for the woman to get on top of the man during sex, because it is against the natural way that Allāh has created men and women and males and females. In this case, the man will not be able to ejaculate all of the semen and whatever remains will get soiled and harm his body. Also, this position might allow some harmful moisture to descend from the woman's sexual organ to the penis. Also, the womb would not be able to hold on to the semen in this position and thus conception will be more difficult. Further, the woman is and should be the receiving party and when this position is turned around and she becomes the giver, the act will go against the natural way.

It was reported that the People of the Scripture used to have sex with their wives while leaning on their sides, saying that this position is the most comfortable for the women.

As for Quraish and the Ansar, they used to have sexual intercourse with their woman from behind (in the vagina), and the Jews criticized them for this practice. Afterwards, Allāh revealed:

$$ ﴿ نِسَآؤُكُمْ حَرْثٌ لَّكُمْ فَأْتُوا حَرْثَكُمْ أَنَّى شِئْتُمْ ﴾ $$

"Your wives are a tilth for you, so go to your tilth, when or how you will..." (2:223)

In the *Sahihain* it is also narrated that Jabir رَضِيَ اللهُ عَنْهُ said, "The Jews used to say that if a man had sex with his wife from behind in the womb the offspring would be cross-eyed. Then Allāh revealed:

$$ ﴿ نِسَآؤُكُمْ حَرْثٌ لَّكُمْ فَأْتُوا حَرْثَكُمْ أَنَّى شِئْتُمْ ﴾ $$

"Your wives are a tilth for you, so go to your tilth, when or how

you will..." (2:223)

In another narration of this *Hadith* by Muslim, the Prophet ﷺ commented (*on the Āyah*),

« إن شاء مُجَبِّيَةً وإن شاء غير مجبِّيةٍ؛ غير أن ذلك في صِمَام واحدٍ »

"If you wish from behind and if you wish from the front, but only in one valve (i.e. the vagina)."

Anal sex with the wife was never allowed by any Prophet, and it is a grave error that some people relate that some of the Salaf allowed men to have anal sex with their wives.

Abu Dāwud narrated in his *Sunan* that Abu Hurairah رَضِيَ الله عَنْهُ related from the Prophet ﷺ that he said:

« مَلْعُونٌ مَن أتَى المَرْأة في دُبُرها »

"Cursed be the person who has sex with a woman in her anal canal."

Also, Ahmad and Ibn Mājah narrated that the Prophet ﷺ said:

« لا ينظُرُ الله إلى رَجُل جامَعَ امْرأته في دُبُرها »

"Allāh does not look at the person who has sex with his wife in her anal canal."

At-Tirmidhi and *Ahmad* mentioned another narration of this *Hadith* in which the Prophet ﷺ said:

« مَن أتى حائضا، أو امْرأته في دُبُرها، أو كاهنًا فصدَّقه: فقد كَفَر بما أنزِل على مُحمَّد صلى الله عليه وسلم »

"Whoever has sex with a woman during her period or in her anal canal, and whoever goes to a soothsayer and believes in him will have committed disbelief in what Allāh has sent down to Muhammad."

In another narration of Al-Bayhaqi, the Prophet ﷺ said:

« مَن أتى شيئًا - من الرِّجال والنِّساء - في الأدْبار: فقد كَفَر »

"Whoever has sex with a man or a woman in the anal canal will have committed Kufr (disbelief)."

Furthermore, *Waki'* narrated that the Messenger of Allāh ﷺ said:

« إن الله لا [يَسْتَحْيِي] من الحقِّ؛ لا تأتُوا النِّساءَ في أعجازِهنَّ »

"Allāh is not shy to say the truth: Do not have sex with women in their anal canals."

Also, *At-Tirmidhi* narrated that Talq bin Ali said that the Messenger of Allāh ﷺ said:

« لا تَأْتُوا النِّساءَ في أعجازِهنَّ؛ فإن الله لا يستحي من الحقِّ »

"Do not have sex with women in their anal canals. Allāh does not shy away from saying the truth."

Further, Ibn 'Adi narrated in his book, *Al-Kamil*, that 'Abdullāh bin Mas'ud related from the Prophet ﷺ that he said:

« لا تأتوا النِّساءَ في أعجازهن »

"Do not have sexual intercourse with women in the anal canals."

Abu Tharr also related from the Prophet ﷺ that he said:

« مَن أتَى الرجال والنساءَ في أدبارهنَّ، فقد كفر »

"Whoever has sexual intercourse with men or women in their anal canals, will have committed disbelief."

In addition, Isma'il bin 'Aiyash narrated that Jabir رَضِيَ الله عَنْهُ said that the Prophet ﷺ said:

« اسْتَحْيُوا من الله – فإن الله لا يستَحي من الحقِّ – لا تأتُوا النساءَ في حُشُوشِهنَّ »

"Be shy with Allāh, but Allāh is not shy to say the truth: Do not have sex with women in their anal canals."

Also, *Ad-Darqutni* narrated this *Hadith* using another chain of narrators and it reads:

« أن الله لا يستَحي من الحقِّ؛ ولا يَحلُّ إتيانُ النساءِ في حُشُوشِهنَّ »

"Allāh is not shy to say the truth: anal sex with women is not allowed."

Al-Baghawi also narrated that once Qatadah was asked about the person who has sex with his wife in her anal canal, and Qatadah related from the Prophet ﷺ that he said:

« تلك اللُّوطِيَّة الصُّغرى »

"That is the small sodomy (or homosexuality)."

Imam Ahmad also narrated that Ibn 'Abbās رَضِيَ الله عَنْهما said:

﴿ نِسَآؤُكُمْ حَرْثٌ لَّكُمْ ﴾

"Your wives are a tilth for you ..." (2:223)

"The *Āyah*, was revealed regarding some people from the *Ansar*. They came to the Prophet ﷺ and asked him and he said, 'Have sex with your wife however you like, but avoid anal sex.'"

Also in the *Musnad* Imam Ahmad it is narrated that Ibn 'Abbās رَضِيَ الله عَنْهما said that Umar bin Al-Khattab رَضِيَ الله عَنْه came to the Prophet ﷺ and said: "O Messenger of Allāh ﷺ! I am destroyed." The Prophet ﷺ said, "What has destroyed you?" 'Umar رَضِيَ الله عَنْه said, "I turned over my Firash (mount, woman) last night (had sexual intercourse from the back in the vagina)." The Prophet ﷺ did not answer him. Soon after, Allāh revealed:

﴿ نِسَآؤُكُمْ حَرْثٌ لَّكُمْ فَأْتُوا حَرْثَكُمْ أَنَّى شِئْتُمْ ﴾

"Your wives are a tilth for you, so go to your tilth, when or how you will..." (2:223)

The Prophet ﷺ said:

« أَقْبِل وأَدْبِرْ، واتَّقِ الحَيْضةَ والدُّبُرَ »

"Do it from the front and from behind if you wish, but avoid menstruation and the anal canal."

Furthermore, *At-Tirmidhi* narrated that Ibn 'Abbās رَضِيَ الله عَنْه related from the Prophet ﷺ that he said:

« لا ينظُرُ الله إلى رجل أتى رجلًا أو امرأة في الدُّبر »

"Allāh does not look at a man who had anal sex with another man or with a woman."

'Uqbah bin 'Amir رَضِيَ الله عَنْه also narrated that the Messenger of Allāh ﷺ said:

«مَلْعونٌ من يأتي النساء في محاشِّهِنَّ »

"Cursed be whoever has sex with women in their anal canals."

Furthermore, *Musnad* Al-Harith bin Abi Usamah narrated that Abu Hurairah رَضِيَ الله عَنْهُ and Ibn 'Abbās رَضِيَ الله عَنْهما said, "The Messenger of Allāh ﷺ gave us a speech just before he died and it was the last speech the Prophet ﷺ gave in Al-Madinah until he went to Allāh. He said:

« مَن نكَح امرأته في دُبُرِها، أو رجلًا أو صبيًّا حُشِرَ يوم القيامة وريحُه أنتَنُ من الجِيفةِ يتأذَّى به الناس حتى يدخُلَ النارَ؛ وأحبطَ الله أجره، ولا يُقْبل منه صَرفًا ولا عَدْلًا، ويدخلُ في تابوتٍ مِن نارٍ، ويُسَدُّ عليه بِمَساميرَ مِن نارٍ »

"Whoever had sex with a woman in her anal canal, or with a man, or with a male child, will be gathered on the Day of Resurrection with an odor emitting from him that is more foul than rotted carrion. The people will be bothered by his smell until he enters Hellfire. Also Allāh will destroy his rewards and will not accept from him a prayer or a fast. He will also be entered into a coffin of fire and the coffin will be shut closed on him using nails of fire."

Abu Hurairah رَضِيَ الله عَنْهُ commented, "This is for whomever did not repent (from sodomy)."

Ash-Shafi'ī narrated that Khuzaymah bin Thabit رَضِيَ الله عَنْهُ said:

« إن رجلا سأل النبي صلى الله عليه وسلم عن إتيان النساءِ في أَدْبارهنَّ، فقال: حَلالٌ. فلمَّا ولَّى دعاه، فقال: كيف قلتَ ؟ في أيِّ الْخُرْبَتَيْنِ؟ أو في أي الْخُرْزَتين؟ أو في أي الخُصْفَتين؟ أمِن دبرها في قُبُلِها: فنَعَمْ، أمَّا من دُبرها في دبرها: فلا . فإن الله لا يستحي من الحق، لَا تأتوا النِّساءَ في أدبارهنَّ »

"A man came to the Messenger of Allāh ﷺ and asked him about having sex with women from the rear. The Prophet ﷺ said, 'It is allowed.' When the man left, the Prophet ﷺ summoned him and asked him, 'What was your question? In which of the two holes?If it from is the rear in the vagina, then it is allowed. As for having sex in the anal canal from the rear, no. Allāh is not shy to say the truth. Do not have sex with women in the anal canal."

Furthermore, Allāh said:

$$ ﴿ فَأْتُوهُنَّ مِنْ حَيْثُ أَمَرَكُمُ اللَّهُ ﴾ $$

"Then go in unto them as Allāh has odained for you."

Mujahid said, "I asked Ibn 'Abbās رَضِيَ اللہ عَنْهُما about the meaning of what Allāh said:

$$ ﴿ فَأْتُوهُنَّ مِنْ حَيْثُ أَمَرَكُمُ اللَّهُ ﴾ $$

"Then go in unto them as Allāh has ordained for you."

He said, 'Have sex with her in the same place where you were not allowed when she is menstruating."

'Ali bin Abi Talhah commented, "Meaning in the vagina."

The *Ayah* has indicated that it is not allowed to have sexual intercourse in the anal canal in two different ways.

First, Allāh has only allowed having sex in the place where the offspring is created not the anus, which is a harmful place. The place of offspring is mentioned in what Allāh said:

$$ ﴿ مِنْ حَيْثُ أَمَرَكُمُ اللَّهُ ﴾ $$

"As Allāh has ordained for you (go in unto them in any manner as long as it is in their vagina)." (2:222)

Having sex with the wife from the rear in the vagina is also entailed in the Ayah, because Allāh said:

$$ ﴿ فَأْتُوا حَرْثَكُمْ أَنَّى شِئْتُمْ ﴾ $$

"So go to your tilth, when or how you will." (2:223)

It means that from wherever you wish, from the front or the rear. Also, Ibn 'Abbās رَضِيَ اللہ عَنْهُما said: meaning the vagina.

Allāh has disallowed vaginal sex with the woman when there is a temporary harmful condition (menstruation). So what about anal sex in the place of harm which will also harm the cause of reproduction. Also, anal sex with the woman will surely encourage the man to have anal sex with young boys.

Also, the wife has a right on her husband to have natural sexual activity and anal sex does not satisfy this right nor fulfill her desire.

Further, the anal canal was not created for this act nor is it suitable for it, unlike the vagina. Those who refrain from sex in the vagina and perform anal sex will have deviated from Allāh's Wisdom and Commandments.

Also, anal sex is very harmful for the man and this is why the wisest doctors advise against it. The vagina has a special quality in extracting the semen and relieving the man from it. The anal canal, on the other hand, does not help extract all of the semen because it is not in its nature.

Anal sex is also harmful to the man because it requires tiresome movements and because it goes against his nature.

The anus is also the place of dirt and filth. Yet, the man faces it with his face and embraces it [during anal sex]!

Anal sex is also very harmful for the woman because it is unnatural, abnormal and not suitable for what she was created for.

Anal sex also causes depression and distress, along with the people feeling hateful and estranged with both parties to the anal sex.

Anal sex also blackens the face, causes distress in the chest, extinguishes the light of the heart and gives the face a darkness that will become a trademark for those who do anal sex.

Anal sex also causes hatred (between the participants to the act) and will soon lead both participants to part from each other.

Anal sex also causes the nature of both participants to be terminally spoiled, unless they repent to Allāh with a sincere heart.

Anal sex also erases all the good qualities and replaces them with their opposites. It also dissipates the affection and good relations between the two parties, who will soon curse and hate each other.

Anal sex is also one of the major reasons behind the destruction of the bounties and the coming of torment and disaster. It also leads to being cursed and hated by Allāh, as He will ignore those who indulge in this act and would not look at them. What good can such people ever gain later on and what evil could they wish to avert? What kind of life can they live after Allāh's curse falls on them, along with His hatred towards them, His ignoring them and His shunning them?

Anal sex also dissipates shyness, and shyness is the life of the heart. When the heart looses shyness, it will like the disliked and dislike the liked. Thus, the heart will have fallen into utter ruin and destruction.

Anal sex also alters human nature from the path that Allāh has created it for, to a type of lower animal behavior. Rather, it is even lower. When the nature is altered and changed, the heart, the deeds and the guidance will also be altered. One will then like the evil things and deeds, leading him to fall into total disarray regarding his condition, deeds, and speech.

More than any other act, anal sex also causes one to have rude behavior and makes him dare to commit evil.

Anal sex also brings one humiliation, degradation and disgrace more than any other act.

Finally, anal sex causes the slave hatred and dislike, and the people will feel despise and disgust with him, as is evident all around us.

May Allāh's peace and blessings be on he whose guidance gives those who follow it the happiness of this and the Next Life. On the other hand, destruction and demise of this and the Next Life are the result of deviating from his guidance and what he was sent with.

There are two types of harmful sexual activity

One type that the religion declares harmful and another type that defies nature.

The harmful sexual intercourse that the religion prohibits is in grades, some are worse than others. Temporarily prohibited sexual activity is less dangerous than those totally prohibited. For instance, sex is disallowed during the Fast, Ihram, I'tikaf, menstruation, and so froth. There is no punishment prescribed when one violates this type of limited prohibition. The second type, which is totally prohibited, falls under two categories, prohibited for eternity, such as marrying whom one is not allowed to marry, which is one of the worst types of illegal sexual activity. This category requires capital punishment according to a segment of the scholars, such as Ahmad bin Hanbal. There is an authentic Hadith that upholds this ruling too. The second category is totally prohibited but not for eternity, such as committing adultery or fornication with whom one is theoretically eligible for marriage. In the case of adultery, it will be violating two rights: Allāh's right and the husband's right. If the woman was forced to this act, it will be a violation of three rights (Allāh's, her husband's and her own). If she had a family and relatives, they will be ashamed by the rape, and thus a fourth right would be violated. If the woman was not allowed for the man even theoretically, a fifth right will be violated. The harm of this type of act varies according to the grade of prohibition it violates.

There is a type of sexual activity that is harmful for one's nature, whether due to the form or the manner it takes. For instance, having excessive sexual intercourse will weaken the strength and harm the nerves. It will also cause convulsive shaking, facial paralysis and spasms. It also weakens the eyesight and the rest of the powers of the body, along with weakening the instinctive heat and energy, widening the body vessels and exposing them to accumulating harmful substances.

The best time to have sex is after the food has been digested in the stomach, but not when the stomach is empty for it weakens the instinctive heat. Also, one should not have sex when he is full, because in this case sexual intercourse causes clogs, nor when one is tired, after taking a bath, after vomiting or when one is nervous, sad, depressed distressed or very happy.

The best time to have sex is after the night falls, especially when the food had been digested. One then takes a bath or ablution and sleeps afterwards so that he regains his strength. One should not indulge in sports activity after sex because it is very harmful in this case.

The Prophet's guidance on treating passion

This is a disease that attacks the heart. Yet, it is a different type of disease concerning its symptoms, causes, and cure. When this ailment becomes acute, the doctors will not be able to cure it nor will the one afflicted be able to bear its effects.

Allāh has mentioned the subject of passion concerning two types of people: women and lovers of beardless boys. For instance, Allāh mentioned the story of the wife of Al-'Aziz (Ruler of Egypt) and the Prophet Yusef عليه السلام. He also mentioned the second type about the people of the Prophet Lut عليه السلام as He said about them when the angels came to visit the Prophet Lut عليه السلام.

﴿ وَجَآءَ أَهۡلُ ٱلۡمَدِينَةِ يَسۡتَبۡشِرُونَ ۝ قَالَ إِنَّ هَٰٓؤُلَآءِ ضَيۡفِى فَلَا تَفۡضَحُونِ ۝ وَٱتَّقُوا۟ ٱللَّهَ وَلَا تُخۡزُونِ ۝ قَالُوٓا۟ أَوَلَمۡ نَنۡهَكَ عَنِ ٱلۡعَٰلَمِينَ ۝ قَالَ هَٰٓؤُلَآءِ

بَنَاتِى إِن كُنتُمْ فَعِلِينَ ۝ لَعَمْرُكَ إِنَّهُمْ لَفِى سَكْرَتِهِمْ يَعْمَهُونَ ۝

"And the inhabitants of the city came rejoicing (at the news of
the young men's arrival). [Lūt (Lot)] said: 'Verily, these are my
guests, so shame me not. And fear Allāh and disgrace me not.'
They (people of the city) said: 'Did we not forbid you from
entertaining (or protecting) any of the 'Ālamīn (people, foreigners
and strangers from us)?' [Lūt (Lot)] said: 'These (the girls of the
nation) are my daughters (to marry lawfully), if you must act
(so).' Verily, by your life (O Muhammad ﷺ), in their wild
intoxication, they were wandering blindly." (15:67-72)

There is a false claim that was started by those who do not give the
Prophet ﷺ his due respect and appreciation, stating that the Prophet ﷺ
once saw Zainab bint Jahsh* and said, "All praise be to He Who changes
the hearts as He wills!" They also claim that the Prophet ﷺ was inflicted
with this disease, passion, and that his heart liked her. Yet, they claimed,
he commanded Zaid to keep her and not divorce her, until Allāh
revealed:

﴿ وَإِذْ تَقُولُ لِلَّذِىٓ أَنْعَمَ ٱللَّهُ عَلَيْهِ وَأَنْعَمْتَ عَلَيْهِ أَمْسِكْ عَلَيْكَ زَوْجَكَ وَٱتَّقِ ٱللَّهَ
وَتُخْفِى فِى نَفْسِكَ مَا ٱللَّهُ مُبْدِيهِ وَتَخْشَى ٱلنَّاسَ وَٱللَّهُ أَحَقُّ أَن تَخْشَىٰهُ ﴾

"And (remember) when you said to him (Zaid bin Hārithah رَضِيَ اللهُ
عَنْهُ — the freed-slave of the Prophet ﷺ) on whom Allāh has
bestowed grace (by guiding him to Islām) and you (O Muhammad
ﷺ too) have done favour (by manumitting him): 'Keep your wife to
yourself, and fear Allāh.' But you did hide in yourself (i.e., what
Allāh has already made known to you that He will give her to you
in marriage) that which Allāh will make manifest, you did fear the
people (i.e., their saying that Muhammad (married the divorced
wife of his manumitted slave) whereas Allāh had a better right
that you should fear Him." (33:37)

Those who uttered this false claim also claimed that the Âyah is talking
about passion. Consequently, some of them collected a book about

---

* **Editor's note**: This is referring to before the prophet was married to Zaynab. She
was at the time still married to Zaid bin Harithah. Therefore it is unimaginable , and
impossible that the prophet of Allah would lust for the wife of another man! A.W.

passion in which they mentioned several Prophets who were afflicted with this disease, including the Prophet ﷺ ! This is an utter ignorance of such people of the Qur'ān and the Messengers and a misunderstanding that alters the true meaning of Allāh's Words. Further, this false claim accuses the Prophet ﷺ with what he is truly innocent of.

Zaid bin Harithah رَضِيَ اللهُ عَنْهُ , whom the Prophet ﷺ had adopted before Islam until he was called Zaid bin Muhammad, married Zainab bint Jahsh. Zainab was not humble with her husband and he asked the Prophet's advice if he should divorce her. The Messenger of Allāh ﷺ said, to him:

« أَمْسِكْ عَلَيْكَ زَوْجَكَ وَاتَّقِ اللهَ »

"Keep your wife to yourself, and fear Allāh."

The Prophet ﷺ thought that if Zaid would otherwise divorce her, he would marry her after him. But, the Prophet ﷺ hid this thought in his heart because he feared what the people might say if he married the ex-wife of his adopted son. This is why Allāh mentioned in this Ayah His favors on the Prophet ﷺ and commanded him not to fear what the people might say in doing what Allāh has allowed for him. Allāh also reminded him that it is He whom the Prophet ﷺ should fear, so he should not be hesitant in doing what Allāh has allowed for him because of fear of what the people might say.

Further, Allāh informed the Prophet ﷺ that He has given Zainab to him in marriage after Zaid رَضِيَ اللهُ عَنْهُ had divorced her so that his nation imitates him when they know that the man is allowed to marry the ex-wife of his adopted son. This is why Allāh said:

﴿ فَلَا جُنَاحَ عَلَيْكُمْ وَحَلَائِلُ أَبْنَائِكُمُ ٱلَّذِينَ مِنْ أَصْلَابِكُمْ ﴾

"But there is no sin on you if you have not gone in them (to marry their daughters), and the wives of your sons who (spring) from your own loins (are forbidden for you to marry)...." (4:23)

And in this chapter (4:40), Allāh said:

﴿ مَّا كَانَ مُحَمَّدٌ أَبَآ أَحَدٍ مِّن رِّجَالِكُمْ ﴾

"Muhammad (ﷺ) is not the father of any of your men." (33:40)

While in the beginning of the chapter Allāh said:

﴿ وَمَا جَعَلَ أَدْعِيَاءَكُمْ أَبْنَاءَكُمْ ذَلِكُمْ قَوْلُكُم بِأَفْوَهِكُمْ ﴾

"...nor has He made your adopted sons your real sons. That is but your saying with your mouths." (33:4)

Therefore, think deeply about Allāh's defense of the Prophet ﷺ that refuted the false accusation directed at him. All success comes from Allāh.

Yes, the Prophet of Allāh ﷺ used to love his wives, especially 'Āishah رَضِيَ الله عَنْها the most beloved to him among them. Yet, his love for them did not reach the level of perfect love, which he reserved for his Lord. The Prophet ﷺ once said:

« لو كنتُ متَّخِذًا من أهل الأرض خليلًا، لا تَّخذْتُ أبا بكرٍ خليلًا»

"If I was going to take an intimate friend from the people of the earth, I would have taken Abu Bakr."

And in another narration, he said:

« وإن صاحِبَكم خليلُ الرَّحْمٰن »

"Your friend (himself, Muhammad) is the intimate friend of the Most Beneficent."

Having passion towards images only afflicts empty hearts

This affects hearts that are deprived of the love of Allāh, ignoring Him and preferring someone else. When the heart is full of the love of Allāh and eagerness to meet Him, this love will fend off the disease of love and passion for images. This is why Allāh said about Prophet Yusef عليه السلام.

﴿ كَذَٰلِكَ لِنَصْرِفَ عَنْهُ السُّوٓءَ وَالْفَحْشَآءَ إِنَّهُۥ مِنْ عِبَادِنَا الْمُخْلَصِينَ ﴾

"Thus it was, that We might turn away from him evil and illegal sexual intercourse. Surely, he was one of Our chosen, (guided) slaves." (12:24)

This Āyah indicated that sincerity is a cause and a remedy that drives away passion which might lead to sin and fornication, which is the culmination of passion. When the cause behind the disease is repelled, the effects of the disease will also be repelled.

Some of our *Salaf* once described passion that it is the act of a heart that is empty of everything except what it has a passion for. Allāh said:

$$\text{﴿ وَأَصْبَحَ فُؤَادُ أُمِّ مُوسَىٰ فَٰرِغًا ۖ إِن كَادَتْ لَتُبْدِى بِهِۦ ﴾}$$

"And the heart of the mother of Mūsā (Moses) became empty [from every thought, except the thought of Mūsā (Moses)]. She was very near to disclosing his case." (28:10)

This *Âyah* indicated that the heart of Moses's mother was empty of every concern except for Moses, because of her great love for him and her heart's affection for him. Passion has two parts, loving an object and an eagerness to possess the loved object. When one of these two parts does not exist, then passion does not exist either.

The ailment of passion has caused bafflement to many wise people and some of them issued some statements in this regard that should not be taken seriously.

We say that Allāh's Wisdom has decided regarding His creation that there are similarities that occur between things and people, and that things and people are driven to their likes and to avoid what is not similar to them. The secret to the harmony that occurs in the world is due to the similarities between various creations. Various things [and people] thus lean towards similar objects, while dissimilar objects ignore each other. Allāh said:

$$\text{﴿ هُوَ ٱلَّذِى خَلَقَكُم مِّن نَّفْسٍ وَٰحِدَةٍ وَجَعَلَ مِنْهَا زَوْجَهَا لِيَسْكُنَ إِلَيْهَا ﴾}$$

"It is He Who has created you from a single person (Adam), and (then) He has created from him his wife [Hawwā' (Eve)], in order that he might enjoy the pleasure of living with her." (7:189)

Allāh has made this the reason why man feels attracted and consequently passionate, for woman. She is similar to him in essence. The reason for the attraction [between men and women] is not only the beauty of the image,but the similarity in the habits, goals, guidance and mannerism, all of which help ignite passion.

In the Sahih it is narrated that the Prophet said:

« الأرواحُ جنودٌ مُجَنَّدةٌ فما تَعارفَ منها ائْتَلفَ، وماتَناكَرَ منها اختَلفَ »

"The souls are similar to recruited soldiers. Those who recognize

each other will be intimate and those who do not recognize each other will be apart."

Also, Imam Ahmad narrated in his *Musnad* the reason behind this *Hadith*, "A woman in Makkah used to be able to make people laugh and when she came to Al-Madinah she resided with a woman who also used to be able to make people in Al-Madinah laugh. The Prophet ﷺ said:

« الأرواحُ جنودٌ مُجَنَّدةٌ »

"The souls are just like recruited soldiers."

The religion of Allāh gives the same rulings to similar matters and thus does not differentiate between similar matters nor join between dissimilar matters. Those who think to the contrary are mistaken due to their lack of knowledge of the religion, or lack of effort on their part to acquire knowledge on the subject of similarities and dissimilarities. Or, their error comes from relating to the religion what is not a part of it without the authority that can justify it. With Allāh's Wisdom and justice, His creation and command have been established by equating similar things and differentiating between dissimilar things. This fact is true both in this life and on the Day of Resurrection. Allāh said:

﴿ احْشُرُوا الَّذِينَ ظَلَمُوا وَأَزْوَٰجَهُمْ وَمَا كَانُوا يَعْبُدُونَ ۝ مِن دُونِ اللَّهِ فَاهْدُوهُمْ إِلَىٰ صِرَٰطِ الْجَحِيمِ ۝ ﴾

(It will be said to the angels): "Assemble those who did wrong, together with their companions (from the devils) and what they used to worship, Instead of Allāh, and lead them on to the way of flaming Fire (Hell); ..." (37:22,23)

Also, Allāh said:

﴿ وَإِذَا النُّفُوسُ زُوِّجَتْ ﴾

"And when the souls shall be joined with their partners (the good with the good and the bad with the bad)." (81:7)

This Âyah indicates that each person will be tied to his likes. Those who have love for each other for Allāh's sake will be together in Paradise, while those who love each other for the devil's sake will be together in Hell. One is with those whom he likes, whether he likes it or not. Al-Hakim narrated that the Prophet ﷺ said:

« لا يُحِبُّ المرءُ قومًا إلّا حُشِر مَعَهم »

"If a man loves a people, he will be gathered with them (on the Day of Resurrection)."

There are several types of love. The best and most honorable of them is love for the sake of Allāh, which requires loving what He loves and also loving Him and His Messenger.

Another type of love is that which occurs when the parties to it have a similar religion or way, or theology, or sect, or relation, or craft, or a goal that they both seek. Another type of love is what occurs when one loves to acquire a matter that the loved object has, whether a position, money, knowledge, or any other purpose that he seeks. This is material love that dissipates when the goal is reached. Indeed, he who likes you for a material purpose goes away when his goal is accomplished.

The love that results because of the similarities between the two parties does not fade away unless there is a reason that makes it fade away. This type of love includes passion because it is a love that the soul and the heart share. No other ailment can cause more profound effects on those afflicted, of obsession, weakness, concern and even destruction, like passion.

If one says that since the reason behind affection is what you have stated, the souls being connected and compatible, why is it not always exchanged between the two parties? Sometimes, love is one sided, although you stated that the reason for it is the similarity and the compatibility between the souls.

The answer is that there are reasons that arise and prevent the love from being exchanged by both sides. One-sided love is the result of one of three reasons: a deficiency in the love because it is accidental and not real. In this case, the loved person might even feel dislike for the other party. Second, sometimes the loved person might be the cause for the love to be one-sided, such as a deficiency in his mannerism, shape, path, actions, appearance, and so forth. Third, due to a specific reason that prevents the loved person from sharing the same feelings with the other party.

When these reasons are not present, and the love is thus real, love will be shared by both parties.

Arrogance, envy, loving various positions and enmity by the

disbelievers were the main reasons the Messengers were not more beloved by them than their own selves, families and offspring. When these barriers were removed from the hearts of the Messengers' followers, their love for the Messengers was indeed more than the love they had for their own selves, wives, children and wealth.

Attainment of one's love object is its cure and other cures for love

The subject is that since love is one of the ailments in general, it does have a cure or several cures. If the lover has a legal path to take to attain his loved object, it will be his cure. In the *Sahihain* it is narrated that Ibn Mas'ud رَضِيَ الله عَنْهما said that the Prophet ﷺ said:

« يا معشرَ الشَّباب؛ من استطاع منكمُ الباءةَ فلْيتزَوَّج؛ ومن لم يستطعْ: فعليه بالصوم، فإنه له وِجَاءٌ »

"O young people! Whoever amongst you can afford marriage, let him marry. Those who cannot afford it should resort to fasting, for it will be a cure for them."

The Prophet ﷺ has directed the people to the best methods to obtain what they love, a major and a minor method. He ordered the men to resort to the first choice, marriage, which is the perfect cure for this disease. Thus, people should not prefer other solutions to the solution that the Prophet ﷺ recommended.

Ibn Mājah narrated that the Prophet ﷺ said:

« لم نَرَ للمُتحابَّيْن مثلَ النِّكاح »

"We never saw anything like marriage for lovers."

This is the meaning that Allāh indicated when He allowed in marriage both free and slave women when needed: Allāh said:

﴿ يُرِيدُ ٱللَّهُ أَن يُخَفِّفَ عَنكُمْ وَخُلِقَ ٱلْإِنسَٰنُ ضَعِيفًا ﴾

"Allāh wishes to lighten (the burden) for you; and man was created weak (cannot be patient to leave sexual intercourse with woman)." (4:28)

Therefore, Allāh mentioned man's weakness in this *Ayah* and stated that He has made matters easy for him by allowing him to marry as many as he wishes, two, three or four. He also allowed him slave women in marriage if he wishes, so as to treat this ailment, passion, to cure the weakness in mankind and as an act of mercy [from Him] to His slaves.

When no legal method exists for the lover to attain his love object

If there is no legal method that the lover can attain his loved object or because of his inability to do so, or both, then passion will become a difficult disease in this case and the afflicted person needs to feel that he cannot satisfy it. It is a fact that when the heart feels hopelessness in something, it will no longer seek to acquire it.

If the disease, passion, still exists even under these hopeless conditions, then the nature of the person would have deviated and the person needs to try another solution, that is, attending to his state of mind. The person afflicted by passion should convince himself that his heart's affection with what it cannot attain constitutes madness, and that this case is similar to whoever loves the sun, the only way to acquire it is to ascend to it! Everyone understands this is madness.

If one cannot attain his loved object because of a legal barrier that the religion erected, he should convince himself that acquiring his passion is not feasible because Allah did not allow it to happen. He should know that for his safety he should abandon such a matter and be certain that it is virtually impossible that he will ever attain it.

If one's whose heart orders him to do evil does not comply with these cures, let the slave abandon the matter for fear of losing whoever is more beloved to him, more beneficial and who offers a longer period of contentment and joy. In this case, the afflicted person will come to realize the difference between the two objects. Therefore, one should not prefer the joy of an hour that would soon turn to pain compared to eternal joy that is incomparable. The reality of the short-lived joy is that it is a daydream or a mirage that will soon end and fade away, but the responsibility would remain.

Also, one should realize that this might lead to a hateful loss that is worse for him than losing the coveted object, and thus his loss would multiply, losing the coveted object and acquiring a hateful outcome. When one realizes these facts, then losing the coveted object becomes less serious in his heart and being patient becomes more worthwhile. The mind, religion, honor and human nature then require the afflicted person to be patient in the face of losing a lesser loved object, for in this case, patience would soon earn him joy, contentment and happiness. On the other hand, one's ignorance, transience, injustice and immaturity orders him to prefer the lesser coveted object whatever the cost. Those whom Allah gives immunity will be saved from this end.

When one's heart does not accept this solution and dislikes using the remedy that we mentioned, let him think about what evil repercussions satisfying his lusts would bring about and what gains it would cause him to lose. He should realize that satisfying his lust is the major cause of an evil outcome in this life, as it prevents the slave from using his mind that is the controller of his actions and which should be used to lead him to benefit instead.

If one's heart still does not accept the remedy we mentioned, let him remember the shortcomings and unlikable characteristics of the coveted object, so that he might dislike the object, as well. When one thinks about this subject, he will realize that such shortcomings supercede the good qualities that made him like that object. Let him also ask the neighbors of his loved one about what he does not know of their attributes and behavior. It is a fact that as much as the good qualities drive loved ones closer, the shortcomings drive them apart. Then, one should weigh the two sides and choose the best and most beloved path to take. He should not be among those who are deceived by the color of an otherwise leprous skin. Let one think beyond the beautiful exterior to the true reality of things. Let one look beyond the beautiful shape to the inner evil of the heart.

If all of these remedies do not work, there will be no resort except seeking Allah Who answers the calls of those in distress when they invoke Him. Let him throw himself before His Door seeking His help with humbleness, humility and meekness.

Those who are led to this type of success should act honorably and keep their affair a secret, so as not to expose the loved one to the people and cause them harm, or else he will be committing a transgression and an injustice.

The Prophet's guidance on preserving the health with perfume

Good scents and perfumes are nutrition for the soul, and the soul is the dynamo of the rest of the body's powers. Perfume helps the brain, the heart and the internal organs and brings comfort to the heart and the soul. Perfumes are also the most suitable and favorable remedy and substance for the soul. Also, there is a close connection between the good soul and scented perfumes. This is why perfumes were among the dearest substances in this world to the heart of the most pure of all people, the Prophet ﷺ.

Al-Bukhari narrated that the Prophet ﷺ used to always accept perfume when presented to him. Also, Muslim narrated that the Messenger of Allah ﷺ said:

« من عُرِض عليه رَيْحانٌ فلا يَرُدَّه: فإنه طيِّبُ الريح، خفيفُ المَحْمِلِ »

"He who is offered Raihan (basil) should not refuse it, because it is easy to wear and has a good scent."

Further, Abu Dāwud and An-Nasai'ī narrated that the Prophet ﷺ said:

« من عُرِض عليه طِيبٌ فلا يَرُدَّه: فإنه خفيفُ المحمِلِ، طيِّبُ الرائحة »

"Whoever is offered some perfume should not refuse it because it is light to wear and has a good scent."

Ibn Abi Shaibah also narrated that the Messenger of Allah ﷺ had a container that had some perfume and he used to perfume himself with it. The Prophet ﷺ also said:

« إن لله حقًّا على كل مسلم: أن يغتسلَ في كل سبعةِ أيام؛ وإن كان له طِيبٌ: أن يمَسَّ منه »

"Allah has a right on every Muslim that he takes a bath (at least once) in every seven days and if he has perfume to wear some of it."

Furthermore, the angels like perfume while the devils dislike it, because the dearest scent to the devils are foul odors, while good souls like good scents. Every soul leans towards and deserves what it likes. Evil men are suitable for evil women and vise versa, while good men are suitable for good women and vise versa. Although this statement applies to men and women in general, it also applies to every type of deed, speech, food, drink, clothing and scent.

The Prophet's guidance on preserving the health of the eyes

Ibn 'Abbās رَضِيَ الله عَنْهُ narrated:

« كان رسولُ الله صلى الله عليه وسلم إذا اكْتَحَلَ : يجعلُ في اليُمنى ثلاثًا، يبتدِىءُ بها ويختم بها، وفي اليُسْرى ثِنتين » .

"Whenever the Messenger of Allah used to wear kohl, he would use it thrice in the right eye - beginning with it and finishing with it - and twice in the left eye."

Also, Abu Dāwud narrated that the Prophet ﷺ said:

« من اكتحَل فلْيوتِرْ»

"Those who use Kohl should use it an odd number of times."

One should use an odd number of times when applying Kohl in both eyes, thrice in the right eye and then twice in the left eye. Or, one should use the Kohl thrice in each eye, as Imam Ahmad has stated.

Kohl preserves the health of the eye, strengthens and clears the sight and removes harmful substances, along with adding a touch of beauty to the eye. When one uses kohl before he goes to sleep, it is beneficial for the eye, especially since the eyes will not be moving and thus the kohl will have its most favorable affect. The Ithmid type of kohl is especially effective in this regard.

Ibn Mājah narrated in his *Sunan* that 'Abdullāh bin Umar رضي الله عنه related from the Prophet ﷺ that he said:

« عليكم بالإثْمِد فَإنَّه يجلُو البَصَر ويُنْبِت الشَعَر »

"Use Ithmid (antimony), because it clears the eye and grows the eyelashes." [Al-Hakim].

Also, Ibn Mājah narrated in his *Sunan* that Ibn 'Abbās related from the Prophet ﷺ that he said:

« خيرُ أكْحالِكم الإثمِدُ: يجلُو البصرَ، ويُنبت الشعرَ »

"The best of your kohl is the Ithmid (antimony), because it clears the sight and causes the eyelashes to grow."

[At-Tirmidhi, Ibn Mājah, Ibn Hibban, Al-Hakim, At-Tabarani and Abu Na'im].

Part IV

Alphabetical Listing*

---

* **Editor's note**: The following is a list in Arabic alphabetical order of different things that were mentioned by the Prophet ﷺ or Qur'ân or were mistakenly attributed to the Prophet ﷺ, in which case the false attribution is cleared up for the reader.

249

The Letter *Hamzah*

1. *Ithmid* (Antimony)

The *Ithmid* is the black Kohl stone. The best type of *Ithmid* is found in Asfahan (Iran), but it is also found in western areas. The best type of *Ithmid* is that which fragmentizes quickly and which has shiny morsels. Also, the interior of the *Ithmid* is polished and does not contain any impurities.

The Kohl tends to be cold and dry and it is beneficial to the eye in that it strengthens it and also strengthens the eye nerve. Ithmid dissolves excess flesh around ulcers and closes the wound while cleansing the area around them. Ithmid also relieves headaches when it is blended with pure watery (not thick) honey. When Ithmid is ground and mixed with tender fat and then used as a bandage over fire burns, it prevents blisters from appearing and also helps cure the skin damage that occurs in cases of burns by fire. *Ithmid* is the best type of Kohl used for the eye, especially for old people whose eyesight has weakened. In this case, it is better that Kohl is mixed with some Musk.

2. *Utrujj* (Citron)

In the *Sahih* it is narrated that the Prophet ﷺ said:

« مَثَلُ المُؤْمِن الذي يَقْرَأُ القُرآن، كَمَثَل الأُتْرُجَّةِ: طَعْمُها طَيِّبٌ، وريحُها طَيِّبٌ »

"The example of the believer who reads the Qur'ān is the example of the Utrujj: its taste is delicious and its scent is pleasant."

The *Utrujj* has many benefits. There are four elements in the *Utrujj*, the peel, heart (or pulp), the pith and the seed. Each of these four elements has its own tendency: the peels, for instance, are hot and dry, while the pulp is hot and wet. The *Utrujj* pith is cold and dry, while its seed is hot and dry.

The peel of the *Utrujj* has many benefits. For instance, when its is placed within the clothes it prevents molding. The peel's scent refreshes decaying and polluted air. The peels of the *Utrujj* also improve the flavor of the foods and dissipate foul scents. Also, when the peels are mixed with the food they help the digestive process. The author of the *Qanoon* said, 'The pith of the (*Utrujj*) peels benefit in cases of snake bite, while the peels are used in bandages for snakebite. The ashes of the peels are used as an effective ointment against leprosy.'

The pulp of the citron *(Utrujj)* soothes the heat of the stomach, helps those who suffer from bile and subdues hot vapors. Further, Al-Ghafiqi said, "Eating the (citron) pulp relieves hemorrhoids."

The extract of the pith contained in the citron constipates, relieves bile, soothes hot pulsation, controls bilious vomiting, and when taken as a drink or a Kohl, relieves jaundice. The extract of the pith is also a good appetite stimulant, constipates and helps in cases of bilious diarrhea. The citron pith extract also soothes the lust of the woman and relieves and combats skin spots when used as a lubricant. It also cures herpes. The proof of the pith's effectiveness against ink is that when it touches the ink on the clothes, it effectively removes the stain. The pith contained in the *Utrujj* also soothes and has a chilling effect, cools the hotness of the liver, strengthens the stomach, eliminates bile and the accompanying depression and also quenches the thirst.

The seeds of the *Utrujj* have a decomposing and drying effect. Ibn Masawaih said that *Utrujj,* "When the skin of the seed is removed and cooked and taken as a drink with warm water, helps against deadly poisons when one drinks as much as two measures, each around twenty-five grams. When the seeds are ground and placed on a sting, they also help. The seeds also constipate and add good scent to the taste. Most of these benefits are also present in its pulp."

It was also said that, "The seeds help against scorpion stings when two measures of it are taken with warm water, and also when it is ground and placed on the affected area." It was also said, "Its seeds help against all types of poisons and all types of venomous stings."

It was also reported that one of the Persian rulers was angry with his doctors and that he ordered them be jailed. He gave them the choice to have only one type of food and they chose the *Utrujj.* They were asked, "Why did you choose it in particular?" They said, "Because it turns into a type of perfume shortly, its sight is pleasant, its peel smells good, its pulp is a fruit, its pith is a food, its seeds an antidote and it contains fat."

Truly, such a beneficial substance deserves to be compared with the best of creation, meaning the believer who recites the Qur'ān. We should mention that some of the *Salaf* used to like looking at the Utrujj because its sight is pleasant and comforting.

3. *Aruzz* (Rice)

There are two fake *Ahadith* regarding rice. The first, "If it was a man it would be forbearing." The second *Hadith*, "Everything that the earth produces has a disease and a cure, except the rice, for it is a cure and has no disease (or side effects)." We mentioned these incorrect Hadiths so that the people do not relate them from the Prophet by mistake.

Rice is hot and dry and it is the most nutritious cereal after wheat. Rice is a beneficial substance as it tightens the intestinal cavity and coats and strengthens the stomach. The doctors of India claim that it is the most beneficial food when it is cooked with cows' milk. Rice is nutritious, enriches the body, increases semen production and purifies the color.

4. *Arz* (Pine)

Arz is also called *Sanawbar*. The Messenger of Allah ﷺ mentioned the pine, when he said:

« مَثَلُ المؤمنِ مَثَلُ الخامةِ من الزَّرع تُفَيِّؤُها الرِّياح: تُقيمُها مرَّةً، وتُميلُها أخرى ومَثَلُ المنافقِ مَثَلُ الأرزة: لا تزالُ قائمةً على أصلِها، حتى يكُونَ انْجِعافُها مرةً واحدةً»

"The example of the believer is the example of the green plant that the wind twists, sometimes leaving it straight and sometimes bending it. The example of the hypocrite is the example of the Arz, it will be standing on its roots then all of a sudden it is completely dry!"

The seed of the *Arz* is hot and wet. It is a relaxing and maturating substance, and has a sting that can be prevented if the *Arz* seeds are soaked in water. Further, the *Arz* seeds are difficult to digest but are nutritious, help relieve coughing and dries the moisture or vapor that accumulates in the lungs. They also energize semen production but constipate, unless one also eats bitter pomegranate seeds with them.

5. The *Ith-khir* (Lemon Grass)

In the *Sahih* it is narrated that the Prophet ﷺ said in Makkah about its plants:

« لَا يُخْتَلَىٰ خَلَاهَا »

"Do not cut its plants."

Al-'Abbās رَضِيَ اللهُ عَنْهُ said, "Except for *Al-Ith-khir*, O Messenger of Allah ﷺ, for their (the people of Makkah) servants use it and it is also used for their houses." The Prophet ﷺ said: *"Except Al-Ith-khir."*

Lemon grass is hot in the second degree and dry in the first degree. It is a light substance that opens clogs and the veins' orifices. It also increases urine and menstruation-flow, dissolves the stones and the hard tumors in the stomach, liver and kidneys, either as a drink or as a bandage. The stems of the lemon grass will strengthen the column of the teeth and the stomach, calm nausea and constipate the stomach.

The Letter *Baa*

I. *Bittikh* (Watermelon)

Abu Dāwud and At-Tirmidhi narrated that the Prophet ﷺ used to eat watermelon with ripe dates, saying:

« يَدفعُ حَرُّ هذا بَرْدَ هذا »

"The hotness of this substance (dates) neutralizes the coolness of that (watermelon)."

There are several *Ahadith* regarding watermelon none of them are authentic, except the *Hadith* that we mentioned above.

Green watermelon is cold and wet and is sweet. It also works as a cleanser (for the stomach and the intestines). Watermelon departs the stomach more quickly than cucumber and quickly blends with whatever substances are present in the stomach. It is beneficial to eat watermelon when it is warm, but when it is cold it is better to have it with some ginger to offset its harm.

Watermelon should be eaten before the meals. Otherwise, it will cause nausea. Some doctors said that when watermelon is, "Eaten before the meal, it cleanses the stomach and removes ailments."

2. *Balah* (Dates)

An-Nasai'ī and Ibn Mājah narrated in their *Sunan* that 'Āishah الله رَضِيَ عَنْها said that the Messenger of Allah ﷺ said:

« كُلُو البَلَحَ بالتَّمْر . فإِن الشيطانَ إذا نَظَر إِلَى ابن آدمَ يأكلُ البَلَحَ بالتَّمر، يقولُ: بَقِيَ ابنُ آدمَ حتى أكل الحَديثَ بالعَتِيق »

"Eat fresh dates with dried dates, for when Satan sees the son of Adam eating fresh and dried dates he comments, 'The son of Adam remained until he started eating the new and the old together."

In another narration, the Prophet ﷺ said:

« كلو البلح بالتمر، فإن الشيطانَ يحزَنُ إذا رأى ابن آدمَ يأكُلُه؛ يقول: عاش ابنُ آدمَ حتى أكل الجَديدَ بالخَلَق »

"Eat fresh and dried dates, because Satan gets sad when he sees the son of Adam eating them, so he says: 'The son of Adam has lived until (now) he eats the fresh and the old together."

Some of the Muslim doctors commented, "The Prophet ﷺ ordered the Muslims to eat fresh and dried dates together rather than green dates with dried dates. Fresh dates are cold and dry while dried dates are hot and humid, thus neutralizing the effect of each other. On the other hand, green dates and dried dates are both hot, although the dried dates are more hot." Medically, it is better to avoid eating two types of foods that incline towards either hotness or coolness.

The *Hadith* indicates that the medical profession is generally correct when it inclines towards neutralizing the effects of medications and foods with other ingredients or foods to preserve good health.

Fresh dates are cold and dry and they benefit the mouth, the gums (gingiva) and the stomach. Yet, dates are not beneficial for the chest and lungs because of their coarseness. Also, the dates are difficult to digest and are not very nutritious. The example of fresh dates is the example of unripe grapes, as both cause flatulence and bloating, especially when one drinks water after eating fresh dates. To neutralize these side effects, one should eat them with dried dates, or honey and butter.

3. *Busr* (Green Dates)

In the *Sahih* it is narrated that when the Prophet ﷺ, Abu Bakr and Umar رَضِيَ الله عَنْهما were guests of Abu Al-Haitham bin At-Taihan رَضِيَ الله عَنْهُ, he brought them a cluster of dates, which is similar to a cluster of grapes. The Prophet ﷺ said:

« هَلَّا انتقَيْتَ لنا من رُطَبه »

"Why do you not choose some ripe dates for us?"

Abu Al-Haitham رَضِيَ الله عَنْهُ replied, "I wanted you to choose whatever you like of its green and ripe dates."

Busr is hot and dry, and its dryness is more than its hotness. Also, the *Busr* dries out excess moisture, coats the stomach, relaxes the bowels and helps the gums and the mouth. The most beneficial type of *Busr* is the tender and sweet *Busr*. Yet, eating excessive amounts of *Busr* (green dates) regularly causes obstructions or clogs in the intestines.

4. *Baydh* (Eggs)

Fresh eggs are better than old eggs, and the best kind of eggs is chicken eggs. The eggs are mild but incline slightly towards being cold.

The author of the *Qanoon* said, "The yolk is hot and wet and makes the blood sanitary, but is not nutritious. It is also digested quickly when it is still soft." Another person said, "Egg yolk relives the pain, polishes the throat and the trachea, helps the throat and relieves coughing and the ulcers of the lungs, liver and prostate. It also eliminates coarseness, especially when blended with the grease of sweet almonds. It also maturates and softens whatever is in the chest and softens the roughness of the throat."

When the albumen is used as an eye drop, it cools the hot tumors in the eye and relieves the pain. When it is used as an ointment and placed on the face, it prevents sunburn. Also, when the albumen is used as an ointment and placed on the forehead, it helps in cases of dysentery.

The author of the *Qanoon* mentioned eggs in the medicines and remedies of the heart. He also said, "Its yolk has a strong effect in strengthening the heart. Egg yolk has three beneficial uses: it turns into blood quickly, it does not produce extensive wastes, and the blood that it produces is light and similar to the blood that feeds the heart. Further, the egg yolk is the most adequate substance against the diseases that affect the essence of the soul."

5. *Basal* (Onions)

Abu Dāwud narrated in his *Sunan* that 'Āishah رَضِيَ اللهُ عَنْها was asked about *Basal* and she said, "The last meal that the Prophet ﷺ had included onions in it."

In the *Sahihain* it is also narrated that the Prophet ﷺ disallowed those who eat onions from entering the mosque.

The *Basal* is hot in the third degree and has an excess wetness, helps against pollution and prevents hot wind (meaning in the stomach). It also excites the sexual drive, strengthens the stomach, helps semen production, makes the color lighter, dissolves the phlegm and cleanses the stomach.

Onion grains help against vitiate (lack of pigment in certain areas of the skin) and are used as an ointment around the area affected by alopecia (A skin disease characterized by loss of hair, partial or total). Further, warts will dissipate effectively when onions are blended with salt (and used as an ointment on the warts). When someone feels nauseous after taking a laxative, smelling onions will help against vomiting. Also, the onion will dissipate the smell of laxatives, and when onion water (extract) is administered through the nose, it will clear the head. Used as ear drops, onion extract also helps against weak hearing, Innitus, pus and water that accumulates in the ear. Also, onion grains are used as an eyeliner, to dry out the water that attacks the eye, i.e. cataracts, when the grains are blended with honey and used on the white part of the eye.

Cooked onions are nutritious and help against icterus, jaundice, coughing and roughness in the chest. It is also diuretic and relaxes the bowels. It also heals dog bites when its water (extract) is blended with salt and rue and squeezed on the affected area. Finally, it will open the orifices of the hemorrhoids when used as suppository.

Onions cause migraines, headaches, flatulence and bring darkness to the sight

Eating onions in excessive amounts or regularly causes forgetfulness, affects the mind and changes the odor of the mouth and the taste of food. It also bothers those in your presence and the angels. Cooking onions dissipates these side effects of the onion. The *Sunan* narrated:

« أنه صلى الله عليه وسلم أمر آكِلَه وآكِلِ الثُّوم: أن يُمِيتَهما طَبْخًا »

"The Prophet ordered those who eat onion and garlic to kill them (make them milder) by cooking."

Also, chewing rue leaves dissipates the odor of the onions.

6. *Bathinjan* (Eggplant)

There is a fake *Hadith* that states that eggplant materializes the goals anticipated from eating it. This statement is not suitable to be related from a sane person let alone the Prophet ﷺ.

There are two types of eggplants: white and black. There is a difference of opinion on if it is hot or cold, although we think it is hot. Eggplants cause black bile, piles, clogs, cancer and leprosy. Eggplants also spoil ones color, make it black and cause bad breath. White eggplants do not have these side effects.

The Letter *Taa*

1. *Tamr* (Dried Dates)

In the *Sahih* it is narrated that the Prophet ﷺ said:

« من تَصَبَّح بَسَبْع تَمَراتٍ - من تمر العالية - لم يضرَّه ذلك اليومَ سُمٌّ ولا سِحْرٌ »

"Whoever ate seven dates in the morning from the area of 'Aaliyah will not be harmed by poison or magic the rest of that day."

He also said:

« بيتٌ لا تمرَ فيه جِياعٌ أهلُه »

"The people of a house where there are no dates are hungry."

Also, the Prophet ﷺ ate dried dates with butter, with bread and alone.

Tamr is hot in the second degree and either wet or dry in the second degree.

Dried dates strengthen the liver, relax the bowels, increase semen production, especially when taken with pine, and relieve soar throat. As for those who are not used to eating dried dates, such as the residents of cold areas, dried dates cause them clogs, harm the teeth and cause headaches, unless they are eaten with almonds and poppy.

Dried dates are among the most nutritious fruits, their essence is hot and wet. Also, when one eats dates in the beginning of the day, they help kill worms. Although dried dates are hot, yet they have the strength of an antidote against worms, killing or at least decreasing their numbers, especially when dried dates are taken frequently on an empty stomach. Dried dates are a fruit, a type of food, a cure, a drink and a sweet.

2. Tin (Figs)

The *Sunnah* does not mention figs because they did not grow in that area of the Hijaz or Al-Madinah. Figs require an environment that is different from that in the areas where dates grow. Allah has sworn by the Tin in His Book because of its tremendous benefits and uses.

Tin is hot and either dry or wet. The best type of figs are the white kind when they are ripe, as they cleanse the sand that accumulates in the liver and prostate and serve as a preventive substance against poisons. Figs are more nutritious than all other type of fruit, and help relieve the roughness in the chest, throat and trachea. It also cleanses the liver and the spleen, purifies the phlegm that accumulates in the stomach and provides good nourishment for the body. Yet, it makes one more susceptible to lice if eaten excessively.

3. Tharid (Meat & Bread Dish)

In the *Sahihain* it states that the Messenger of Allah ﷺ said:

« فضلُ عائشةَ على النِّساء: كفَضل الثَّريدِ على سائِر الطَّعام »

"The virtue of 'Aishah رَضِيَ الله عَنْها *as compared to other women, is like the virtue of* Tharid *as compared to the rest of the foods."*

Tharid is composed of some bread, which is the best food, and meat, which is the best flavoring. When these two are combined together, no other food can surpass them.

There are conflicting opinions regarding which is better, the bread or the meat. The correct opinion is that bread is used more while meat is better and superior to bread. Also, the meat resembles the true essence of the human body more than any other food. It is also the food of the people of Paradise. Allah said about those who sought to eat herbs, cucumbers, Fum (wheat or garlic), lentils and onions,

$$ \text{﴿ أَتَسْتَبْدِلُونَ ٱلَّذِى هُوَ أَدْنَىٰ بِٱلَّذِى هُوَ خَيْرٌ ﴾} $$

"Would you exchange that which is better for that which is lower?
(2: 61)

Many among the *Salaf* said that *Fum* is wheat. Hence this *Ayah* states that meat (quails) is better than wheat. Allah has the best knowledge.

The Letter *Jeem*

1. *Jummar* (Palm Pith)

In the *Sahihain* it is narrated that 'Abdullāh bin Umar رَضِيَ الله عَنْهما said." "While we were sitting with the Messenger of Allah ﷺ, he was brought a *Jummar* of a date tree. The Prophet ﷺ said:

« إِنَّ مِنَ الشَّجَرِ شَجَرَةً مِثْلَ الرَّجُلِ الْمُسْلِم لا يَسْقُط وَرقُها »

'There is a tree that resembles the Muslim as its leaves never fall."

Jummar is cold and dry in the first degree, and it seals the ulcers and relieves hemorrhage, diarrhea, yellow bile and blood pressure. Also, the *Jummar* is not harmful, but is not nutritious and is difficult to digest. The *Jummar* is all benefit and this is why the Prophet said it resembled the Muslim, because of his tremendous usefulness and goodness.

2. *Jubn* (Cheese)

In the *Sunan* of Abu Dāwud it is narrated that 'Abdullāh bin 'Umar said that the Prophet ﷺ was brought some cheese while in the area of Tabuk and that he asked for a knife, mentioned Allah's Name and then cut it. Also, the Companions used to eat cheese in Iraq and Sham (Greater Syria) areas.

Unsalted cheese is good for the stomach, easy on the body organs, produces flesh and relaxes the stomach. Salted cheese, on other hand, is less nutritious and is bad for the stomach and the intestines. Old and grilled cheese heats the stomach and is beneficial in cases of ulcers and diarrhea.

Cheese is cold and wet and is better when it is grilled because the fire makes it milder, softer and better tasting and scented. The old salted cheese is hot and dry, and boiling also makes it softer and less sour because the fire extracts the hot residue from the cheese. Salted cheese makes the body weak and causes stones in the liver and prostate. It is also bad for the stomach, and mixing it with what people think will make it milder is even worse because these substances allow the cheese an easy access to the stomach.

The Letter *Haa*

1. *Henna'*

We mentioned the benefits of *henna'* before and mentioned the *Ahadith* on this subject.

2. *Habbah Sawdaa* (The Black Seed)

In the *Sahihain* it is narrated that Abu Hurairah رَضِيَ الله عَنْه related from the Prophet ﷺ that he said:

« عليكم بهذه الحَبّةِ السَّوْداء. فإن فيها شفاءً من كُل داءٍ، إلا السامَ »

"Use the Black Seed, because it contains a cure for every type of ailment, except for death." [At-Tirmidhi, Ahmad and Ibn Hibban].

The Black Seed (or *Habbat Al-Barakah*) is called Shuneiz in Persian, black cumin and Indian cumin. Al-Harbi narrated that Al-Hasan said, "It is the mustard seed" while Al-Harawi said that it is the green seed which is the seed of the terebinth. These are not correct opinions, because the Prophet ﷺ stated that it is the Black Seed, which is the Shuneiz as we stated.

The Black Seed has many benefits, as indicated by the Prophet's statement:

"It is a cure for every type of disease." This statement is just like what Allah said:

﴿ تُدَمِّرُ كُلَّ شَيْءٍ بِأَمْرِ رَبِّهَا ﴾

"Destroying everything by the Command of its Lord!" (46:25)

Its means destroys everything that is prone to destruction.

The Black Seed helps against all types of cold ailments. Also, the Black Seed helps introduce the effective ingredients of cold medications to the areas affected by hot and dry ailments, as it helps the body absorb the medicine quickly when taken in small dosages.

The author of the 'Qanoon' and other people stated that saffron blended with camphor has similar effects, because saffron helps the camphor reach the affected area quickly. There are several types of plants that have similar effects as saffron. It is possible that the hot substance benefits in cases of hot diseases. For instance, the Anzarut, which is a type of eyeliner, is mixed with other remedies for Ophthalmia, conjunctivitis, and so forth. Ophthalmia is a hot tumor as the doctors agree. Also, sulfur is a remedy for hot mange.

Shuneiz is hot and dry in the third degree, eliminates flatulence, extracts the helminthes (worms), relieves leprosy, and phlegmy fevers, opens clogs, decomposes accumulating gas and excess moisture in the stomach. When the *Shuneiz* is ground, blended with honey and drunk with some warm water, it will dissolve the stones that appear in the kidney and the prostate, and it is also diuretic. It increases the flow during menstruation and the production of milk if it is drunk for several days. When it is heated with vinegar and placed on the stomach, it will eliminate helminthes (worms). When it is blended with wet or cooked colorynth water, it is more effective in removing helminthes (worms). It also clears up, decomposes and relieves cold symptoms when it is ground in a rag and inhaled through the nose on a regular basis until the ailment is cured.

Black seed oil helps against snakebites, hemorrhoids and spots. When around twenty-five grams of it is drunk with water it will help against gasping and hard breathing.

When the black seeds are cooked in vinegar and then one rinses his mouth with it, it will relieve toothache resulting from sensitivity to cold. When one inhales powdered black seed, it will help against water that accumulates in the eye. When it is used in a bandage while blended with vinegar, it heals spots and exposed skin ulcers and decomposes the acute mucus tumors and also hard tumors.

The oil of the Black Seed also helps against facial paralysis when administered by the nose. When one drinks around twenty-five grams of its oil, it helps against spider bite. When it is ground finely and blended with the oil of the green Seed and used as ear drops, only up to three drops, it helps against cold symptoms, flatulence and various clogs.

When the Black Seed is fried and finely ground, soaked in oil and then drops are administered in the nose, it will help against cold conditions accompanied by intensive sneezing.

When the Black Seed is burned and mixed with melted wax along with *henna'* or iris oil, it helps remove the ulcers that appear on the skin of the legs, after washing the skin with vinegar.

When the Black Seeds are crushed in vinegar and laid on leprous skin, the skin affected by black pigmentation and on the head that is affected by dandruff, it helps relieve these ailments.

When the Black Seeds are ground finely and one swallows around twenty-five grams of it each day with cold water, it instantly helps against the bite of rabid dogs, and might prevent death as a result of hydrophobia. When one administers the oil of the Black seed in the nose, it will help against facial paralysis and tetanus by eliminating their causes. Finally, when the Black seeds are burned, they help repulse the venomous beasts.

When Persian kohl is dissolved in water and then placed on the interior of the throat and then the Black seeds are sprinkled on it, it acts like an effective remover of hemorrhoids. There are many other benefits for the Shuneiz. We should state that the dose should be around twenty-five grams, as some people claim that using excessive dosages of it might cause death.

3. *Harir* (Silk)

We mentioned that the Prophet ﷺ allowed Az-Zubayr and Abdur-Rahman bin 'Awf to wear silk because of a rash that they suffered from. We mentioned the benefits of the silk in that chapter.

4. *Hurf* (Cress)

Abu Hanifah Ad-Daynoori said, "Cress seeds are used in remedies and are also called Ath-Thuffaa, which the Prophet ﷺ mentioned. Its plant is called Al-Hurf while Rashad seeds is its popular name." Also, Abu Ubayd said that Ath-Thuffaa is the Hurf.

The *Hadith* that Abu Hanifah referred to is what Abu Ubay and other scholars have related from Ibn 'Abbās that the Prophet ﷺ was reported to have said:

« ماذا في الأَمَرَّين من الشِّفاء ! : الثُّفَّاءِ والصَّبِرِ»

"What a cure do the two bitter remedies carry: the Thuffaa and aloe."

Cress is hot and dry in the third degree, and it heats and relaxes the stomach, removes different types of worms, decomposes the spleen tumors, excites the sexual drive and heals the ulcers of mange and herpes.

When the cress is used as a bandage along with honey, it will decompose spleen tumors. When it is cooked with henna, it will extract harmful accumulations in the chest, while taking it as a drink helps against venomous bites and stings.

When it is burned, its smoke repulses venomous beasts and also prevents the hair form falling. Also, when it is mixed with barley flour and vinegar and used as a bandage it helps against sciatic nerve and decomposes hot tumors.

Further, when it is used as a bandage with water, it brings the pustules to maturity and helps against flabbiness in various organs, strengthens the sexual drive and works as an appetite stimulant. It also helps against asthma, hard breathing, relieves the thickness in the spleen, purifies the chest and increases the menstrual flow. It also helps against sciatic nerve and the cavity of the hip, due to the extraction power of the cress when one drinks it or is injected with it. It also purifies the chest and the lungs from phlegm.

When cress is crushed and taken in a drink with warm water, it will work as a laxative, decomposes flatulence and helps against the pain caused by constipation. Further, cress also helps against leprosy when it is crushed and used in a drink.

Also, when the cress is blended with vinegar and used as an ointment on leprous skin and on white pigmentation disorder, it helps relieve these conditions. It also relieves headaches that are caused by colds and by phlegm accumulation. When it is fried and drunk (with water), it constipates, especially when it is not crushed, as its consistency will be softened when it is fried.

Galinus said that the strength of the cress, "Is similar to the effectiveness of mustard grains. Hence it could be used to heat the pain in the hip, which is known as *Nasa* and headaches, as each of these symptoms requires heat, similar to mustard seed. Sometimes, cress is mixed with other remedies and used to treat asthma, as it is known that it dissolves thick mixtures, again just as mustard seed does. It is similar to mustard seed in every respect."

5. *'Hulbah* (Fenugreek)

The Prophet ﷺ was reported to have visited Sa'd bin Abi Waqqas رَضِيَ اللهُ عَنْهُ once when he was ill while in Makkah and he asked that a doctor be brought to examine him. They brought Al-Harith bin Kaladah who examined him and said, "There is no harm with him, just cook some fenugreek with dates and let him eat them." Sa'd was reported to have done that and was then healed.

Hulbah is hot in the second degree and dry in the first degree.

When the fenugreek is cooked in water, it will soften the throat, chest and the stomach. It also relieves coughing, dryness, asthma, hard breathing and increases the sexual drive. It also relieves flatulence, phlegm, piles and the various accumulations in the intestines. It also dissolves the phlegm from the chest and helps against gastric ulcer and lung diseases. *'Hulbah* is used to heal the intestines, mixed with some ghee and fanith.

When five measures of fenugreek is taken in a drink, it will increase the flow of menstruation, and when it is cooked and the hair is washed with it, it will make it curly and will combat dandruff.

When the flour of the fenugreek is blended with some vinegar and natron and used as a bandage on the tumor of the spleen, it will dissolve it. Also, the woman who suffers from pain in the vagina due to a tumor will benefit if she sits in the water in which the fenugreek was cooked.

When it is used as a bandage and placed on hard, cold tumors, it will help dissolve these tumors. Also, when its water is drunk, it will help against the pain in the stomach that results from accumulating gaseous materials and will cleanse the intestines.

When one eats the *Hulbah* cooked in honey, dates or figs on an empty stomach, it will dissolve the phlegm that accumulates in the chest and stomach, and will also help against coughing that accompanies such ailments.

Hulbah also relieves urine retention and works as a laxative. When it is placed on the erratic nail, it will heal it, while its oil helps against cracked skin due to extreme cold, when it is mixed with wax. There are many other benefits for the *Hulbah* (fenugreek).

Some doctors stated, "If the people had knowledge of its benefits, they would buy it with its weight worth of gold."

The Letter *Khaa*

I. *Khubz* (Bread)

In the *Sahih* it is narrated that the Prophet ﷺ said:

« تكونُ الأرضُ يوم القيامةِ خُبْزةً واحدةً، يَتَكَفَّؤُها الجبَّارُ بيده نُزُلًا لأهل الجَنة »

"On the Day of Resurrection, the earth will look like one piece of bread which the Most Mighty would prepare with His Hand as a residence for the people of Paradise."

There is a fake *Hadith* that disallows cutting bread with a knife. There is also another fake *Hadith* that disallows cutting meat with a knife. Muhanna said that he asked Imam Ahmad about the *Hadith* related from ʿAishah رَضِيَ الله عَنْها which narrates that the Prophet ﷺ disallowed using a knife to cut meat, because it is an act of non-Arabs. Imam Ahmad said that it is not correct and that it contradicts the *Hadith* narrated by ʿAmr bin Umayyah and Al-Mughirah. The *Hadith* that he referred to is what ʿAmr bin Umayyah related that the Prophet ﷺ used to cut some pieces of ewe meat with a blade. Also, Al-Mughirah narrated that when he asked the Prophet ﷺ to be his guest, he ordered that a piece of meat be broiled and he then started cutting the meat with a blade.

The best type of bread is yeasty and kneaded

The next best is furnace bread, then oven baked bread, then bread cooked under hot ashes, using fresh flour.

The most nutritious kind of bread is semolina bread, because it digests slowly and because it does not have excessive amounts of bran, then chalky bread and lastly black bread.

The best time to eat the bread is in the last part of the day when it is baked. Also, unlike dry bread, soft bread is lighter, more nutritious, humidifying and digests faster.

Wheat bread is hot in the second degree and is mild concerning wetness and dryness, unless dried by fire.

Wheat bread also fattens the body rapidly. The Qatayif (similar to pancakes) cause a thick condition, while breadcrumbs provoke swelling in the stomach and digests with difficulty. Further, bread made with milk causes clogs and is difficult to digest, although it is nutritious.

Barley bread is cold and dry in the first degree and it not as nutritious as wheat bread.

2. *Khall* (Vinegar)

Muslim narrated in his *Sahih* that Jabir bin 'Abdullāh رَضِيَ الله عَنْهُما said, "The Messenger of Allah ﷺ asked his wife for food and she said that I have vinegar. He asked for some of it and started eating from it while saying:

$$ \text{« نِعْمَ الإِدامُ الخَلُّ »} $$

"What an excellent food is vinegar." (He ate it with bread.)

Khall is a substance that is both hot and cold, although coldness is usually more apparent. It is also dry in the third degree and a strong drying agent. Vinegar also soothes the body and softens the nature.

Wine vinegar helps against gastric inflammation and bile and prevents the harm of toxic medications. It also decomposes milk and the blood when coagulated, and helps the spleen, coats the stomach, constipates, quenches the thirst and prevents tumors from occurring. It also helps the digestion process, works against phlegm, softens thick foods and softens the consistency of the blood.

When vinegar is drunk with salt, it will help against poisonous mushrooms. When vinegar is sipped, it will dissolve the clogs that occur in the blood in the lower jaw. When one rinses his mouth with warm vinegar, it relieves toothache and strengthens the gingival.

Vinegar also helps against a septic finger when it is anointed with it, and also relieves pustules, hot tumors and fire burns. Vinegar is an appetite stimulant, softens the stomach, and favorable for young people and for those who live in warm areas.

3. *Khilal* (Toothpick)

Toothpicks are helpful for the gingival and teeth and preserve their health, and help keep the breath fresh. One of the best types of toothpicks are those made from olive wood. It is not advised to use reed, myrtle, or basil to pick the teeth.

The Letter *Dal*

I. *Duhn* (Fat or Grease)

Fat closes the pores of the body and prevents the skin from decomposing. When it is used after one takes a bath with hot water, it will humidify the body and polish it. When the hair is anointed with grease, it will beautify it and make it longer. It also helps against measles and most other ailments that could affect the hair.

At-Tirmidhi narrated that Abu Hurairah رَضِيَ اللهُ عَنهُ related from the Prophet ﷺ that he said:

« كلو الزَّيت، واذَّهِنوا به »

"Use grease in your food and as an ointment."

In the warm areas, such as Hijaz, grease works as one of the best preservers of health and as a remedy, making it necessary for the residents of such areas. As for those who live in cold areas, it is not as necessary for them. We should mention that using grease on the head on a regular basis causes harm to the sight.

The most beneficial simple kinds of grease are regular oil, then fat and then sesame oil.

As for the compound greases, some kinds are wet and cold, such as the essence of violet, which helps against hot headaches and brings sleep to the eye. It also moisturizes the brain, helps against cracks (or fractures) and excessive dryness of the skin. It is also a beneficial ointment against mange and dry rashes, along with helping the joints be flexible. It is also suitable for those who tend to be hot during the summer.

Some types of compound greases are hot and wet, such as ben-tree grease, which is the extract of white seeds that look like dusty pistachio and which is greasy and fatty. This type of grease relaxes the nerves and helps against spots and lack of pigment in certain areas of the skin. It also draws thick phlegm, softens dry ligaments and heats the nerves. It also cleans the teeth, makes them shiny and helps them against corrosion. Also whoever anoints his head and face with ben-tree grease will not come down with measles or cracks. Anointing the sexual organs and groins with it also helps against the coldness of the kidneys and dripping urine.

The Letter *Thal*

1. *Tharirah* (Hemarthria/Arum)

In the *Sahihain* it is narrated that 'Āishah رَضِيَ الله عَنْها said that during the Farewell *Hajj*, she perfumed the Messenger of Allah ﷺ with *Tharirah* for his *Ihram* and otherwise.

We mentioned the *Tharirah* and its benefits before.

2. *Thubab* (Flies)

We mentioned the *Hadith* by Abu Hurairah رَضِيَ الله عَنْه in the *Sahihain* about the Prophet's command to dip the housefly in the food or drink when it falls in it to get the antidote that its wing carries. This antidote works as the antidote of the poison that the fly carries on the other wing. We also mentioned the benefits of the flies before.

3. *Thahab* (Gold)

Abu Dāwud and At-Tirmidhi narrated that the Prophet ﷺ allowed Arfajah bin As'ad, who lost his nose during the battle of Kulab and had to use a nose made of silver that later rotted, to wear a nose made of gold. 'Arfajah is only mentioned in this one *Hadith*.

Gold is the joy of the life of this world and the precious material possession of this existence that brings joy to the hearts and strength to the back. It is also Allah's secret on His earth. Gold's condition is suitable in all types of environments and has a soft hotness that is used in various light and soothing remedies. It is also the most mild of all minerals.

When gold is buried in the ground, sand does not affect it adversely. When gold is used in certain remedies, it helps cure weak hearts and the fibrillation that accompanies black bile. It also helps against obsession, sadness, depression, fear and love. It brings fatness to the body, dissipates pallor and lightens the color. It also helps against leprosy and the various other ailments including black bile. Drunk or used as an ointment, gold is an effective ingredient in the remedies for treating alopecia (a skin disease characterized by loss of hair, partial or total), and viper stings. It also clears the eye and strengthens it, and helps against several ailments while brining strength to the various organs of the body.

Foul breath would dissipate if one holds some gold in his mouth. Also, those who have a disease that requires cauterization and use gold for this purpose it will heal quickly and the wound would not be covered with blisters. Also, when gold is used as kohl, it purifies and strengthens the eyes. Further, when a golden ring is heated and applied on pigeon wings, the pigeons will be accustomed to their homes and will not abandon them.

Gold is especially effective in strengthening the hearts and this is why it was allowed in times of war and in times of peace, except when there is proof to the contrary. At-Tirmidhi narrated that Buraydah Al-'Asri said, "The Messenger of Allah ﷺ entered (Makkah) the Day of *Al-Fath* (conquering of Makkah) with gold and silver on his sword."

Gold is such a beloved object to the hearts that when they acquire it, it will be sufficient for the people to forget the other beloved objects of this earthly life.

Allah said:

﴿ زُيِّنَ لِلنَّاسِ حُبُّ ٱلشَّهَوَٰتِ مِنَ ٱلنِّسَآءِ وَٱلْبَنِينَ وَٱلْقَنَٰطِيرِ ٱلْمُقَنطَرَةِ مِنَ ٱلذَّهَبِ وَٱلْفِضَّةِ وَٱلْخَيْلِ ٱلْمُسَوَّمَةِ وَٱلْأَنْعَٰمِ وَٱلْحَرْثِ ﴾

"Beautified for men is the love of things they covet; women, children, much of gold and silver (wealth), branded beautiful horses, cattle and well-tilled land." (3:14)

Also, in the *Sahihain*it is narrated that the Prophet ﷺ said:

« لَوْ كَانَ لِابْنِ آدَمَ وَادٍ مِنْ ذَهَبٍ: لَابْتَغَى إِلَيْهِ ثَانِيًا . وَلَوْ كَانَ لَهُ ثَانٍ: لَابْتَغَى

ثَالِثًا . وَلَا يَمْلَأُ جَوْفَ ابْنِ آدَمَ إِلَّا التُّرَابُ؛ وَيَتُوبُ اللهُ عَلَى مَنْ تَابَ »

"If the son of Adam had a valley of gold, he would seek a second.
If he had two, he would seek a third. Nothing fills the stomach of
the son of Adam except dirt, and Allah forgives those who
repent."

Gold is the biggest barrier that stands between mankind and acquiring the ultimate success on the Day of Resurrection. It is also the biggest object with which Allah has been disobeyed. Because of gold, relations of the womb were severed, blood was shed, prohibitions were violated, rights were unjustly taken and slaves committed injustice against each other. Gold is the reason behind liking the life of this world and its shortness, and the cause behind disliking the Next Life and what Allah has prepared in it for His loyal supporters. With gold, so many truths were and are buried, so much falsehood was and is brought to life, so many unjust people were and are given support and so many innocent people were and are being dealt with unjustly.

The Letter *Raa*

I. *Rutab* (Ripe Dates)

Allah said to Mary:

﴿وَهُزِّي إِلَيْكِ بِجِذْعِ ٱلنَّخْلَةِ تُسَٰقِطْ عَلَيْكِ رُطَبًا جَنِيًّا ۞ فَكُلِي وَٱشْرَبِي وَقَرِّي عَيْنًا﴾

"And shake the trunk of date palm towards you, it will let fall
fresh ripe dates upon you. So eat and drink and be glad. And if
you see any human being, say: 'Verily, I have vowed a fast unto
the Most Gracious (Allāh) so I shall not speak to any human
being this day." (19: 25, 26)

Also, in the *Sahihain* it is narrated that 'Abdullāh bin Ja'far رَضِيَ الله عَنْهما said:

"I saw the Messenger of Allah ﷺ eating cucumbers with ripe
dates."

Abu Dāwud also narrated in his *Sunan* that Anas رَضِيَ اللهُ عَنهُ said:

> *"The Messenger of Allah ﷺ used to break his fast on some ripe dates, and if he did not have any, on dry dates. Otherwise, if he did not have dry dates, he would have several sips of water."*

Ripe dates are just like water, hot and wet, and they are favorable for and strengthen the cold stomach, increase the production of semen and fertility, are suitable for cold temperaments and are very nutritious.

Ripe dates are the best types of fruit for the people of Al-Madinah specifically and for all others in general where ripe dates grow. It is also a very beneficial fruit for the body, although ripe dates spoil quickly in the stomach of those who are not used to eating them and thus produce putrid blood. Also, eating excessive amounts of ripe dates cause headaches and black bile and also harms the teeth. Oxymel (Sakanjabin) helps neutralize the irritants that accompany eating ripe dates.

When the Prophet ﷺ used to break his fast, he used to first eat ripe or dry dates, or would drink some water. This is a wise decision, because fasting empties the stomach of food. Thus the liver would not find any sufficient energy that it could transfer to the various organs. Sweets are the fastest food to reach the liver and are also favored by the liver, especially when one eats ripe dates, in which case the liver accepts it even more favorably, benefits from it and then transfers the benefit to the rest of the organs of the body. If there are no ripe dates available, one should eat dried dates because they are sweet and nutritious. Otherwise, some sips of water would extinguish the heat of the stomach and the Fast. The stomach's appetite would then increase and become ready to accept (and digest) food.

2. Raihan (Myrtle / Basil)

Allah said:

> *"Then, if he (the dying person) be of the* Muqarrabūn *(those brought near to Allāh), (There is for him) rest and provision, and a Garden of Delights (Paradise)."* (56:88,89)

And He said:

﴿ وَٱلْحَبُّ ذُو ٱلْعَصْفِ وَٱلرَّيْحَانُ ﴾

"And also corn, with (its) leaves and stalk for fodder, and sweet-scented plants." (55:12)

Muslim narrated that the Prophet ﷺ said:

« مَن عُرِض عليه رَيْحانٌ فلا يرده: فإنه خفيفُ المَحْمَلِ، طيِّب الرائحة »

"Whoever was presented with Rayhan should not refuse it, because it is easy to wear and has a good scent."

Ibn Majah narrated in his *Sunan* that Usamah رَضِيَ الله عَنْهُ related from the Prophet ﷺ that he said:

« أَلا مُشَمِّرٌ لِلْجِنَّةِ؛ فإن الجَنَّةَ لا خطَرَ لها هي – ورِبِّ الكعبة –: نورٌ يَتَلأْلأُ وَرَيْحانَةٌ تَهْتَزُّ، وقصْرٌ مَشيدٌ، ونهرٌ مُطَّرِدٌ، وتمْرَةٌ نَضِيجَةٌ، وزَوْجَةٌ حَسْناءُ جميلَةٌ، وحُلَلٌ كثيرةٌ، ومُقامٌ في أبدٍ في دارٍ سليمةٍ؛ وفاكهةٌ وخُضْرَةٌ، وحَبَرَةٌ ونِعمَةٌ، في مَحَلَّةٍ عاليةٍ بَهِيَّةٍ » .

"Is there anyone who is ready to enter Paradise, for Paradise is all good (and pure). It is, by the Lord of the Ka'bah, a shining light, a twinkling Raihan, a luxurious palace, a running river, a ripe date, and a beautiful, pretty wife. It has many suits, eternal residence in a good place of dwelling, fruits, vegetables, comfort and bounty in an exalted, comfortable dwelling."

They said, " 'Yes, O Messenger of Allah ﷺ! We are ready for it!' He said, 'Say, by Allah's Leave.' They said, By Allah's Leave.' "

Every plant that has good scent is called 'Raihan'. Therefore, every area gives a certain plant that name. For instance, the people to the west, as well as, the Arabs call the aromatic plants *Raihan*. The people in Iraq and Sham call the Hibk (a type of mint) a *Raihan*.

Raihan or myrtle is cold in the first degree and dry in the second degree. Yet, it is a compound of several qualities, most of which consist of earthly cold essence. Myrtle also consists of a soft hot substance. Myrtle dries the head nicely and is effective as a constipating agent.

Myrtle prevents bile diarrhea and dissipates hot and wet vapor when one smells its scent. Its scent also brings relief to the heart and prevents various ailments, especially when the plant is spread around the house.

Also, myrtle heals the tumors that occur in the two ureters when it is coated on them. When fresh myrtle leaves are ground and blended with vinegar and then placed on the head, they will stop nose bleeding. When dried myrtle leaves are crushed and the powder is sprinkled on wet ulcers it will heal them and will help weak organs when used as a bandage, relieve septic finger and heal spots and the ulcers on the hands and feet.

When myrtle is used to rub the body it eliminates sweat, dries the excess wetness and dissipates underarm odor. When one sits in the water that myrtle was cooked in, it will help against infections on the buttocks and vagina and will heal weak joints and also broken bones, when it is poured on the wound.

Also, myrtle helps eliminate dandruff and the wet ulcers and the spots that appear on the head. It also helps the hair against falling and gives it a black color. When myrtle leaves are ground with a little water and then blended with some oil or rose grease and then used as a bandage, it will be suitable against fresh (or humid) ulcers, canker sores, erysipelas (skin infection), acute tumors, urticaria (hives) and hemorrhoids.

Myrtle seeds also help against hemoptysis (spiting up blood) of the chest and lungs. It also coats the stomach and does not harm the chest or the stomach and cleanses them. It also helps against diarrhea and coughing, and this is a special quality for myrtle that is rarely found in other medications. Myrtle seeds also help urine production and heal vesica (bladder) infections, spider bites and scorpion stings. Using myrtle roots to clean between the teeth is harmful, though.

Persian *Raihan*, which is also called *Hibq*, is hot, and when its scent is smelled, it helps against hot headaches when water is sprinkled on the *Hibq* and then is allowed to cool down. It is also said that this kind of myrtle is cold, but it looks like it has some of the four types of temperament. It also helps bring sleep to the eye.

The seeds of Persian myrtle relieve diarrhea of the bile, stomach, strengthen the heart and help against black bile ailments.

3. *Rumman* (Pomegranate)

Allah said:

﴿ فِيهِمَا فَاكِهَةٌ وَنَخْلٌ وَرُمَّانٌ ﴾

"In them (both) will be fruits, and date palms and pomegranates." (55:68)

Also, 'Ali رَضِيَ اللهُ عَنْهُ was reported to have said: "Eat *Rumman* with its pulp, because it coats the stomach."

Sweet pomegranate is hot and wet, good for the stomach, and strengthens it because of its being a mild constipating agent. It is also good for the throat, chest and lungs, along with relieving coughing. The water (or juice) in the pomegranate softens the stomach and is a nutrient for the body. It also digests quickly because it is light and produces heat along with some air in the stomach. It helps increase the semen production and is not favorable for those who have fever. Pomegranate has a special quality, that is, when one eats bread with it, it prevents it from being spoiled.

Bitter pomegranate is cold and dry and constipates mildly. It is also good for overheated stomach and helps produce more urine than the other types of pomegranate. It also softens bile symptoms, relieves diarrhea, prevents vomiting and is slightly tarry. It also stops the heat in the liver, strengthens the organs, helps against bilious shaking, heartaches and the ache of the tip of the stomach. It also helps the stomach and rids it of excrements and extinguishes the bile and benefits the blood.

When pomegranate's juice is extracted and is cooked with some honey until it becomes like an ointment and used as eye drops, it will clear the yellow color from the eye and will dissipate the thick wetness. When it is placed on the gingival (gums), it will help against the rashes that appear on the gingival. Also, pomegranate juice extracted with the rind will work as a laxative and will rid the body from septic bilious moistures, along with helping against short-term fever.

As for sour pomegranate, its qualities are in the middle between the two other kinds we mentioned, although this kind leans more towards being sour. Pomegranate seeds that are mixed with honey will alleviate septic finger and malignant ulcers. Pomegranate flowers also help heal wounds. It is said that if one swallows three pomegranate flowers each year, he will be immune from ophthalmia (conjunctivitis) for an entire year.

The Letter *Zay*

I – *Zait** (Olive Oil)

Allah said:

﴿ يُوقَدُ مِن شَجَرَةٍ مُّبَـٰرَكَةٍ زَيْتُونَةٍ لَّا شَرْقِيَّةٍ وَلَا غَرْبِيَّةٍ يَكَادُ زَيْتُهَا يُضِىٓءُ وَلَوْ لَمْ تَمْسَسْهُ نَارٌ ﴾

"Lit from a blessed tree, an olive, neither of the east (i.e. neither it gets sun-rays only in the morning) nor of the west (i.e. nor it gets sun-rays only in the afternoon, but it is exposed to the sun all day long), whose oil would almost glow forth (of itself), though no fire touched it." (24:35)

At-Tirmidhi and Ibn Mājah narrated that Abu Hurairah رَضِيَ الله عَنْهُ related from the Prophet ﷺ that he said:

« كلوا الزَّيْت وادَّهِنُوا به؛ فإنه من شَجَرةٍ مباركةٍ »

"Eat the Zait and use it as an ointment, because it is produced by a blessed tree."

Al-Bayhaqi and Ibn Mājah also narrated that 'Abdullāh bin 'Umar رَضِيَ الله عَنْهما said that the Messenger of Allah ﷺ said:

« ائْتَدِموا بالزيتِ وادَّهِنوا به، فإنه من شَجَرة مباركةٍ »

"Eat oil and use it as an ointment because it is from a blessed tree (olive tree)."

Zait is hot and wet in the first degree. Also, the quality of the oil depends on the tree that produces it. For instance, the best type of olive oil is that squeezed from ripe olives, while oil from unripe olives is cold and dry. Red olives produce oil that is between these while black olives produce hot and wet oil. Olive oil helps against poisons, works as a laxative and rids the body of worms. Old olive oil leans more towards being hot and decomposing. When the oil is blended with water, it becomes less hot and milder and thus more beneficial. All kinds of olive oil soften the skin and slow the aging process. The salty water blended with oil helps burned skin against blistering. It also strengthens the gingiva

---

* **Editor's note**: Oil was understood to mean olive oil.

(gums), while olive leaves help against erysipelas (skin infections), sores, septic ulcers and urticaria (hives). There are many other benefits for olive oil.

2. *Zubd* (Butter)

Abu Dāwud narrated in his *Sunan* that the two children of Busr said, "The Messenger of Allah ﷺ came by us and we offered him some butter and dried dates, as he used to like eating butter and dried dates."

Butter is hot and wet and has many benefits, such as maturing the mixtures (bodily wastes) and decomposing them, along with relieving the tumors that appear next to the ears and ureters (tubes leading from the kidney to the bladder). When butter is used alone it also heals mouth cankers and the various other types of tumors that attack children and women. When one licks butter, it will help against lung hemoptysis (spitting up blood) and will mature the tumors of the lungs.

Butter softens the nature, the nerves and the hard tumors that result from black bile and phlegm and relieves the dryness in the body. When butter is laid on the place where children's' teeth emerge, it will help the teeth grow. Butter also soothes the coughing that accompanies colds and dryness. It also heals herpes and the roughness in the body and works as a laxative. Yet, butter reduces the appetite and the sweetness of honey and dates.

The wisdom behind the Prophet ﷺ eating dried dates with butter is that they would neutralize the effect of each other.

3. *Zabib* (Raisins)

The best type of *Zabib* is the largest in size, the fattest and that has thin skin and small seeds, especially when the seeds are removed before eating them. Raisins are hot and wet in the first degree, while their seeds are cold and dry.

Raisins are similar to the type of grape they are made of, as sweet raisins are hot, sour raisins are cold and constipating and white raisins are more effective constipating agents. Raisin pulp is suitable for the windpipe and relieves coughing and liver and prostate pain. It also strengthens the stomach and soothes the intestinal cavity.

Sweet raisin pulps are more nutritious than grapes, but less nutritious than dried figs. Also, sweet raisin pulps possess maturing qualities and mildly constipate. In general, raisins strengthen the stomach, the spleen and the liver and benefit the throat, chest, lung, liver and prostate.

The best way to have raisins is to eat them without the seeds. Raisins provide good nutrition and do not cause clogs like dates do. Eating raisins with their seeds will increase the nutritious intake and will benefit the stomach, liver and spleen. When one is suffering from loose nails and places raisin pulps on them, they will remove the nails quickly. Sweet, seedless raisins benefit those who suffer from excessive wetness and phlegm and help the liver.

Raisins also help memory power, as Az-Zuhri said, "Those who seek to memorize the Hadith should eat raisins." Also, it was reported that Abdullah Ibn 'Abbās described the raisins that, "Their seeds are an ailment while their pulp is a cure."

4. Zanjabil (Ginger)

Allah said:

$$ \text{﴿ وَيُسْقَوْنَ فِيهَا كَأْسًا كَانَ مِزَاجُهَا زَنجَبِيلًا ﴾} $$

"And they will be given to drink there of a cup (of wine) mixed with Zanjabīl (ginger)." (76:17)

Abu Nu'aym also narrated in his book on the Prophetic medicine that Abu Sa'id Al-Khudri رَضِيَ الله عَنْهُ said:

« أَهْدَى مَلِكُ الرُّومِ إِلَى رَسُولِ الله صلى الله عليه وسلم جَرَّةَ زَنْجَبِيلٍ، فَأَطْعَمَ كُلَّ إِنْسَانٍ قِطْعَةً، وَأَطْعَمَنِي قِطْعَةً »

"The Byzantine king gave the Messenger of Allah ﷺ a barrel of ginger as a gift and he gave each person a part of it. I too got a piece."

Ginger is hot in the second degree and wet in the first degree. It heats the body, helps the digestion process, softens the stomach mildly, helps open the clogs of the liver that are caused by coldness and wetness and helps against the wetness that causes sight impairment, when it is eaten or used as kohl. Ginger also strengthens the sexual power and decomposes the thick gases accumulating in the intestines and the stomach.

In general, ginger is good for the cold temperament of the liver and the stomach. When one takes some ginger along with two measures of sugar and some hot water, it will work as a laxative and will rid the body of harmful excrements. Ginger is an effective ingredient in the ointments that dissolve the phlegm.

Sour ginger is hot and dry and it excites the sexual drive, increases semen production, heats the stomach and the liver, helps the digestion process, dries the phlegm that prevails in the body and increases the memory power. It is also suitable for the coldness in the liver and stomach and washes the harmful effect of eating fruit. It also makes the scent better and fends off the harm of thick, cold foods.

The Letter *Seen*

1. *Senna*

We mentioned *Senna* before and stated that it is also called Sanut. There are seven opinions regarding what the word *Senna* means.

Senna is said to mean honey, the thick juice that appears on the surface of the butter and which looks like black stripes, cumin like seeds, Persian cumin, dill, dried dates or fennel.

2. *Safarjal* (Quince)

Quince is cold and dry, constipates and benefits the stomach. Sweet quince is cold and dry and is somewhat mild. Sour quince constipates more than sweet quince and is colder and drier. All types of *Safarjal* quench the thirst, stop vomiting, help produce urine and constipate. *Safarjal* also helps against stomach ulcers, hemoptysis (spitting up blood), diarrhea and nausea. *Safarjal* also prevents the ascending of gaseous material when one eats it after the meal. Also, the ashes of washed *Safarjal* leaves and stems are similar to zinc in benefit.

Consuming Safarjal before the meal constipates, while consuming it after the meals softens the stool and helps the digestion process. Eating excessive amounts of *Safarjal* harms the nerves and causes painful constipation. *Safarjal* helps extinguish the yellow bile of the stomach.

When the quince is broiled, it will become softer and milder. When one removes the pips of the quince, stuffs them with honey, dips them in a paste and then broil them under hot ashes, they will become very beneficial.

The best way to eat the quince is broiled or cooked in honey. The seeds of *Safarjal* also help against dryness in the throat, the windpipe and several other ailments. Its oil stops sweating and strengthens the stomach. *Safarjal* jam also strengthens the stomach and the liver and relieves the heart and the soul.

3. Siwak

In the *Sahihain* it is narrated that the Prophet ﷺ said:

«لَوْ لَا أَن أَشُقَّ على أُمَّتي : لأمرتُهم بالسِّواك عند كل صَلَاة »

"If it was not for the fact that my nation would not be able to bear it, I would have ordered them to use Siwak before every prayer."

Also, in the *Sahihain* it is narrated that:

« أنه صلى الله عليه وسلم كان إذا قامَ من اللَّيل : يَشُوصُ فاهُ بالسِّواك »

"Whenever the Prophet ﷺ would wake up at night, he would clean his mouth with Siwak."

Al-Bukhari also narrated that the Prophet ﷺ said:

« السِّواك مَطْهَرَةٌ لِلْفَم، مرضَاة للربِّ »

"*Siwak* cleans the mouth and pleases the Lord."

Further, Muslim narrated that:

« أنه صلى الله عليه وسلم كان إذا دخل بيتَه : بدأ بالسِّواك »

"Whenever the Prophet ﷺ would enter his house, he would first use the Siwak."

There are many other *Ahadith* on this subject.

An authentic *Hadith* also stated that just before he died, the Prophet ﷺ used the *Siwak*. The Prophet ﷺ also said:

« أكثرت عليكم في السِّواك »

"I have troubled you by frequently stressing using the Siwak."

The best type of *Siwak* is made from Arak trees. Further, one should not use an unknown tree for *Siwak* for it might be poisonous. Also, *Siwak* should be used moderately, because it might cause the coating of the teeth to wear away and thus the teeth will be susceptible to the hot vapors or gasses that ascend from the stomach and to all kinds of dirt. When the *Siwak* is used moderately, it will polish the teeth, strengthen the roots of the teeth, help the tongue, prevent plaque, perfume the breath, clear the mind and strengthen the appetite.

The best way to use the *Siwak* is by soaking it in rose water. Also, the best type of *Siwak* is made from walnut stems. The author of At-Taysir said, "It was said that when one uses the *Siwak* once every five days, it will clear the head, sharpen the senses and alert the mind."

Siwak is beneficial for many reasons, such as perfuming the breath, strengthening the gingiva, clearing the phlegm and the sight and preventing cavities. It also preserves the health of the stomach, clears the voice, helps the digestion process, helps make the speech clear and encourages one to recite the Qur'ān, remember Allāh and pray. *Siwak* also fights sleepiness, pleases the Lord, delights the angels and increases the number of the good deeds.

Siwak is preferred at any time, especially before the prayer, ablution, when waking up and when the mouth emits foul odor. It is also preferred for those who are fasting and all other people at all times. There are *Ahadith* that allow this practice for those who are fasting, because it is beneficial for them and pleases the Lord. Pleasing the Lord when one is fasting is even more desired than at other times. Also the *Siwak* cleans the mouth, and cleanliness for the fasting person is one of his best deeds.

In the *Sunan* it is narrated that 'Amir bin Rabī'ah رَضِيَ الله عَنْهُ said: "I saw the Messenger of Allāh ﷺ on numerous occasion using the *Siwak* when he was fasting."

Al-Bukhari also said that Ibn 'Umar رَضِيَ الله عَنْهما said that the Prophet ﷺ used the *Siwak* at the two ends of the day.

There is a consensus that the fasting person rinses his mouth while performing ablution, and rinsing the mouth is an obligation or a more preferred act than using the *Siwak*. Also, Allāh does not have a use for the people to worship him while their mouths are emitting foul odor, nor is it an act of worship. When the Prophet mentioned that the odor that the mouth of the fasting person emits is better in His Sight than the scent of *Musk*, he meant to encourage the practice of fasting, not the practice of allowing the mouth to emit foul odor. Hence the fasting person needs the *Siwak* more than anyone else. Also, Allāh's Pleasure is much better than His preferring the odor that the mouth of the fasting person emits.

Further, Allāh prefers using the Siwak more than for the odor that comes out of the mouth of the fasting person to remain.

Also, using *Siwak* does not prevent the good scent that Allāh creates in the fasting person's mouth on the Day of Resurrection. Rather, the mouth of the fasting person will smell better than Musk on the Day of Resurrection as a sign of his observing the Fast, even if the odor that used to come from his mouth was removed by the *Siwak*. Similarly, whoever suffers a wound [for the sake of Allāh] in this life is commanded to remove the blood from his body in this life, but his wound would still have the color of blood on the Day of Resurrection.

Furthermore, The *Siwak* does not completely remove the odor of the mouth for the fasting person because its reason still remains, that is, the stomach being empty of food. Only the effect of this fact will be lessened from the teeth and gums.

The Prophet ﷺ taught his nation the preferred and the disliked acts of the Fast. He did not mention the *Siwak* among the disliked acts although he knew they were using it. Rather, he encouraged them in general to use the *Siwak* and they saw him using it himself at innumerable times, knowing that they would imitate him. Never did he discourage them from using the *Siwak* in the afternoon (when they are fasting). It is a fact that the Prophet ﷺ is required to offer the religious ruling when it is needed.

4. *Samn* (Shortening)

There is a weak *Hadith* that narrates that the Prophet ﷺ encouraged the Muslim to drink cow milk, because it is a remedy and because the butter of that milk is a cure, while stating that cow meat is an ailment. The chain of narrators for this *Hadith* is not authentic.

Samn is hot and wet in the first degree and it is mild and helps eliminate the various tumors that attack the soft parts of the body. *Samn* is stronger than butter as a maturing agent. Galinus said that he used shortening to cure the tumors that occur in the ear and the tip of the nose. Also, when the base of the teeth is anointed with shortening, the teeth will emerge faster.

When shortening is blended with honey and bitter almonds, it will clear the chest and the lungs and will dissipate various ailments. Shortening is harmful for the stomach, especially if the person has a mucus condition.

When the shortening made of cow and goat milk is mixed with honey, it helps against toxic materials and snake and scorpion stings. Ibn As-Sunni mentioned that 'Ali عَنهُ اللهُ رَضِيَ said that the people never use a better remedy than shortening.

5. Samak (Fish)

Imam Ahmad and Ibn Mājah narrated that 'Abdullāh Ibn 'Umar اللهُ رَضِيَ عَنهُ said that the Prophet ﷺ said:

« أُحِلَّتْ لَنا مَيتَتَان وَدَمَان : السَّمَكُ والجَراد، والكَبِد والطِّحال »

"We were allowed two dead animals and two bloods: fish and locust, and liver and spleen."

There are many kinds of fish, the best of which is the most delicious, the best scented, moderate in size, which has fine scales, the softest meat, which live in fresh water that flows on pebbles and which eat plants and not organic waste. The best areas for the fish to live are those with the freshest water that runs through rocks, then the areas that have sandy ground void of filth or wastes and which are mildly calm and exposed to the sun and wind.

Sea fish are also soft and delicious. The meat of sea fish that has soft skin is cold and wet, difficult to digest and produces excessive amounts of phlegm, but also produce acceptable temperament, increase semen production and fertility and suit hot conditions.

The best kind of salted fish is the most recently salted. Salted fish is hot and dry, and the older they get the hotter and drier they become. Silurid (similar to catfish) is very viscous, and the Jews do not eat this type of fish. Yet, soft silurid meat softens the stomach, and when it is salted, kept and then eaten, it will clear the windpipe and make the voice finer. When it is ground and used as an external ointment, it will extract the wastes that accumulate inside the body, as it has the quality of extracting such substances.

Sitting in the salty water of silurid relives the effects of newly formed ulcers and extracts the harmful substances to the surface. Salty water of silurid also relieves sciatic nerve ailment when one is injected with it.

The best part of fish meat is closer to the tail, and the soft and fatty fish meat produces fatness and flesh.

In the *Sahihain* it is also narrated that Jabir bin 'Abdullāh رَضِيَ الله عَنْهُ said, "The Prophet ﷺ sent us with three hundred riders under the leadership of Abu 'Ubaidah bin Al-Jarrah. We went by the seashore and were soon very hungry until we ate tree leaves. The sea then threw out a whale that is called 'Anbar. We ate from it for a half a month and also used its fat in our food. Abu Ubaidah then took a rib of the fish and asked a man to ride on his camel and then pass under the rib, which he easily did."

6. *Silqh* (Chard)

At-Tirmidhi and Abu Dāwud narrated that Umm Al-Munthir said, "The Messenger of Allāh ﷺ came by along with 'Ali رَضِيَ الله عَنْهُ, when he was still recovering from an illness. Then, we had some hanging clusters of dates. The Messenger of Allāh ﷺ started eating from it, and he (Ali) joined him. The Messenger of Allāh ﷺ then said to him:

« مَهْ يا عليُّ ! فإِنك ناقِهٌ » . . . . « يا عليُّ، فأَصِبْ من هَذا : فإِنه أَوفَقُ لك »

"You are still recuperating, until 'Ali stopped eating.' I then made some barley with chard and brought it to them. The Prophet ﷺ said, to 'Ali رَضِيَ الله عَنْهُ 'Eat from this; this more beneficial for you.'"

Silqh is hot and dry in the first degree and has a soothing coolness in it. Chard also decomposes and opens the clogs. The black chard constipates and helps against alopecia (A skin disease characterized by loss of hair, partial or total), spots, dandruff and warts if its water is used as ointment. It also kills lice and is used as ointment when blended with honey to cure herpes. Silqh also opens the clogs in the liver and spleen.

The black chard constipates as we have stated, especially when taken with lentils, both of which are not suitable for the stomach. However, white chard with lentils softens the stomach and is used as a laxative and is used to treat hemiplegia (Paralysis affecting only one side of the body), when blended with food aliments and condiments. Yet, it is not nutritious, produces harmful mixtures and burns the blood. Eating it with vinegar and mustard helps neutralize these side effects. Finally, eating it excessively causes constipation and flatulence.

The Letter *Shin*

1. *Shuneiz* (The Black Seed)

We talked about the Black Seed before under the letter *'Haa*.

2. *Shubrum* (Euphorb)

At-Tirmidhi and Ibn Mājah narrated that the Messenger of Allāh ﷺ asked Asmā' bint 'Umais رَضِيَ الله عَنْها

« بِمَاذَا كُنتِ تَسْتَمْشِينَ؟ قَالَت: بِالشُّبْرُوم. قال: حَارٌّ جَا رٌّ»

"How do you treat constipation? She said, 'with Shubrum'. The Prophet ﷺ said, 'Hot and too strong of a laxative."

Shubrum is a small tree that sometimes grows to be as tall as a man. The *Shubrum* has red branches with some whiteness, while the tips of its branches end with a cluster of leaves. *Shubrum* flowers are small and yellowish with some whiteness. When its flowers they fall they are replaced by small stems that have small grains and which look like terebinth. The color of these stems is reddish and has red peels that cover its ribs. The parts of the *Shubrum* that are used are its peels, ribs and stem extract.

Shubrum is hot and dry in the fourth degree and drives away the black bile, yellow water and phlegm. It also causes nausea and distress. Using it in excessive amounts might even case death. When intending to use the *Shubrum*, it should first be soaked in milk for a day and a night, and the milk should be changed twice or thrice during the day. Then, the *Shubrum* should be dried in the shadow and blended with roses, tragacanth (also known as goats' horn) and then consumed with honey water or grape juice.

Two to four small measures of the *Shubrum* constitute one dose. We should state that Hunain said, "As for *Shubrum* milk, I do not see any goodness in it and thus do not recommend it. Common doctors have killed many people with it."

3. Sha'ir (Barley)

Ibn Mājah narrated that 'Āishah رَضِيَ الله عَنْها said: "When a member of the family of the Messenger of Allāh ﷺ would fall sick, he would order that barley soup is made and then the ill person would be commanded to have some of it. He used to say, 'It strengthens the heart of the sad person and relieves the heart of the ill person, just as one of you would wash the dirt off of her face with water.' "

We mentioned that the remedy mentioned in this *Hadith* entails boiled barley water which is more nutritious than its flour. Barley water helps against coughing and throat roughness, relieves the irritant excess excrement, produces more urine, cleanses the stomach, quenches the thirst and extinguishes heat. It also provides comfort and has a decomposing quality.

This remedy entails preparing a portion of a good type of barley and five times as much water, placing them in a clean pot and cooking them under moderate temperature until only two fifths of the mixture remains in the pot. The resulting soup is then purified and used as much as needed.

4. Shawii (Roasted Meat)

Allāh said that when Prophet Ibrahim عليه السلام had the honorable guests:

$$ \text{﴿ فَمَا لَبِثَ أَن جَآءَ بِعِجْلٍ حَنِيذٍ ﴾} $$

"And he hastened to entertain them with a roasted calf." (11:69)

Ibrahim عليه السلام had roasted the calf on heated stones.

At-Tirmidhi narrated that Umm Salamah رَضِيَ الله عَنْهُ said that she once brought the Prophet ﷺ a roasted piece of meat and that he ate from it and then stood up to pray without repeating the ablution. At-Tirmidhi then commented that this *Hadith* is authentic. At-Tirmidhi also narrated that 'Abdullāh bin Al-Harith said, "We ate some roasted meat with the Messenger of Allāh ﷺ inside the mosque." Further, At-Tirmidhi narrated that Al-Mughirah bin Shu'bah رَضِيَ الله عَنْهُ said, "I was a guest of the

Messenger of Allāh ﷺ one night and he ordered that a piece of meat be roasted and then took the blade and started to cut pieces of it for me. Then, Bilal came to make the call to prayer and the Prophet ﷺ dropped the blade and said, 'What is the matter with him?'"

The best type of roast is the meat of a one-year old sheep, then a fat sheep. This type of food is hot and wet, produces black bile, but is one of the most nutritious foods for healthy, ill and recovering persons alike. Cooked meat is better, lighter on the stomach and also has more wetness. Fried meat is less beneficial while meat dried in the sun is the worst kind. Also, roasting meat on burning stones is better than flame broiled meats.

5. *Sha'hm* (Fat or Grease)

In Al-Musnad it is narrated that Anas رَضِيَ اللهُ عَنْهُ said that a Jewish man asked the Prophet ﷺ to be his guest and that he offered him some barley bread and melted grease.

In the *Sahih* it is also narrated that 'Abdullah bin Mughaffal said, "On the Day of Khaibar, a bag full of grease was lowered and I took possession of it and said, 'By Allāh! I will not give anyone any of it!' When I turned around I found that the Messenger of Allāh ﷺ was laughing and did not comment.' "

The best type of grease is that taken from a grown animal. Grease is hot and wet but less wet than clarified butter. This is why when both grease and clarified butter are melted, grease hardens faster.

Grease helps against throat roughness, it represses and causes rotting. To neutralize the harmful effects of grease, one should use lemon, salt and ginger. Also, goat grease constipates more than any other type of grease, while billy goat grease is more decomposing and helps against stomach ulcers. Goat grease helps against stomach ulcers and is used as an injection to relieve excoriation (the rubbing away of skin from injury or disease), and tenesmus (spasms of the bladder or anus).

The Letter *Sad*

I. The *Salat* (The Formal Prayer)

Allāh said:

﴿ وَٱسْتَعِينُوا۟ بِٱلصَّبْرِ وَٱلصَّلَوٰةِ ۚ وَإِنَّهَا لَكَبِيرَةٌ إِلَّا عَلَى ٱلْخَٰشِعِينَ ﴾

*"And seek help in patience and As-Salāt (the prayer) and truly, it
is extremely heavy and hard except for Al-Khāshi'ūn [i.e. the true
believers in Allāh – those who obey Allāh with full submission, fear
much from His punishment, and believe in His Promise (Paradise)
and in His Warnings (Hell)]."* (2:45)

And:

﴿ يَٰٓأَيُّهَا ٱلَّذِينَ ءَامَنُوا۟ ٱسْتَعِينُوا۟ بِٱلصَّبْرِ وَٱلصَّلَوٰةِ ۚ إِنَّ ٱللَّهَ مَعَ ٱلصَّٰبِرِينَ ﴾

*"O you who believe! Seek help in patience and As-Salāt (the
prayer). Truly, Allāh is with As-Sābirūn (the patient)."* (2:153)

Also, Allāh said,

﴿ وَأْمُرْ أَهْلَكَ بِٱلصَّلَوٰةِ وَٱصْطَبِرْ عَلَيْهَا ۖ لَا نَسْـَٔلُكَ رِزْقًا ۖ نَّحْنُ نَرْزُقُكَ ۗ وَٱلْعَٰقِبَةُ لِلتَّقْوَىٰ ﴾

*"And enjoin As-Salāt (the prayer) on your family, and be patient in
offering them [i.e. the Salat (prayers)]. We ask not of you a
provision (i.e. to give Us something: money): We provide for you.
And the good end (i.e. Paradise) is for the Muttaqûn (the pious)."*
(20:132)

Furthermore, in the *Sunan* it is narrated:

« كان رسولُ الله صلى الله عليه وسلم إذا حَزَبه أمرٌ فزع إلى الصَّلاة »

*"Whenever the Messenger of Allāh would be concerned about a
matter, he would turn to prayer."*

We also mentioned using the prayer as a cure for various types of
illnesses before these illnesses progress.

The prayer brings about sustenance, preserves the health, discards
harm, eradicates illness, strengthens the heart, radiates the face with light,
brings joy to the soul and dissipates laziness. Also, the prayer energizes
the limbs, sustains power, opens the chest, nourishes the soul, brings
light to the heart, protects the bounty, shields from the anger (of Allāh),
brings about blessings, takes one away from Satan and draws him closer
to the Most Beneficent.

In general, the prayer has a profound effect in preserving the health of
the body and the heart. The prayer also discards harmful substances. No

two persons would catch a type of disease or suffer an affliction, but whoever prays among them would suffer the minimal effects of the illness or the affliction.

The prayer has a profoundly wonderful effect in repelling the evils of this life, especially when the prayer is given its due right inwardly and outwardly. Certainly, the evils of this life and the Next Life would be most effectively repelled while their good would be most effectively brought forth through prayer. The secret in this is that the prayer is the connection with Allāh. The closer the connection is between the slave and his Lord, the more open the doors of all types of good will be for him, while closing the ways to evil. In this case, the tools of success will descend on the slave from his Lord, along with good health, many bounties and riches, comfort, delight, joy, happiness and the good things of life.

2. *Sabr* (Patience)

Sabr, patience, is one half of Faith, which is half patience and half praise and thankfulness. Some of the *Salaf* said, "Iman has two halves, one half patience and one half praise (and appreciation)." Allāh said:

$$\text{﴾ إِنَّ فِي ذَلِكَ لَآيَٰتٍ لِّكُلِّ صَبَّارٍ شَكُورٍ ﴿}$$

"Verily, in this are indeed signs for every steadfast, grateful (person)." (34:19)

To Faith, *Sabr* is just like the head to the body. There are three types of *Sabr*. First, there is the *Sabr* while performing Allāh's Commands, so that one does not ignore [or get bored with] them. There is a *Sabr* with shunning the prohibitions, so that one does not violate them. There is also a *Sabr* with the appointed destiny and decisions of Allāh, so that one is not enraged because of them. When one acquires all three types of *Sabr*, his *Sabr* will be complete and the delight of this and the Next Life will be whole, along with gaining and winning in both lives. No person shall achieve these great prizes except by passing on the bridge of *Sabr*, just as no person will reach Paradise except by passing over the *Sirat* (the bridge over hell). Umar رَضِيَ اللهُ عَنْهُ said, "We achieve the best living by *Sabr*."

When one thinks about the grades of perfection achieved in this life, he will realize that all of them are connected to *Sabr*. On the other hand, when one thinks about the blame worthy types of failure that one can and should avoid, he will realize that they are all connected to impatience. For instance, courage, honor, generosity and preferring others with good things are patience for a short time only (meaning this life is short).

Much of the illnesses and the sicknesses that attack the body and the heart are a result of impatience. Also, *Sabr* is the best preserver for the health of the heart, the body and the soul, as it is the great distinction and the biggest cure. If *Sabr* only carries the reward of Allāh being with the patient slaves and His love for them, it would be sufficient. Allāh loves *Sabr* and supports its people:

$$\text{« فإن النَّصْرَ مع الصبر »}$$

"Certainly, victory comes with patience"

Also, patience is good for its people.

$$\text{﴿ وَلَئِن صَبَرْتُمْ لَهُوَ خَيْرٌ لِّلصَّـٰبِرِينَ ﴾}$$

"But if you endure patiently, verily, it is better for As-Sābirūn (the patient)." (16:126)

Further, patience is the tool to achieve success.

$$\text{﴿يَـٰٓأَيُّهَا ٱلَّذِينَ ءَامَنُوا۟ ٱصْبِرُوا۟ وَصَابِرُوا۟ وَرَابِطُوا۟ وَٱتَّقُوا۟ ٱللَّهَ لَعَلَّكُمْ تُفْلِحُونَ﴾}$$

"O you who believe! Endure and be more patient (than your enemy), and guard your territory by stationing army units permanently at the places from where the enemy can attack you, and fear Allāh, so that you may be successful." (3:200)

3. Sabir (Aloe)

Sabir has many benefits, especially the Indian *Sabir*, as it rids the body of bilious excrements in the brain and the optic nerves. When the *Sabir* is used as an ointment on the forehead and the cheeks, after blending it with rose oil, it helps relieve headaches. It also helps relieve the sores and cankers that appear in the mouth and nose and helps against black bile and depression.

The Persian *Sabir* sharpens the mind and brings firmness to the heart, and also releases from the body bilious mixtures and the phlegm that accumulates in the stomach, when one takes two spoons of *Sabir* mixed with water.

Caution: drinking *Sabir* in cold weather might cause diarrhea with blood.

4. *Sawm* (Fasting)

Fasting is a shield from many illnesses of the soul, the heart and the body and has tremendous benefits. Fasting also preserves the health and rids the body of harmful substances while preventing it from consuming what might harm it, especially when one fasts in the best times that the religion states or when the body needs it. Fasting relieves the muscles and the rest of the body and ensures regenerating its strength. Fasting also has a characteristic that should make one eagerly prefer it, that is, bringing joy and relief to the heart sooner or later (i.e. on the Last Day). Fasting is the best resort for those suffering from excess bodily moistures and substances and also protects and preserves their health.

Fasting is a type of spiritual and physical remedy. When the fasting person observes various rulings and guidelines regarding the Fast, his heart and body will benefit from the Fast the most. Also, the body will get rid of the harmful foreign substances that his body is susceptible to receive, along with getting rid of the harmful substances that have already penetrated the body. The Fast also helps the fasting person to stay away from what he is supposed to avoid and to implement and seek the goals behind the Fast and what it is supposed to achieve for him. Fasting does not only entail abstaining from food and drink. There is another goal that fasting seeks to achieve which made it an act that Allāh will specify its reward [only on the Day of Judgment]. The Fast is also a shield between the slave and what might harm his body and soul sooner or later, and this is why Allāh said,

﴿ يَـٰٓأَيُّهَا ٱلَّذِينَ ءَامَنُواْ كُتِبَ عَلَيْكُمُ ٱلصِّيَامُ كَمَا كُتِبَ عَلَى ٱلَّذِينَ مِن قَبْلِكُمْ لَعَلَّكُمْ تَتَّقُونَ ﴾

"O you who believe! Observing As-Saum (the fasting) is prescribed for you as it was prescribed for those before you, that you may become Al-Muttaqūn (the pious)." (2:183)

Fasting is a shield and a protection making it a type of tremendously beneficial diet. Another goal that the Fast seeks to achieve is the heart being busy with Allāh, thus enlisting and recruiting the various powers of the body to implement what Allāh loves and the requirements of worshiping Him. We mentioned some of the secrets of the Fast when we mentioned the Prophet's guidance on this subject.

The Letter Dhad

1. Dhabb (Lizards)

In the Sahihain it is narrated that Ibn 'Abbās رَضِيَ الله عَنْهُما said that the Messenger of Allāh ﷺ was asked if eating the Dhabb was disallowed, because he did not eat from it when it was presented to him. The Prophet ﷺ replied:

« لا؛ ولكنْ لم يكن بأرْضِ قَوْمي، فأجِدُني أعافُه »

"No. But this food is not found in my people's land and I do not have the appetite to eat it."

The Dhabb was then eaten in the presence of the Prophet ﷺ. Also, the Sahihain it is narrated that Ibn 'Umar رَضِيَ الله عَنْهُ related from the Prophet ﷺ that he said:

« لا أُحِلُّه، ولا أُحَرِّمُه »

"I neither allow it nor disallow it."

The meat of the Dhabb is hot and dry and strengthens the sexual drive. When it is ground and placed on a thorn that pierced someone's skin, it will extract the thorn.

2. Dhifdi' (Frog)

Imam Ahmad said, "(Killing) frogs is not allowed for medicinal purposes, because the Messenger of Allāh ﷺ has disallowed killing them." Ahmad was referring to the Hadith that he narrated in his Musnad in which Uthman bin Abdur-Rahman said that a doctor mentioned using frogs for medicinal purposes, and the Messenger disallowed killing them.

The author of 'Al-Qanoon said, "Eating the meat or the blood of the frog might cause swellings in the body, pale color and [uncontrollable] ejaculation until death. This is why the doctors hesitate to use it for medicinal purpose because of its harm." There are two types of frogs, land and water frogs. Some of the land frogs are poisonous.

The Letter *Ta'*

I. *Taīb* (Perfume)

The Messenger of Allāh ﷺ said:

«حُبِّبَ إِلَيَّ مِن دُنياكم النساءُ والطِّيبُ؛ وجُعِلَتْ قُرَّةُ عيني في الصَّلاة »

"From your world, women and Taīb (perfume) were made beloved to me and the comfort of my eye is the prayer."

The Messenger of Allāh ﷺ used to frequently use *Taīb* and did not like foul odors.

Taīb (perfume) is the fuel of the soul, which is the engine of the powers of the body. Therefore, various strengths and powers in the body are nurtured in the presence of *Taīb*. Similarly, the powers of the body are nurtured by consuming food and drink, feeling comfort and elation, being close to loved ones, receiving good news and by the absence of hateful, disliked persons whose presence is heavy on the heart. Indeed, associating with disliked persons weakens the strength and causes sadness and depression, just as the effects that fever and foul odor have on the body. This is why the companions of the Messengers were disallowed from acquiring the characteristics that would bother the Prophet and make them detested and disliked by him. Allāh said:

﴿ إِذَا دُعِيتُمْ فَٱدْخُلُوا۟ فَإِذَا طَعِمْتُمْ فَٱنتَشِرُوا۟ وَلَا مُسْتَـٔنِسِينَ لِحَدِيثٍ إِنَّ ذَٰلِكُمْ كَانَ يُؤْذِى ٱلنَّبِىَّ فَيَسْتَحْىِۦ مِنكُمْ وَٱللَّهُ لَا يَسْتَحْىِۦ مِنَ ٱلْحَقِّ ﴾

"But when you are invited, enter, and when you have taken your meal, disperse without sitting for a talk. Verily, such (behaviour) annoys the Prophet, and he is shy of (asking) you (to go); but Allāh is not shy of (telling you) the truth." (33:53)

In short, the *Taīb*, perfume, was one of the dearest objects to the Prophet of Allāh ﷺ. It also has a good effect on preserving good health and removing many ailments because it arouses the power of the body.

2. *Teen* (Clay or Argil)

Several invented *Ahadith* were mentioned regarding the benefits of clay. We should state that every *Hadith* that talks about the benefit of clay is untrue and must not be related from the Messenger of Allāh. Clay is harmful and causes clogs in the veins, and it is cold, dry and a strong drying agent. Also, clay prevents diarrhea and causes hemorrhages and sours in the mouth.

3. *Talh* (Banana or Acacia)

Allāh said:

﴿ وَطَلۡحٖ مَّنضُودٖ﴾

"And among Talh *(banana-trees) with fruits piled one above another."* (56:29)

The majority of the scholars said that *Talh* means bananas, as they grow in piles one over the other just as the comb's teeth. It was said that the *Talh* is the tree that has thorns and which get replaced by fruits, each in the place of a thorn, just like what occurs on banana trees. This is the best opinion about the meaning of *Talh*. Hence, the *Salaf* (righteous predecessors) who said that the *Talh* means banana trees are just using the banana tree as an example to explain the meaning of the word *Talh*, not that it only means banana trees. Allāh has the best knowledge.

Bananas are hot and wet. The best type of bananas are ripe and sweet.

Bananas help against the roughness of the chest and lung, relieve coughing and help against the ulcers of the kidney and prostate. Bananas also produce urine (diuretic), stimulate semen production, soften the stomach and arouse the sexual drive; and they should be eaten before meals. Bananas harm the stomach and aggravate the bile and the phlegm, but eating them with sugar and honey reduces their harmful side effects.

4. *Tal'* (Shoots or Clusters of dates)

Allāh said:

﴾ وَالنَّخْلَ بَاسِقَاتٍ لَّهَا طَلْعٌ نَّضِيدٌ ﴾

"And tall date-palms, with ranged clusters." (50:10)

And He said:

﴾ وَنَخْلٍ طَلْعُهَا هَضِيمٌ ﴾

"And green crops (field) and date-palms with soft spadix."
(26:148)

The *Tal'* of the date trees is the fruit when it is still young.

There are two types of *Tal'* (clusters): male and female. The reproduction process of date trees requires transferring pollen, which resembles the male organ and which looks like a fine powder, and placing it on the female organ. This process is called *Ta'bir*.

Muslim narrated in his *Sahih* that Talhah bin 'Ubaidullah said:

"I and the Messenger of Allāh ﷺ passed by some date trees and found some people doing *Ta'bir*. The Prophet ﷺ asked about what they were doing and they said that they were removing the male sexual organ and placing it in the female sexual organ. The Prophet ﷺ said, 'I do not think that this process will be of much help.' When they heard what the Prophet ﷺ said, they abandoned what they were doing and the trees did not reproduce. The Prophet ﷺ then said, 'It was only a guess on my part. If (the *Ta'bir*) does help, then do it. I am only human just like you and my guess is either correct or incorrect. But, whatever I inform you from Allāh (is true), I will never utter a lie on Allāh."

The *Tal'* stimulates semen production and strengthens the sexual drive. When a woman takes the powder of the *Tal'* before having sex, it will help her get pregnant. The clusters of date trees are cold and dry in the second degree, strengthen the stomach and dry it out, and calm irritated blood, but are hard to digest.

Only those who have hot temperament can tolerate eating the *Tal'*. In addition, those who eat the *Tal'* regularly should also eat hot sweets with it. The *Tal'* constipates and strengthens the intestines, just as the *Jummar*, fresh dates and Busr that we mentioned before. Eating the *Tal'* in excessive amounts harms the stomach and the chest and might cause painful constipation, while taking it with butter and sweets helps reduce these side effects.

The Letter 'Ayn

1. 'Inab (Grapes)

The Messenger of Allāh ﷺ was reported to have liked eating grapes and watermelon. Also, Allāh has mentioned grapes in six instances in the Qur'ān while listing the various bounties that He has bestowed on His slaves in this and the Next Life. Grapes are among the best and most beneficial fruits, and they are eaten fresh, dried, green and ripe. Further, Grapes are a type of fruit and nutritious food, along with their benefits as a remedy and a drink. Wetness and hotness are among the characteristics of grapes just as other grains. The best type of grapes are the big grapes that are full of juice, while white grapes are better than the black grapes when both are equal in sweetness. Also, eating fresh grapes two or three days after harvest is better than eating them immediately otherwise they cause diarrhea and flatulence. The grapes are left on their hanging grapevines until their skin becomes thin. They are a source of good nutrition, just like raisins and figs, and also strengthen the body.

When the seeds of the grapes are removed, the grapes become a more effective laxative. Eating grapes excessively causes headache, unless one also eats sour pomegranate. Grapes in general are a good laxative and provide a good source of nutrition. The best types of fruits are three: grapes, dates and figs.

2. 'Asal (Honey)

We mentioned the benefits of honey before.

Ibn Jurayj said that Az-Zuhri said, "Eat honey because it is good for the memory." The best type of honey is the white, pure, light and sweet honey. Also, the honey that is collected from trees and mountains is better than the honey that is grown in cells. Further, the quality of the honey varies according to the area where the bees collected their food.

3. 'Ajwah (Pressed, Dried Dates)

Sa'd bin Abu Waqqas رَضِيَ اللهُ عَنْهُ narrated that the Prophet ﷺ said:

« مَن تصبَّحَ بسَبْع تَمَراتٍ عجوةٍ، لم يضُرَّه ذلك اليومَ سُمٌّ ولا سِحْرٌ »

"Whoever eats seven dates of 'Ajwah in the morning will not be

harmed by poison or magic the rest of that day."

Also, An-Nasai'ī and Ibn Mājah narrated that the Prophet ﷺ said:

« العَجْوَةُ مِنَ الجنة، وَهِيَ شِفَاءٌ مِنَ السُّمِّ. والكَمْأَةُ مِنَ المَنِّ، وماؤُها شِفَاءٌ للعين »

"The 'Ajwah is from Paradise, and it is an antidote against poison. The Kamah (truffles) is a type of Manna and its water (extract) cures the eye."

There is an opinion that this *Hadith* is talking about the *'Ajwah* of Al-Madinah in particular, which is one the best types of dates in the area of Hijaz. The *'Ajwah*, pressed dried dates, is a good type of dates, has firm skin and is one of the softest and most delicious types of dates.

We mentioned the various benefits of the dates and the *Tamr* when we talked about the letter *Taa*. We also mentioned the benefits of the *'Ajwah* in treating poison and fending off the harm of magic.

4. 'Anbar (Ambergris; Whale)

We mentioned the *Hadith* that is narrated in the Two *Sahihs* about Abu 'Ubaydah and the Muslim army finding a huge fish, or whale, and that they ate from it for a half a month. They also took some of its meat with them to Al-Madinah and gave the Prophet ﷺ some of it. This *Hadith* indicates that it is allowed for Muslims to eat whatever comes from the sea even when it is dead.

Some people who [disagree with what we stated above] said that the whale was thrown on the shore while still alive and that when the water receded it died. So, they say, the whale died because of the lack of water not naturally.

This opinion is incorrect, because the companions found the whale dead at the seashore. They did not see it alive and then the water receded causing its death as claimed. Further, if the whale were still alive, the sea would not have thrown it on the shore, since the sea usually throws dead animals and dead fish on the shore.

Furthermore, even if what they claimed had happened to the whale, it will not affect the ruling of permissibility [to eat dead marine creatures]. The Prophet ﷺ disallowed eating game if one finds it dead in the water because there is a doubt if it had died from drowning and not from his weapon. So, if what the opponents say were true, then the fact that there is a doubt concerning how the whale died would disallow eating it [i.e. if their suggestion that the whale died because of lack of air and that dead marine creatures are disallowed dead were both true].

As for Al-'Anbar, amber, which is a type of *Taīb* (perfume), it is one of the best types of perfume after *Musk*. Some people mistakenly preferred *'Anbar* to *Misk*. However, the Prophet ﷺ described *Musk:*

« هو أطيبُ الطِّيب »

"It is the best Taīb (perfume)."

Soon afterwards, we will mention the benefits and characteristics of Musk, which is the *Taīb* of Paradise. In addition, the seats in Paradise that belong to the truthful believers are made of *Musk* not *'Anbar.*

Those who thought that *'Anbar* is better than *Musk* were deceived by the fact that the *'Anbar* does not spoil, just like gold. This fact alone does not indicate that the *'Anbar* is better than *Musk.*

There are several types of *'Anbar:* white, gray, red, yellow, green, blue, black and multicolored. The best type of the *'Anbar* is gray, then the blue and then the yellow in color, while the black *'Anbar* is the worst type.

People have conflicting opinions regarding the origin of *'Anbar,* where some people said that it is a plant that grows on the seabed and which sea reptiles eat and then discard to later be thrown on the seashore. Some people say that *'Anbar* is the waste of sea creatures that looks like cow manure. Some people even said that it is a type of foam that the sea discards on the shore. The author of the 'Qanoon' discounted the last two opinions but said that the amber might originate from an undersea spring.

'Anbar is hot and dry and strengthens the heart, the mind and the senses. It also strengthens the body and helps relieve facial paralysis, hemiplegia (paralysis), phlegmy ailments, stomach and flatulence. *'Anbar* also helps open various clogs if it is used as an ointment or as a drink. When it is inhaled, *'Anbar* will relieve cold symptoms, headaches and migraines.

5. *'Ud* (Indian Aloe Tree)

The Indian *'Ud* comes in two types. One type is used for medicinal purposes, which is called Al-Kust and some people called it Al-Qust. We will mention this type under the letter *Qaf.* The second type of *'Ud* is called Aluwwah, aloe wood, which is used as perfume.

Imam Muslim narrated in his *Sahih* that Ibn 'Umar رَضِيَ اللهُ عَنْهُ used to burn dry aloe wood along with some *Kafur* (camphor), and states that the Messenger of Allāh used to do the same. Also, the Messenger of Allāh has described the bounties that the people of Paradise will be enjoying, such as having the aloe wood.

The *'Ud* is hot and dry in the third degree, opens the clogs and does away with gas. Also, *'Ud* dries unnecessary moisture while strengthening the intestines and brings relief and comfort to the heart. *'Ud* also helps the mind, sharpens the senses, constipates and helps relieve the enuresis, bed wetting that results from coldness of the prostate.

Ibn Samjun said, "There are several kinds of *'Ud*, and they all carry the general name of Aluwwah. *'Ud* is used in and out of the body and is burned alone or with other substances. There is a medicinal significance when the *'Ud* is mixed with *Kafur* (camphor), as each of them makes the other milder. Also, burning the *'Ud* helps cleanse the air, which is one of the six necessary elements for the body's well-being."

6. *'Adas* (Lentils)

It was reported that the *'Adas* (lentils) was described as the lust of the Jews that they preferred over Manna and quails.

The *'Adas* is the companion of garlic and onions. It is cold and dry and has two opposing effects, one that constipates and one that works as a laxative. The skin of the *'Adas* is hot and dry in the third degree and also works as a laxative. The benefit in the lentils is concentrated in the peelings, and this is why whole lentils are more beneficial than ground lentils, less heavy on the stomach and less harmful.

Lentils cause black bile and harm the melancholy profoundly, along with having a negative effect on the nerves and the eyesight.

'Adas produces thick blood; and those who suffer from black bile should avoid eating it, for when they eat lentils excessively, the lentils will

beget obsession, leprosy, quartran fever (a fever that occurs on every fourth day), and other ailments. However, eating lentils with chard and large amounts of grease will lessen their negative side effects. Also, one should avoid eating lentils with sweets, because lentils could cause clogs in the liver in this case. Further, eating 'Adas on a regular basis causes harm to the eyesight because they are very dry. Lentils also cause urine retention, cold swellings and excessive flatulence. The best type of 'Adas is the fat, white 'Adas that digests faster.

Some ignorant people claimed that Prophet Ibrahim عليه السلام used to cook lentils for his guests. However, the Qur'ān mentioned that he hosted his guests with a fat roasted calf.

The Letter Ghayn

1. Ghayth (Rain)

The Ghaith is mentioned in the Qur'ān in many instances. The word Ghaith is soft on the ear and delightful for the body and the soul. The ears like to hear the word Ghaith, while the hearts enjoy its falling.

Rainwater is the best type of water there is and the softest, most beneficial and most blessed. This is especially the case when the rainfall is accompanied by lightning and thunder and is then collected in mountainous areas.

Rainwater is lighter than the other types of water because it is fresh and did not remain on the ground for a long time, in which case it would acquire some of the earth's dryness and hard substances. This is why rainwater gets spoiled quickly because it is pure and light.

There are two opinions regarding which is softer and lighter: rainwater that falls in the spring or winter.

Those who prefer winter rainwater say that in winter, the sun's heat is less and it thus evaporates the softest parts of the seawater. Also, the air then would be clean and void of dust, and consequently, would not be polluted. Hence, rainwater will not dissolve any pollutants while falling, and this is why rainwater is the softest and the lightest.

Those who prefer spring rainwater say that the hot sun then evaporates heavy substances in the air and makes the air itself lighter and cleaner. In this case, rainwater will be the lightest and the softest, at a time when the plants, the trees and the air become ready to receive rainfall.

Ash-Shafi'ī narrated that Anas bin Malik رَضِيَ اللهُ عَنْهُ said, "Once, we were with the Prophet ﷺ when the rain fell. The Prophet ﷺ removed his outer garment (until the rain fell on him) saying:

« إِنَّه حَدِيثُ عَهْدٍ بَرَبِّه »

"It has just come from its Lord."

We mentioned the Prophet's guidance in invoking Allāh for rain and stated that he used to seek the blessings [that Allāh endows] in the rain when it falls.

The Letter *Faa*

1. *Fātihah Al-Kitab* (the First Chapter in the Qur'ān)

Fātihah is the mother of the Qur'ān, the seven frequently recited Versus that the Prophet ﷺ was given and the ultimate cure and beneficial remedy that contains the prefect *Ruqiah*, Islamic prayer formula. The *Fatihah* is the key to acquiring the richness, success and strength. The *Fatihah* also removes sadness, depression, anguish and fear. Only those who appreciate the value of the *Fatihah* and give it its due consideration, reciting it as it should be recited and knowing the secret of its value as a medicine and as a cure, will acquire such bounties.

One of the Companions unveiled a few of the secrets of the *Fatihah* when he used it as a *Ruqyah* for scorpion stings. The affected person was instantly cured and the Prophet ﷺ asked the Companion:

« مَا أَدْرَاكَ أَنَّهَا رُقْيَةٌ »

"How did you know it is a cure?"

They are successful ones who uncover some of the secrets of the *Fatihah* and what it contains of *Tawhid*, knowing Allāh and His Names, Attributes, Actions and Decisions. Those who acquire knowledge of what the *Fatihah* contains of affirming the religion, Predestination, Resurrection, Allāh's Oneness in worship and in Lordship and trusting and depending on He Who owns all affairs, the praise and all pure things and to Whom everything must return. Those who acquire the habit of showing meekness to Allāh seeking correct guidance which is the basis of the ultimate happiness in this and the Next Life. Those who acquire knowledge in the connection between the meanings contained in the *Fatihah* and acquiring the good and fending off the harm of both lives. Those who understand that their ultimate well-being and receiving the perfect Favor of Allah are all linked to implementing these meanings. It is they who will be able to substitute the *Fatihah* in place of many medicines and use it as an Islamic prayer formula (*Ruqiah*), and will use it to open the doors of goodness and drive away the elements of evil.

Understanding this subject requires a new nature, a new heart and a new type of Faith. By Allāh! You will not find any evil statement, nor misguiding innovation, but the *Fatihah* will contain what nullifies and refutes it with the best, most correct and most direct manner. Also, you will not find a door that leads to acquiring divine knowledge, correct guidance of the heart and the remedy of the soul against its ills, but that the *Fatihah* will possess its key and the method to best use it. Finally, you will not find a path on which those who seek the Lord of the Worlds are passing, but you will find the *Fatihah* in its beginning and end.

By Allāh! The *Fatihah* is much more important than what we have emphasized. The slave who holds fast to the *Fatihah,* comprehends it in the proper manner, relies on it as a perfect remedy, a shield, an immunity, and as a light of guidance. He understands its implications as they should be understood. It is he who will not fall into an innovation, or Shirk, or catch an ailment in the heart except briefly!

The *Fatihah* is the ultimate key for the treasures of the earth and Paradise, as well. But not every person knows how to use this key so as to have access to these treasures. If those who seek these treasures were able to uncover the secrets of this chapter [in the Qur'ān] and acquire knowledge of its implications, they would add teeth to the key and would have easy access to these treasures.

We are certain of the statements that we have asserted herein because they are true. Allāh has Perfect Wisdom in hiding the secrets [of Al-Fatihah] from the hearts of the majority of mankind, just as He has a perfect Wisdom in hiding the treasures of the earth from them.

The hidden treasures of the earth are surrounded by the devils that stand between mankind and these treasures. Only the good souls will be able to defeat these devils with True Faith, which is the weapon that the devils cannot withstand. However, the majority of the souls of mankind are not of this type (are not truly faithful). Therefore, they cannot resist the evil or defeat them to acquire their possessions for, "Whoever kills a combatant will have his possessions."

2. *Faghiyah* (Henna Blossom)

Faghiyah, henna blossom, is one of the best kinds of perfumes. *Faghiyah* is mild in its hotness and dryness and constipates mildly. When Faghiyah is placed between folded wool clothes it protects them from mold and mites. Also, *Faghiyah* is used in ointments against facial paralysis and aneurysm (dilatation of a portion of the wall of an artery), while its oil helps the organs and relaxes the nerves.

3. *Fiddah* (Silver)

There is an authentic narration that states:

« أن رسولَ الله صلى الله عليه وسلم كان خاتَمُه من فضة، وفضُّه منه . وكانت
قَبيعةُ سيفه فضةً »

"The Messenger of Allāh had a silver ring with a silver face. Also, the grip of his sword was made from silver."

Unlike disallowing drinking in silver containers, there are no authentic narrations that disallow wearing silver. The category of containers for food and drink is more specific than the category of clothes and adornments. For instance, women are allowed to wear all types of clothes and adornments, while there are specific containers for food and drink that are not allowed to be used (i.e., gold and silver containers). Therefore, the fact that Muslims are not allowed to use some types of containers does not necessarily apply to clothes and adornments [which are a wider category as we have stated]. In the Sunan it is narrated that the Prophet ﷺ said:

« وأما الفضة فالعَبُوا بها لَعْبًا »

"As for silver, play with it as you like."

Furthermore, disallowing wearing silver adornments needs a specific Text (Qur'ān or *Sunnah*) or a consensus (of the scholars) for the heart to accept it with certainty. Once, the Prophet ﷺ held some gold in one hand and some silk in the other hand and said:

« هذان حرامٌ على ذُكور أمتي، وحِلٌّ لإناثهم »

"These two are not allowed for the males of my nation and allowed for the females among them."

Silver is one of the wonders that Allāh has created on the earth. It is the key to acquiring ones needs and high positions among the people of the earth. Those who have silver are honorable in the eyes of the people and respected in their hearts, allowing them to sit at the head of various meetings and opening all doors in front of them. Also, the people do not feel bored by sitting next to owners of silver, nor will their presence be heavy. Fingers point at them, while eyes look at them [in admiration]. If they speak, people listen and if they intervene, their mediation will be accepted. If they present their witness, their testimony will be accepted and if they give a speech, they will not be blamed for being incompetent; and even the white hair that they have will be considered more youthful than youth itself!

Silver is one of the remedies that bring joy to the hearts and drive away sadness, depression, and weakness in the heart and its heartbeat. Also, silver is used in some of the best kinds of ointments and helps extract the harmful substances or conditions of the heart, especially when blended with pure honey and saffron.

Silver is originally cold and dry but also produces hotness and wetness.

There are four types of gardens that Allāh has prepared for His loyal slaves when they meet Him: two made of gold and two made of silver, including all their containers, adornments and whatever is in them.

In the *Sahih* it is narrated that the Prophet ﷺ said:

« الذي يشرَب في آنية الذَّهَب والفضة، إنما يُجَرْ جرُ في بطْنه نارَ جهنم »

"Those who drink from golden or silver bowls are only pushing the Fire of Jahannam down into their stomachs."

He also said, as narrated in the *Sahih*:

لا تشرَبُوا في آنية الذَّهَب والفضة، ولا تأكلوا في صِحَافِهما . فإنها لهم في الدنيا، ولكم في الآخرة »

"Neither drink from golden or silver bowls nor eat on golden on silver plates. It is for them (the disbelievers) in the life of this world and for you in the Next Life."

Some people said that the wisdom behind disallowing using golden and silver containers is to tighten the money supply. They say that if people use silver and gold as containers, then the interests of mankind will not be served well. In addition, some people said that they are disallowed so that whoever uses them does not become arrogant and proud, or so that the poor persons do not become humbled when they see such items, and so forth. These opinions are not sound.

For instance, tightening the money supply should also include disallowing wearing golden and silver adornments and canes [not only golden and silver containers]. Further, pride and arrogance are not allowed regarding anything. In addition, making the poor feel humbled is not a precise subject that we can define, for they could also feel humbled when they see luxurious homes, spacious gardens and lavish means of transportation, clothes and delicious foods. All these items are allowed for people.

What we think is the valid reason for this prohibition, and Allāh has the best knowledge, is that using gold and silver in this manner affects the heart in such a way that contradicts true slavery to Allāh. This is why the Prophet ﷺ said that it is for the disbelievers in this life, because the disbelievers do not have a share in the true slavery [to Allāh] that will give them the rewards of the Next Life. The slaves of Allāh should not use these items in this manner, because only those who do not implement the requirements of their slavery (to Allāh) use them in this life, as they prefer the life of this world to the Next Life. Allāh has the best knowledge.

The Letter *Qaf*

I. *Qur'ān*

Allāh said:

$$ ﴿ وَنُنَزِّلُ مِنَ ٱلْقُرْءَانِ مَا هُوَ شِفَاءٌ وَرَحْمَةٌ لِّلْمُؤْمِنِينَ ﴾ $$

"And We send down of the Qur'ān that which is a healing and a

mercy to those who believe (in Islāmic Monotheism and act on it)." (17:82)

And He also said:

﴿ يَٰٓأَيُّهَا ٱلنَّاسُ قَدْ جَآءَتْكُم مَّوْعِظَةٌ مِّن رَّبِّكُمْ وَشِفَآءٌ لِّمَا فِى ٱلصُّدُورِ ﴾

"O mankind! There has come to you a good advice from your Lord (i.e. the Qur'ān, enjoining all that is good and forbidding all that is evil), and a healing for that which is in your breasts..." (10:57)

The Qur'ān is the ultimate cure from all types of illnesses and sicknesses that attack the body and the heart and from all the calamities of life and death. Yet, not everyone is suitable or guided to successfully seek the Qur'ān as a cure.

When the ill person successfully uses the cure contained in the Qur'ān and applies it on his ailment with faith, sincerity, complete acceptance and trust, all the while observing the necessary guidelines in this regard, no illness can resist the cure.

How can any ailment resist [the Book that contains] the Words of the Lord of the earth and heaven, which if it were revealed to a mountain, it would cause it to humble itself and render it asunder. Further, if the Qur'ān were revealed to the earth, it would tear it apart. No ailment that attacks the body or the heart, but the Qur'ān contains its remedy and cure and would provide immunity against it, that is, for whomever Allāh has endowed with the bounty of comprehending His Book.

We stated before that the Qur'ān contains the major aspects and basis of the knowledge of medicine: preserving health, diet and extracting of harmful substances. As for the ills that attack the heart, the Qur'ān mentions them in detail and directs the people to the cures and remedies to treat them. Allāh said:

﴿ أَوَلَمْ يَكْفِهِمْ أَنَّا أَنزَلْنَا عَلَيْكَ ٱلْكِتَٰبَ يُتْلَىٰ عَلَيْهِمْ ﴾

"Is it not sufficient for them that We have sent down to you the Book (the Qur'ān) which is recited to them?" (29:51)

May Allāh never cure those whom the Qur'ān does not cure, nor suffice for those for whom Allāh is not Sufficient as a Helper.

2. Qith-tha' (Wild Cucumber)

In the *Sunan* it is narrated that Abdullah bin Ja'far said:

« أن رسول الله صلى الله عليه وسلم كان يأكل القِثَّاءَ بالرُّطَب »

"The Prophet ﷺ used to eat Qith-tha' with ripe dates." [At-Tirmidhi].

Qith-tha' is cool and wet in the second degree and it cools the hotness in the stomach. it does not spoil quickly and helps relieve prostate pain. Also, *Qith-tha'* helps relieve nausea while its seeds are a diuretic. When *Qith-tha'* leaves are used as a bandage, they help against dog bites.

Qith-tha' does not digest easily and its coolness sometimes hurts some parts of the stomach. Hence, one should eat *Qith-tha'* with what would make its coolness and wetness milder, just as the Prophet did by eating ripe dates with it. Also, eating it with raisins or honey makes it milder on the stomach.

3. Qust, or Kust (Costus)

In the *Sahihain* it is narrated that Anas رَضِيَ الله عَنْهُ related from the Prophet ﷺ that he said:

« خيرُ ما تداوَيْتُم به : الحِجامةُ، والقُسْطُ البَحريُّ »

"Cupping and marine costus are the best of your remedies."

Also, Imam Ahmad narrated that the Prophet ﷺ said:

« عَلَيكم بهذا العُودِ الهنديِّ؛ فإن فيه سبعةَ أشفِيةٍ، منها : ذاتُ الجَنْب »

"Use this Indian wood, because it contains seven types of cures, among them a cure for pleurisy."

There are two kinds of *Qust*, the white kind that is called *sea-Qust* and the *Indian Qust*, which is the hottest among them while the white type is the mildest. Both kinds have many benefits.

Both kinds of *Qust* are hot and dry in the third degree, and they dry out the phlegm and colds. When they are taken as a drink, they help weak liver and stomach and the colds associated with such cases. Costus also helps against victular and quartan fever (fever that comes on every fourth day), the pain on the side of the body and poisons. When the face is anointed with *Qust* that is kneaded with water and honey, they heal the spots that appear on the face. Galinus said that the costus, "Heals tetanus, the pain in the sides and kills spots (which he called the seeds of the pumpkin)."

Some ignorant doctors are unaware of and deny the *Qust* as an effective remedy against the pain in the sides of the body. If these ignorant doctors become aware of what Galinus has stated about the *Qust*, they will quickly embrace it as if it was a divine text. Moreover, many doctors have also stated that *Qust* helps against the pain in the flank that is accompanied by phlegm, as Al-Khattabi related from Muhammad bin Al-Jahm.

We stated before that the difference between the remedies contained in the Prophetic medicine and the remedies of regular doctors, is much larger than the difference between folk medicine as compared to regular medicine. We also stated that what is sent down of the divine revelation, as compared to what is proven by experimentation, compares to the difference between the noble master and the commoner.

In addition, if any of the ignorant doctors [who ignore the Prophetic medicine] were able to discover a remedy that the Jews, the Christians and the polytheist doctors have prescribed, they would embrace it and would certainly prescribe it.

We do not deny that habits have a role in making the cure work or fail. Those who are used to certain foods and medicines would benefit from such items more than those who are not used to them and who sometimes would not benefit at all from them.

The statements of the best doctors do not apply in all cases and places. Taking the statements of these doctors as being specific and not general does not lessen the degree of their knowledge. The same ruling applies even more to the statements of the Prophets. Yet, the hearts of mankind have a built-in degree of ignorance and injustice, except for those whom Allāh has endowed with the light of correct Faith and enlightened their hearts with true guidance.

4. *Qasab As-Sukkar* (Sugarcane)

Sugar is a relatively new substance that the people of old did not mention or even have knowledge that it existed. This is why they did not describe its role in various types of drinks or cures. Honey, on the other hand, was extensively used as a drink and as a medicine.

Sugarcane is hot and wet, helps relieve coughing and dissipates the excess moistures in the body, prostate and chest. It is more effective as a laxative than sugar itself. Also, sugarcane induces vomit, is diuretic and stimulates semen production.

'Affan bin Muslim As-Saggar said, "Those who suck on sugarcane after eating their meal, will find comfort for the rest of his day." When sugarcane is broiled, it relieves the roughness in the throat and chest. Yet, it causes the accumulation of gasses that would be pacified when sugarcane is peeled and washed in hot water.

Sugar is hot and wet. The best type of sugar is white crystalline, especially when it is old. When sugar is boiled and skimmed, it quenches the thirst and relieves coughing. Sugarcane is not good for the stomach that suffers from bile. The side effects of sugarcane could be pacified by mixing it with lemon water (juice), Naranj (bitter orange) and peeled pomegranate.

Some people prefer sugarcane to honey because it is not as hot as honey and because it is milder on the stomach. This is not fair for honey, which is much more profitable than sugarcane. Also, Allāh has made honey both a cure and a type of sweet. So how can anyone compare the benefits of honey and the benefits of sugarcane? Honey strengthens the stomach, soothes the natural process, strengthens the eyesight and heals diphtheria when gargled, facial paralysis and hemiplegia (paralysis affecting only one side of the body). It also helps against all types of cold illnesses that occur in the body because of excess moistures. Honey extracts and pulls excess moistures from the body, preserves the health, increases semen production, cleanses and decomposes the contents of the stomach. Also, honey cleanses the intestines, fights worms and prevents septic repletion (over eating). Further, honey is a good type of food and favorable for those who suffer from phlegm and for old people. In short, no substance is more beneficial for the body as a food, as a remedy and as an ingredient and a preserver of medications, which also strengthens the stomach, than honey. There are many more benefits for honey. So how can anyone compare it to sugarcane, which does not have even a fraction of the benefits contained in honey?

The Letter *Kaf*

Kitab (Books or Writings)

This chapter contains books or writings of divine remedies, Islamic prayer formulas, as Islamic amulets (prayer formulas written down and worn for a specific purpose).*

I. An Amulet for Fever

Al-Mirwazi said, "Abu 'Abdullāh (Imam Ahmad) was informed that I was suffering from fever and he wrote to me a supplication for fever that reads like this, 'In the Name of Allāh, the Most Gracious, the Most Beneficent. In the Name of Allāh, and depending on Allāh.

﴿ قُلْنَا يَنَارُ كُونِي بَرْدًا وَسَلَـٰمًا عَلَىٰٓ إِبْرَٰهِيمَ ﴿٦٩﴾ وَأَرَادُوا بِهِۦ كَيْدًا فَجَعَلْنَـٰهُمُ الْأَخْسَرِينَ ﴾

"We (Allāh) said: 'O fire! Be you coolness and safety for Ibrāhīm (Abraham)! And they wanted to harm him, but We made them the worst losers. (21:69,70)

O Allāh, the Lord of (angels) Gabriel, Michael and Israfil: cure this person with this supplication by Your Power, Strength and Might, O Lord of the creation. *Āmeen.'"*

Also, Al-Mirwazi said that Abu Ja'far, Muhammad bin 'Ali was asked about wearing [a written] *Ruqyah* (divine remedy, Islamic prayer formula or amulet). He said, "If it was from the Book of Allāh or a *Hadith* [correctly] related from the Prophet, then wear it and use it as a remedy as much as possible." Abu 'Abdullāh was listening to this narration and

---

* **Editor's Note**: The issue of the permissability of writing *Tamā'im* (prayer Formulas to be worn or hung) and *Ta'weedh* (amulets of protection) from Qur'anic verses and supplications is one of difference amongst the Muslim Scholars. Even the Companions of the Prophet are reported to have differed concerning its legality. The author was clearly of the view that such writings were permissable. Other scholars of the early predecessors (including Ibn Mas'ood, and Ibn 'Abbās) held such amulets to be prohibited due to their understanding of various statements of the Prophet. Shaikh Muhammad bin Sālih Al-Uthaymeen concludes in his book Al-Majmoo' Ath-Thameen that the correct view is that such Qur'anic amulets are not permissable to use. Allāh knows best AW.

Al-Mirwazi commented, "Should I write this *Ruqyah* for quartan fever, 'In the Name of Allāh...?' " Imam Ahmad said, "Yes."

Imam Ahmad said that 'Aishah رَضِيَ اللهُ عَنْهَا and other Companions have agreed to this practice. 'Harb added that Imam Ahmad also agreed to this practice, although he narrated that Ibn Mas'ud used to strongly dislike it.

Also, Imam Ahmad did not object when he was asked about wearing a *Ruqyah* amulet after an illness or a calamity strikes. Al-Khallal also narrated that 'Abdullāh bin Ahmad told him that his father used to write some supplication in a *Ruqyah* amulet for those who have a certain fear and for fever after it strikes.

An Amulet for Difficult Pregnancies

Also, Al-Khallal narrated that Abdullah bin Ahmad said that his father wrote a *Ruqyah*, Islamic prayer formula, as an Islamic amulet, on a pure object for women who suffered from difficult pregnancies. In the, amulet, Ahmad wrote the *Hadith* narrated by Ibn Abbas, "There is no deity worthy of worship except Allāh, the Most Forbearing, the Most Generous. All praise is due to Allāh, the Lord of the Mighty Throne.

$$ ﴿ اَلْحَمْدُ لِلَّهِ رَبِّ ٱلْعَٰلَمِينَ ﴾ $$

"All the praises and thanks are to Allāh the Lord of the 'Alamīn (mankind, jinn and all that exists)"

$$ ﴿ كَأَنَّهُمْ يَوْمَ يَرَوْنَهَا لَمْ يَلْبَثُوٓا۟ إِلَّا عَشِيَّةً أَوْ ضُحَىٰهَا ﴾ $$

"The Day they see it, (it will be) as if they had not tarried (in this world) except an afternoon or a morning." (79:46)

$$ ﴿ كَأَنَّهُمْ يَوْمَ يَرَوْنَ مَا يُوعَدُونَ لَمْ يَلْبَثُوٓا۟ إِلَّا سَاعَةً مِّن نَّهَارٍ بَلَٰغٌ فَهَلْ يُهْلَكُ إِلَّا ٱلْقَوْمُ ٱلْفَٰسِقُونَ ﴾ $$

"On the Day when they will see that (torment) with which they are promised (i.e. threatened, it will be) as if they had not stayed more than an hour in a single day. (O mankind! this Qur'ān is sufficient as) a clear Message (or proclamation to save yourself from destruction). But shall any be destroyed except the people who are Al-Fāsiqūn (rebellious against Allāh's Command, disobedient to Allāh)?" (46:35)

Al-Khallal said that a man came to Abu Abdullah and asked him to write a Islamic prayer formula as an Islamic amulet for a woman who had gone into labor for two days. Imam Ahmad asked the man to bring a wide cup with some Saffron [and wrote the amulet for the man's wife]. He also narrated that Imam Ahmad wrote the same amulet for several other people.

It was reported that 'Ikrimah narrated that Ibn 'Abbās رَضِيَ الله عَنْهما said, "Jesus, the Messenger of Allāh ﷺ, once passed by a cow that was suffering from hard labor. The cow said [to Jesus], 'O, Word of Allāh (be and he was)! Ask Allāh to relieve me from what I am suffering from.' He said, 'O Creator of the soul from another soul, Who brings to life a soul from within another soul, relieve her.' The cow then gave birth and soon started to smell her newly born." Ibn 'Abbās رَضِيَ الله عَنْهما then said, "Therefore, when the woman is suffering from hard labor, write [and recite] this supplication for her."

The types of Islamic prayer formulas as Islamic amulets that we mentioned are beneficial, Allāh willing. Further, several scholars among the Salaf have allowed writing the Qur'ān and drinking its water as a cure.

Another Amulet for Pregnant Women

One should write the following Āyah in a pure pot:

﴿ إِذَا ٱلسَّمَآءُ ٱنشَقَّتۡ ۝ وَأَذِنَتۡ لِرَبِّهَا وَحُقَّتۡ ۝ وَإِذَا ٱلۡأَرۡضُ مُدَّتۡ ۝ وَأَلۡقَتۡ مَا فِيهَا وَتَخَلَّتۡ ﴾

"When the heaven is split asunder, And listens to and obeys its Lord and it must do so. And when the earth is stretched forth, And has cast out all that was in it and became empty." (84:1-4)

Then the pregnant woman should drink from this pot and pour some of it on her stomach.

An Amulet for Nosebleeds

Ibn Taymiyyah used to write the following Āyah on his forehead:

﴿ وَقِيلَ يَٰٓأَرۡضُ ٱبۡلَعِى مَآءَكِ وَيَٰسَمَآءُ أَقۡلِعِى وَغِيضَ ٱلۡمَآءُ وَقُضِىَ ٱلۡأَمۡرُ ﴾

"And it was said: 'O earth! Swallow up your water, and O sky! Withhold (your rain). And the water was made to subside and the Decree (of Allāh) was fulfilled (i.e. the destruction of the people *of Nuh (Noah)."* (11:44)

I also heard him say, "I wrote [this *Āyah*] for several people and they were cured." He also said [about the *Āyah*], "It is not allowed to write it with the blood of the nosebleed as some ignorant people do, because blood is impure and one is not allowed to use it to write Allāh's Speech."

Another Amulet for nose bleeds

It was reported that Prophet Musa عليه السلام once went out wearing an outer garment and then suffered from nosebleed and covered [his nose] with his garment while reciting:

﴿ يَمْحُوا۟ ٱللَّهُ مَا يَشَآءُ وَيُثْبِتُ وَعِندَهُۥٓ أُمُّ ٱلْكِتَٰبِ ﴾

"Allāh blots out what He wills and confirms (what He wills). And with Him is the Mother of the Book (Al-Lauh Al-Mahfūz)" (13:39)

An Amulet for fungus

One should write [the following *Āyah*] for it:

﴿ فَأَصَابَهَآ إِعْصَارٌ فِيهِ نَارٌ فَٱحْتَرَقَتْ ﴾

"...then it is struck with a fiery whirlwind, so that it is burnt...?" (2:266)

By Allāh's Will and Power.

Another Amulet for fungus

When the sun becomes yellow, one should write [the *Āyah*],

﴿ يَٰٓأَيُّهَا ٱلَّذِينَ ءَامَنُوا۟ ٱتَّقُوا۟ ٱللَّهَ وَءَامِنُوا۟ بِرَسُولِهِۦ يُؤْتِكُمْ كِفْلَيْنِ مِن رَّحْمَتِهِۦ وَيَجْعَل لَّكُمْ نُورًا تَمْشُونَ بِهِۦ وَيَغْفِرْ لَكُمْ وَٱللَّهُ غَفُورٌ رَّحِيمٌ ﴾

"O you who believe [in Mūsā (Moses) (i.e. Jews) and Mūsā (Jesus) (i.e., Christians)]! Fear Allāh, and believe in His Messenger (Muhammad ﷺ) He will give you a double portion of His Mercy, and He will give you a light by which you shall walk (straight). And He will forgive you. And Allāh is Oft-Forgiving, Most Merciful." (57:28)

An Amulet for three-day Fever

One should write on three separate papers, "In the Name of Allāh it is running away. In the Name of Allāh it has subsided. In the Name of Allāh it has decreased."

Every day [that the fever lasts], one should swallow the paper with some water.

An Amulet for sciatica

One should write, "In the Name of Allāh. O Allāh, Lord of everything, Owner of everything and Creator of everything! You have created me and the sciatic nerve. Do not give it power over me, nor allow me to cut it. Heal me completely and eradicate the illness. There is none who can heal except You."

An Amulet for bleeding veins

At-Tirmidhi narrated that Ibn 'Abbās رَضِيَ الله عَنْهُما said that the Messenger of Allāh ﷺ used to teach them to recite [the following *Ruqyah*], against fever and various pains, 'In the Name of Allāh, the Most Great. I seek refuge with Allāh, the All-Mighty, from the evil of bleeding veins and from the evil of the fire's heat."

An Amulet for Toothache

One should write on the cheek that is closer to the pain, "In the Name of Allāh, Most Gracious, Most Merciful.

﴿ وَهُوَ ٱلَّذِىٓ أَنشَأَ لَكُمُ ٱلسَّمْعَ وَٱلْأَبْصَٰرَ وَٱلْأَفْـِٔدَةَۚ قَلِيلًا مَّا تَشْكُرُونَ ﴾

"It is He Who has created for you (the sense of) hearing (ears), eyes (sight), and hearts (understanding). Little thanks you give."
(23:78)

Or,

﴿ وَلَهُۥ مَا سَكَنَ فِى ٱلَّيْلِ وَٱلنَّهَارِۚ وَهُوَ ٱلسَّمِيعُ ٱلْعَلِيمُ ﴾

"And to Him belongs whatsoever exists in the night and the day, and He is the All-Hearing, the All-Knowing." (6:13)

An Amulet for abscess

One should write [this amulet and place it] on the abscess,

﴿ وَيَسْـَٔلُونَكَ عَنِ ٱلْجِبَالِ فَقُلْ يَنسِفُهَا رَبِّى نَسْفًا ۝ فَيَذَرُهَا قَاعًا صَفْصَفًا ۝
لَّا تَرَىٰ فِيهَا عِوَجًا وَلَآ أَمْتًا ﴾

"And they ask you concerning the mountains: say, "My Lord will blast them and scatter them as particles of dust. Then He shall leave them as a level smooth plain." (20:105,106)

2. *Kamah* (Truffles)

In the *Sahihain* it is narrated that the Prophet said:

« الكَمْأَة من المَنِّ، وماؤُها شفاءٌ للعين »

"The Kamah is among the Manna and its water (extract or juice) cures the eye."

The *Kamah* grows wild underground, and it is called *Kamah* because it grows hidden beneath the earth. The *Kamah* does not have leaves or stems.

The essence of the *Kamah* is partly earthly and partly steamy and remains concealed underground during winter and then starts to grow above the ground with spring rainfall. This is why it is called the smallpox of the land, for it is similar to smallpox, which is caused by moistures clogged with blood that get aggravated during the early childhood years when the body starts to gain strength.

Kamah (*truffles*) grow in the spring and are eaten raw or cooked. The Arabs used to call *truffles* 'the plant of the thunder', because they grow in the aftermath of thunderstorms. The nomads in the desert use mushrooms in their regular diet. Further, the best type of *truffles* grow on sandy dry land. There are several types of *Kamah,* among which is a poisonous plant which is reddish in color and which causes asphyxiation.

The *Kamah* is cold and wet in the third degree, and it is not favorable for the stomach and not easily digested. Eating *Kamah* on a regular basis causes constipation, gastric pain, facial paralysis, stomachache and dysuria (painful urination). Humid kinds of mushrooms are less harmful than dry ones. Therefore, those who wish to eat *Kamah* should bury them in a muddy area and then boil them in water, add salt and mint, and then eat them with oil and spices. This is because the *Kamah* has a heavy earthly essence, although it contains a fair amount of water in its essence that makes it a little light. Also, using the *Kamah* as kohl helps in cases of bad eyesight and ophthalmia (conjunctivitis).

Some of the best doctors have agreed that truffle water or juice helps strengthen the eyesight.

There are two opinions regarding the meaning of what the Prophet ﷺ said:

« الكَمْأة من المَنِّ »

"The Kamah is among the Manna."

Some people said, 'the *Manna* that Allāh has sent down to the Children of Israel was not only the sweetmeat that we know, but also several other plants that grow in the wild without effort or planting on the people's part to grow. The *Manna*, in their opinion, means the Favor, and thus, every type of plant or bounty that Allāh grants to mankind without effort on their part is called *Manna*. All of Allāh's bounties that He grants to mankind are a Favor from Him. Yet, Allāh specifically mentioned the types of His Favors concerning which the slave does not make any effort, whether in growing or producing them, and called these Favors, *Manna*.

During the years of wandering in the earth with which Allāh tested the Children of Israel, they used to sustain themselves on truffles that sufficed for bread. Also, Allāh gave them quails that sufficed as meat, and made their sweet the Manna that descends from trees. Therefore, their diet was complete.

Further, the Prophet's statement:

« الكَمْأة من المنِّ الذي أنزل الله على بني إسرائيل »

"The Kamah is a type of the Manna that Allāh has sent down on the Children of Israel."

Some considered that the *Kamah* is a type of *Manna*, although the word '*Manna*' is usually used to describe the dew that descends on trees, which is originally called *Taranjabin*.

The second opinion states that the *Kamah* was called *Manna* because it resembles the Manna that descends on trees, in that it is collected without effort to plant or water.

If one asks, this is the case with *Kamah,* then what about the harm that it contains?

Know that Allāh created everything in a perfect shape and essence. What Allāh created is free from defects and harm and is beneficial for mankind. The various types of ailments occur later on when what Allāh creates becomes spoiled somehow by being mixed or polluted by other substances, and so forth. If what Allāh creates is left in its original shape that Allāh has created, it does not contain any harm.

Those who have knowledge of the world and of the creation realize that all types of evil or harm in the air, land, plants and various creations occur after they are created. Also, ever since mankind started disobeying their Prophets, all types of general and private evil occurred, that which causes them pain, illnesses, diseases, plagues, famines and loss of blessings in the land and in what it produces. The fruits and plants have thus lost their value and benefit gradually.

If one does not comprehend these facts, the following *Āyah* should be enough for him to understand.

﴿ ظَهَرَ ٱلْفَسَادُ فِى ٱلْبَرِّ وَٱلْبَحْرِ بِمَا كَسَبَتْ أَيْدِى ٱلنَّاسِ ﴾

"Evil (sins and disobedience to Allāh) has appeared on land and sea because of what the hands of men have earned (by oppression and evil deeds)." (30:41)

One should apply this *Āyah* to what occurs in this world and compare them together.

Further, the people notice how various illnesses and sicknesses occur in plants, animals and fruits. These illnesses only produce other types of illnesses and diseases. The more mankind starts a new type of evil and sin, the more illnesses and diseases Allāh brings to their foods, fruits, air, water sources, bodies, shapes and outer appearance. Also, the people's behavior suffers a type of harm or alteration that is compatible with what their bodies commit of injustice and sin.

Before this time, the crops and grains used to be larger in size than at the present time, for the blessings in such items was bigger than at the present time. Imam Ahmad narrated, "A bundle that contained some wheat seeds as big as date seeds was found in a safe that belonged to members of the Umayyad dynasty. On it, these words were written, 'This used to grow during the times when justice prevailed.' "Imam Ahmad mentioned this story after narrating one of the Prophet's *Ahadith*.

The majority of the diseases and illnesses are the remnant of the torments that were inflicted on the nations that lived before our time. These illnesses and diseases remained for those who followed their lead and imitated the previously tormented nations. This is a just judgment that the Prophet ﷺ mentioned when he stated that the Plague:

« إنه بَقِيَّةُ رِجْزٍ – أو عَذَابٍ – أُرْسِلَ على بَني إِسْرَائِيلَ »

"It is the remnant of an affliction that Allāh has sent on the Children of Israel."

Also, Allāh sent the wind on the people of 'Ad for seven nights and eight days. Allāh has left some of this strong wind for the people who came after them to serve as a reminder [of what happened to 'Ad].

Allāh made the works of the righteous and the sinning people as reasons behind much of what has happened in this world. For instance, when the people do not work righteousness or give in charity, the rain does not fall on them, and thus famine occurs. Also, when the meek and powerless people are dealt with unjustly, when the people cheat in weights, and when the strong transgress the rights of the weak, the injustice committed by the [tyrant] rulers intensifies as a consequence. Such unjust rulers do not grant mercy if they are asked for mercy, nor are they kind when they are called on to be kind. In reality, what the rulers do and commit is a mere reflection of what their subjects do and commit. Allāh, with His Wisdom and Just Decisions, makes people's work appear to them in various forms that are compatible to their works. Sometimes Allāh strikes mankind with famines, sometimes with an enemy, sometimes with unjust rulers, sometimes with diseases, and sometimes with depression and sadness that will remain with them. Sometimes Allāh strikes mankind with preventing the blessings from descending on them and by allowing the devils to have power over them, and leading them to what is certain torment. In this case, mankind will revert to what they were created for [either Paradise or the Fire].

The wise person thinks about the world and seeks the areas where Allāh exerts His Justice and Wisdom. Then he will realize that the Prophets and their followers are passing on the path of safety, while the rest of mankind are leading themselves to the path of destruction and the land of failure. Allāh will certainly bring His judgement and command to a successful conclusion, none can avert His decisions or commands. All success comes from Allāh.

There are three opinions regarding the meaning of the Prophet's statement:

« وماؤُها شِفاءٌ لِلْعَيْن »

"And its water cures the eye."

First: that the *Kamah* water is an ingredient in the remedies for eye ailments, not that it is used alone.

Second: that *Kamah* is used alone after broiling it and extracting its juice. The fire matures and softens the *truffles*, thus dissolving the harmful wetness and excrements that the *Kamah* contains and leaving the beneficial ingredients.

Third: that the meaning of 'its water' entails the rain that makes the mushroom grow and which is the first patch of rain that falls. In this case, the *Hadith* will be talking about the rain not the mushrooms themselves. Ibn Al-Jawzi mentioned this opinion, which is the weakest among the three opinions mentioned herewith.

Other people said that this portion of the *Hadith* entails using *Kamah* water to cool the eye. Hence its water alone is a cure, while the other parts are used as ingredients in compound remedies.

Al-Ghafiqi said, "The *Kamah* water (juice) is the best remedy for the eye when kneaded with the Ithmid (antimony type of Kohl) and then used as kohl (i.e. eyeliner). It also strengthens the eyelid and the eyesight and prevents many illnesses from attacking the eye."

3. *Kabath* (Arak Tree Fruit)

In the *Sahihain* it is narrated that Jabir bin 'Abdullāh رَضِيَ اللهُ عَنْهُما said, "We were with the Messenger of Allāh ﷺ collecting *Kabath* when he said, "Collect the black type of *Kabath* because it is the best type."

The *Kabath* is the fruit that grows on the plant called *Arak* which grow in the area of Hijaz [and whose branches are used for *Siwak* as we have stated]. It is hot and dry and carries the same benefits as the Arak tree: strengthening the stomach, helping the digestion, dissolving phlegm and relieving back pain and several other illnesses. Ibn Juljul said, "Drinking its soup produces urine as a diuretic, and cleanses the prostate." Also, Ibn Radhwan said, "[The *Kabath*] strengthens the stomach and constipates (mildly)."

4. *Katam* (Plants Used to Dye the Hair Black)

Al-Bukhari narrated that Uthman bin 'Abdullāh bin Mawhab said, "We came to Umm Salamah رَضِيَ اللهُ عَنْها and she took out some of the

Messenger's hair that was dyed with *henna* and *Katam*." Also in the four books of *Sunan* (Abu Dāwud, At-Tirmidhi, An-Nasai'ī and Ibn Mājah) it is narrated that the Prophet ﷺ said:

« إِنَّ أَحْسَنَ مَا غَيَّرْتُمْ بِهِ الشَّيْبَ، الحِنَّاءُ وَالْكَتَمُ »

"Henna and Katam are the best of what you use to change (the color of) white hair."

Also, in the *Sahihain* it is narrated that Anas عَنْهُ اللهُ رَضِيَ said, "Abu Bakr once dyed (his hair) with *henna* and *Katam*." Further, Abu Dāwud narrated that Ibn 'Abbās said, "A man who tinted (his hair) with *henna* passed by the Prophet ﷺ who said, 'How good this is.' Then another man who tinted (his hair) with both *henna* and *Katam* passed by and the Prophet ﷺ said, 'This is even better.' Then another man who tinted with *Sufrah* (a black dye) passed by and the Prophet ﷺ said, 'This is the best of all.'"

Al-Ghafiqi said, "*Katam* is a plant that grows in valleys and its leaves are similar to olive-leaves and grows higher than a (man's) shoulders. Its fruit grows to the size of peppers and have seeds in the middle. When the seeds are crushed, they turn black and when the leaves are squeezed and one drinks a small measure [of the extract], it causes vomiting. *Katam* also benefits against dog bites. When the stem is boiled in water, it is used as ink." Al-Kindi also stated that, "If one uses the Katam's seed as Kohl (i.e., eyeliner), it will clear the eye from the water that accumulates in it."

Some people thought that *Katam* is the *Wasmah* or the Nile-Leaves. This is not true, because *Wasmah* is a different plant. The author of the *Sahih* said, "*Katam*, which is used to dye the hair, is a plant that is mistakenly taken for *Wasmah*." The *Wasmah* has long leaves that are bluish in color and which are larger than the *Khilaf* (Chalef) leaves and are similar to pea leaves but larger in size. Further, *Wasmah* is collected in Hijaz and Yemen.

If someone asks, "In the *Sahih* it is narrated that the Prophet ﷺ did not dye (his hair)." We answer that Imam Ahmad said that other Companions have narrated that the Prophet ﷺ dyed (his hair). Those who were witnesses to an act are not like those who did not witness it. Hence, Imam Ahmad affirmed that the Prophet ﷺ had indeed used *Khidhab* (dyed the hair), although Imam Malik denied it.

If someone says that in *Sahih* Muslim it is narrated the *Hadith* that disallows dying the hair black, when Abu Bakr's father was brought to the Prophet ﷺ with all his hair being white. The Prophet ﷺ said at that time:

« غيِّروا هذا الشَّيْبِ، وجنِّبوه السَّواد »

"Change this white hair but avoid the black color."

Katam changes the color of the hair to black.

There are two ways to answer this argument.

First, the Prophet ﷺ disallowed dying the hair black. But if the black color is mixed with *henna* and *Katam*, there is no harm in it. *Katam* and *henna* dye the hair between red and black colors, unlike *Wasmah*, which turns the hair black. This is the most plausible answer to the argument.

The second answer is that dying the hair black sometimes occurs for the purpose of deceiving others, such as when an old woman dyes her hair black to deceive the husband or other people, or when an old man dyes his hair black to deceive a woman. This is a type of cheating that is disallowed. On the other hand, if dying the hair black does not entail deceit, it is allowed. There are authentic narrations that Al-Hasan and Al-Husayn used to dye their hair black, as Ibn Jarir has reported. He also reported that this is the opinion of Uthman bin 'Affan, 'Abdullāh bin Ja'far, Sa'd bin Abu Waqqas, 'Uqbah bin 'Amir, Al-Mughirah bin Shu'bah, Jarir bin 'Abdullāh and 'Amr bin Al-'Aas رَضِيَ الله عَنْهُم. He also related this opinion to several of the Tabi'in, the second generation of Islam, such as 'Amr bin Uthman, 'Ali bin 'Abdullāh Ibn 'Abbās, Abu Salamah bin Abdur-Rahman, Abdur-Rahman bin Al-Aswad, Musa bin Talhah, Az-Zuhri, Ayyub and Isma'il bin M'ad Yakrib. Ibn Al-Jawzi also related this opinion to Mu'harib bin Dithar, Yazid, Ibn Jurayj, Abu Yusuf, Abu Is'haq, Ibn Abu Layla, Ziyad bin 'Alaqah, Ghaylan bin Jami', Nafi' bin Jubayr, 'Amr bin 'Ali Al-Muqaddami and Al-Qasim bin Sallam.

5. *Karm*, which is the grapevine

It is not preferred that one calls the grapevine *Karm*, as Muslim narrated that the Prophet ﷺ said:

« لا يقولَنَّ أحدكم للعِنَبِ الكَرْمُ؛ الكَرْمُ: الرجلُ المسلم »

"None of you should call the grapevine Karm, for Al-Karm is the

Muslim man."

In another narration the Prophet ﷺ said:

«إنما الكَرْم: قلبُ المؤمن »

"The Karm is the believer's heart."

Also another narration states:

«لا تقولوا الكرمُ وَ قولوا: العنب وَ الحبلة»

"Do not say (for grapes) Al-Karm, rather say 'Inab (grape), and Hablah (grapevine)."

This *Hadith* entails two meanings that the Arabs used to call the grapevine *Al-Karm* because of its tremendous benefits. This is why the Prophet ﷺ disliked calling it *Karm* because this exotic name drives the heart to like it and to later like what it is used to produce: alcohol, which is the mother of all impure things. The Prophet ﷺ disliked calling what is used to produce alcohol with one of the best names.

The second, this *Hadith* is similar to the *Ahadith,*

« ليس الشديد بالصّرعة »

"The strong person is not one who overpowers others physically."

And

« ليس المِسْكين بالطَّوَاف »

"The Miskin (poor) is not one who keeps wandering in the land."

In this case, the *Hadith* (about *Al-Karm*) means, "You call the grapevine *Karm* because of its many benefits, while the believing heart or the Muslim person deserves this good name even more, for indeed, the believer is all pure and beneficial." The *Hadith* then draws the attention to what the believer's heart has of goodness, generosity, faith, enlightenment, guidance, fear from Allāh and the rest of the good characteristics because of which the believer deserves the name *Karm* more than the grapevine.

The grapevine is cool and dry, while its leaves are cool in the first degree. When the grape leaves are crushed and their powder is used as a bandage for headache, they relieve the pain and also relieve swelling and stomach infections.

When one drinks the juice of grapevine stems, it will get rid of nausea sensation and will constipate the stomach, and when its hearts are chewed wet, they also produce the same benefits. Also, the extract of grapevine leaves helps relieve stomach ulcers, hemoptysis (spitting up blood), vomit and stomach ache in general.

The sap contained in hanging grapevine stems acts just like gum extracts if one drinks it, as it dissipates stones. Further, when it is used as ointment, it will bring relief to the hearts and will heal the open sores caused by mange, but it is better to wash the affected wound beforehand with water and Natron. When one uses it as an ointment along with oil, it will remove the hair effectively.

The ashes of grapevine stems are also used as a bandage, blended with vinegar, rose oil and rue, to relieve spleen swellings. Also, just as rose oil (or essence), the oil of vine blossoms constipates the stomach and has many other benefits. In general, grapevines have as much benefit as the date tree.

6. *Karfas* (Celery)

Karfas has a good aroma and when it is hung under the neck, it relieves toothache.

Karfas is hot and dry, and it opens the clogs of the liver and the spleen. Wet celery leaves helps the stomach and the cold liver, causes urine as a diuretic, menstrual flow, and dissolves stones. Celery grains are more effective in this regard. Karfas also stimulates semen production and relieves offensive breath. Ar-Razi said, "One should avoid eating it if he fears he might suffer a scorpion sting."

7. *Kurrath* (Leek)

There are two types of *Kurrath*, a Nabatean type and a Shami (Syrian) type. People eat the Nabatean type, which is a vegetable, while the Syrian type has many heads. *Kurrath* is hot and dry and causes headaches. When *Kurrath* is cooked, one could eat it or drink its water to help against cold hemorrhages. When its seeds are crushed and kneaded with some tar and then applied on decaying teeth, they will cleanse the rotted teeth and will relieve the pain. Further, the smoke of burnt *Kurrath* seeds helps dry out hemorrhages. All these benefits are for the Nabatean *Kurrath*.

Yet, the Kurrath is harmful for the teeth and the gums, causes headaches and nightmares and brings darkness to the sight. Also, it provokes offensive breath, is diuretic, stimulates menstruation flow and semen production, and is not easily digested.

The Letter *Lam*

I. *Lahm* (Meat)

Allāh said:

$$﴿ وَأَمْدَدْنَـٰهُم بِفَـٰكِهَةٍ وَلَحْمٍ مِّمَّا يَشْتَهُونَ ﴾$$

"And We shall provide them with fruit and meat such as they desire." (52:22)

$$﴿ وَلَحْمِ طَيْرٍ مِّمَّا يَشْتَهُونَ ﴾$$

"And with the flesh of fowls that they desire." (56:21)

In the *Sahih* it is also narrated that the Prophet ﷺ said:

« فضلُ عائشةَ على النساء، كفضل الثَّريد على سائرِ الطعام »

"The virtue of 'Âishah رَضِيَ اللهُ عَنْها *as compared to the rest of the women is like the virtue of the Tharid as compared to the rest of the foods." (Tharid means bread and meat).*

Az-Zuhri said, "Eating meat brings about strength in seventy different ways." Also, Muhammad bin Wasi' said, "Eating meat strengthens the sight." Also, 'Ali رَضِيَ اللهُ عَنْهُ was reported to have said, "Eat meat, because it makes the skin's color lighter, the stomach firmer and the behavior better." Nafi said, "Ibn 'Umar رَضِيَ اللهُ عَنْهما used to eat meat frequently when Ramadhān started and when traveling." Finally, 'Ali رَضِيَ اللهُ عَنْهُ was reported to have said, "Whoever refrains from eating meat for forty days will acquire bad behavior."

There are different types of meat that we will mention, describe briefly and elaborate on their benefit or harm.

Sheep Meat (Mutton)

Mutton is warm in the second degree and wet in the first degree. The best type of mutton comes from the one-year old animal, which generates good blood if digested properly. This type of meat is suitable for those who have hot or cold temperaments and for those who practice sports activity in cold areas and cold weather. It is also beneficial for those who suffer from black bile, and it also strengthens the mind and the memory. However, the mutton of old, thin animals is not good, as is the ewe's meat.

The best type of mutton is the dark meat of the male animal, for it is lighter, tastier and more beneficial. The mutton of castrated sheep is even better and more beneficial. The red meat of fat sheep is lighter and more nutritious, while the chest of the goat is less nutritious and floats in the stomach.

The best parts of mutton meat are the meat that covers the bones, the right side, which is lighter and tastier than the left side, and the front parts rather than the back parts. The best part of sheep meat to the Prophet ﷺ was the front part, which is closer to the head, but not the head itself. The front part is lighter and tastier. Once, Al-Farazdaq gave a man some money to buy meat for him, saying, "Buy the front parts and avoid the head and the intestines, because that is where disease resides."

The meat on the neck is also tasty and easy to digest. The meat that covers the arm is the lightest meat, the tastiest, the healthiest and the easiest to digest. In the *Sahihain* it is narrated that the Messenger of Allāh ﷺ used to like eating the meat of the sheep arm. Furthermore, the meat on the back of the sheep is nutritious and produces sanitary blood.

Goat Meat

It is cold and dry, and the mixtures that goat meat produces are harmful. Goat meat is not digested easily and is not significant nutrition-wise. The meat of billy goats is not beneficial, because it is rather dry, heavy on the stomach and produces black bile.

Al-Jahith once said, "A skilled doctor once said to me, 'O Abu Uthman! Avoid goat meat because it causes depression, causes black bile, forgetfulness, and spoils the blood. By Allāh! It also drives children wild.'"

Some doctors say that the goat meat that is not preferred is the meat of old goats, especially for old people. They also say that goat meat is not bad for whoever is used to eating it.

When the doctors state that goat meat is not beneficial, they specifically mean those who have weak stomachs and those who are not used to eating it, such as the people who live in luxury in cities and who are used to the better types of foods. But this is not the majority.

The meat of young – but not very young – goats is milder, especially when the goat is still nursing. This type of goat meat is digested faster, because it still possesses the strength of its mother's milk. The meat of young goats is also milder for most people and lighter than camel meat. Also, young goat's meat produces moderate blood.

Cow Meat

Cow Meat is cold and dry, heavy on the stomach and produces black, bilious blood that is only suitable for hard workers. Eating cow meat excessively for those who are not used to it causes such black bilious illnesses as vitiligo (a skin condition of unknown cause, characterized by patchy loss of pigment), mange, herpes, leprosy, elephantiasis, cancer, obsession, quartran fever and various tumors. The harm that this meat causes will be neutralized when one eats it with spices, garlic, ginger and cinnamon. The meat of male cows is colder than female cows' meat, which is less dry.

The meat of fat calves is one of the best, mildest and tastiest types of food. It is warm and wet, and if fully digested, it provides good nutrition.

Horse meat

In the Sahih it is narrated that Asmā' رَضِيَ الله عَنْها said, "We slaughtered a horse during the time of the Messenger of Allāh ﷺ and ate it." Also, the Prophet ﷺ:

« أنه أُذِن في لُحوم الخيل، و نَهى عن لحوم الحُمُر »

"Allowed eating horsemeat but disallowed eating (domesticated) donkey meat." [Al-Bukhari and Muslim].

The fact that Allāh mentioned horses along with mules and donkeys [in the Qur'ān] does not indicate that the ruling about their meat is identical. Sometimes Allāh mentions several similar things together and sometimes mentions several different things together. What Allāh said is:

﴿ لِتَرْكَبُوهَا ﴾

"For you to ride." (16:8)

This does not indicate that horsemeat is not allowed, just as it does not indicate that one is not allowed to benefit from horses except by riding. Rather, the *Āyah* only mentioned the best benefit and value that the horse represents, which is its being a means of transportation. Furthermore, the two *Ahadith* we mentioned unequivocally indicate that horsemeat is allowed.

Horsemeat is hot, dry, tough and dark. It is also harmful for soft stomachs and bodies.

Camel Meat

The difference between the *Shiites* and the *Sunnis* and between the Jews and Muslims is that the Muslims eat camel meat. In addition, the *Shiites* and the Jews neither praise nor eat camel meat. It is well established in the religion that Muslims are allowed to eat camel meat and that the Messenger of Allāh ﷺ and his Companions used to eat it while traveling and otherwise.

Young camel meat is one of the tastiest and most nutritious types of foods, and those who are used to eating it find it as light and beneficial as sheep meat. Some doctors did not like eating camel meat for residents of the cities because they are not used to it. Camel meat is hot and dry, difficult to digest and begets black bile.

Camel meat has an especially strong effect on the body and this is why the Prophet ﷺ ordered the Muslims to perform ablution after eating it.* We should state here that it is an erroneous method to alter the meaning of the two correct *Ahadith* on this subject so that 'ablution' only means washing the hands, thus altering the true meaning of the word. Also, the Prophet ﷺ made a distinction between eating camel meat and sheep meat, as he gave the choice to Muslims if they want to perform ablution after eating sheep meat. Meanwhile, the Prophet ﷺ commanded the Muslims to perform ablution after eating camel meat. If ablution in these *Ahadith* was held to mean just washing the hands, it should also apply to what the Prophet ﷺ said:

« مَن مَسَّ فَرْجه فليَتَوَضَّأ »

"Whoever touched his sexual organ is obliged to perform ablution."

---

* **Editor's note**: This is the ritual washing before prayer. It is called, and wudhu in Arabic translated into English as ablution.

Furthermore, those who eat camel meat might not touch the meat with their hands. So if 'ablution' in this case means just washing the hands, it would be a senseless act and would alter the true meanings desired by the *Ahadith*. Also, claiming that the *Hadith* which states,

"The last ruling that the Prophet ﷺ chose is that he abandoned performing ablution from eating what is cooked by fire," includes camel meat is not correct.

First, this *Hadith* carries a general meaning, while the *Hadith* about camel meat is specific.

Second, the two *Ahadith* are not talking about the same subject. For instance, one should perform ablution even if he eats dried, cooked or uncooked camel meat. Using fire does not have a bearing on the ruling about camel meat. As for abandoning performing ablution after eating what is cooked by fire, it only indicates that using fire does not require ablution. Therefore, there is a difference between the two *Ahadith,* as one of them orders the Muslims to perform ablution after eating camel meat while the other indicates that performing ablution is not required after eating the food that was cooked by fire.

Third, the *Hadith* about the Prophet ﷺ abandoning performing ablution after eating the food that was cooked on fire came after the Prophet ﷺ had performed ablution from eating such meat earlier. The *Hadith* states that the Prophet ﷺ was once brought meat and that he ate from it and then performed ablution and prayed. Later on, he was brought meat and he ate from it and then prayed without performing ablution. The *Hadith* states, the last ruling on this matter is that it is not necessary to perform ablution after eating what was cooked by fire. So there are two rulings regarding the same subject [eating what was touched by fire], one came earlier than the second ruling. Some of the narrators of the *Hadith* only mentioned the latter incident to make the story short. Therefore, how can anyone use this *Hadith* to prove that it overrules performing ablution from eating camel meat (when the earlier *Hadith* that was overruled talks about another subject)? Even if the *Ahadith* in general allow not performing ablution after eating what was cooked on fire, the specific *Hadith* still stands because it entails a specific ruling [concerning camel meat].

Dhabb **Meat**

We stated before that eating *Dhabb* meat is allowed. This type of meat is hot and dry and excites the sexual drive.

Gazelle meat

Gazelle meat is the best among the meats of wild game. It is hot and dry and beneficial for the healthy body, especially the fawn's meat.

Antelope **Meat**

Antelope meat is hot and dry in the first degree, dehydrates the body and is beneficial for the humid bodied.

The author of the 'Qanoon' said, "The best type of game meat is the antelope's, although it tends to cause black bile."

Rabbit **Meat**

Rabbit meat was mentioned in the *Sahihain*, as Anas رَضِيَ الله عَنْهُ said, "We hunted a rabbit after pursuing it for a while. Afterwards, Abu Talhah رَضِيَ الله عَنْهُ sent its hip to the Messenger of Allāh ﷺ who accepted it."

Rabbit meat is mildly hot and dry, and the best part of it is the hip. The best way to eat rabbit meat is by roasting it. Rabbit meat constipates, produces urine, as a diuretic, and dissolves stones. Eating the rabbit's head benefits against convulsive shaking.

Zebra meat

In the *Sahihain* it is narrated that Abu Qatadah رَضِيَ الله عَنْهُ said that the Companions were once with the Messenger of Allāh ﷺ during an Umrah trip and that he hunted a zebra and the Prophet ﷺ told them to eat it. They were assuming the state of Ihram then, unlike Abu Qatadah.

Ibn Mājah also narrated that Jabir رَضِيَ الله عَنْهُ said, "During the battle of Khaibar, we ate horsemeat and zebra meat."

Zebra meat is hot and dry, nutritious and produces thick, bilious blood. Its fat is beneficial when mixed with Qust oil to treat toothache and flatulence that weakens the kidneys. Further, when its grease is applied on spots, it will heal them.

In general, all types of wild-game meat produce thick, bilious blood. In addition, the best type of wild-game meat is gazelle then rabbit meat.

The meat of animal fetuses is not preferred because the blood is still trapped in it. However, it is still allowed, for the Prophet ﷺ said:

« ذَكاةُ الجَنينِ : ذَكاةُ أُمِّه »

"Slaughtering the fetus is included in slaughtering its mother."

The scholars of Iraq do not allow eating fetus's meat except if one kills it before it dies. They altered the meaning of the last *Hadith* saying that the fetus should be slaughtered as its mother was slaughtered according to the *Hadith,* as they claimed.

However, this claim is false. The *Hadith* states that the Prophet ﷺ was asked, "O Messenger of Allāh ﷺ! We slaughter a sheep and sometimes find a fetus still in its womb, should we eat it?" The Prophet ﷺ said, "Eat it if you wish, because slaughtering it is included in slaughtering its mother."

Also, when one studies this matter further, his analysis will also demonstrate that it is allowed to eat animal fetuses. The fetus is still a part of the mother, and since slaughtering the mother allows us to eat all of its parts, then the fetus should be included, as well. This is the meaning that the Prophet ﷺ meant when he said:

« ذَكاتُه ذَكاةُ أمه »

"Slaughtering it is included in slaughtering its mother."

If the authentic *Sunnah* had not specifically allowed eating the fetus, the correct mind would still guide us that it is allowed.

Eating *Dried* (Jerked) Meat

It the *Sunan* it is narrated that Thawban رَضِيَ اللهُ عَنْهُ said, "I slaughtered a sheep for the Messenger of Allāh ﷺ while we were traveling, and he said to me:

« أصلِحْ لَحْمها »

"Dry its meat."

I kept feeding the Prophet ﷺ from its meat until we reached Al-Madinah."

Dried meat is better than old meat and strengthens the body, although it causes skin rashes sometimes, a side effect that could be neutralized with cold, humid spices. Also, jerked meat is favorable for hot conditions. Old meat is hot and dry, favorable for hot conditions and the best type of this meat is that which is fat and wet. Finally, old meat constipates unless cooked in milk and grease.

Fowl meat

Allāh said:

$$\textram{\{ وَلَحْمِ طَيْرٍ مِّمَّا يَشْتَهُونَ \}}$$

"And with the flesh of fowls that they desire." (56:21)

Some types of fowl meats are allowed and some are prohibited. The prohibited types include the birds that have claws, such as the falcon, hawk and peregrine, and those that eat carrion, such as the eagle, vulture, stork, magpie, spotted and black crows. Also, this list includes the birds that we are not allowed to kill, such as the hoopoe and the shrike, and some of the birds that we are allowed to kill, such as kite and crow.

There are many types of fowl that are allowed, such as chicken meat. In the *Sahihain* it is narrated by Abu Musa رَضِيَ اللهُ عَنْهُ that the Prophet ﷺ ate chicken meat.

Chicken Meat

Chicken meat is hot and dry in the first degree and it is easy on the stomach and digests quickly. Chicken meat strengthens the mind and increases the production of semen. It also makes the voice softer, the mind stronger and produces healthy blood. It was said that eating chicken meat on a regular basis causes gout, but this is not confirmed by fact.

The cock' meat, on the other hand, is hotter and less wet. The meat of old cocks helps against constipation, asthma and thick flatulence when cooked with safflower, canella and chabt (Shibit). The castrated cock' meat is nutritious and easy to digest. Pullet meat is easy to digest and mild on the stomach and produces mild blood.

Francolin Meat

Francolin meat is hot and dry in the second degree, soft and light, easy to digest and produces mild blood. Eating this type of meat also strengthens the sight.

Partridge meat

This type of meat produces good blood and is easily digested.

Goose Meat

Goose meat is hot and dry and is not healthy if eaten on a regular basis, and it does not produce extensive excrement.

Duck Meat

Duck meat is hot and wet, and it is not suitable for the stomach, difficult to digest and produces excessive excrements.

Bustard Meat

Bustard meat is hot and dry, heavy on the stomach but good for those who perform sports activities and for hard workers.

Crane Meat

This type of meat is dry and light. It produces bilious blood, and it is good for hard workers. It is better to eat the crane's meat one or two days after it is slaughtered.

Bird and Lark Meat

An-Nasai'ī narrated in his *Sunnan* that 'Abdullāh bin Umar رَضِيَ الله عَنْهما said that the Prophet ﷺ said:

« ما من إنسان يقتل عُصْفورًا فما فوقه – بغير حقه – إلا سأله الله عز وجل.

قيل: يا رسول الله؛ وما حقّه ؟ قال: تذبحه فتأكله، ولا تقطع رأسه وترمي

به »

"No person kills a bird and a larger animal without justification, but will be asked about it on the Day of Resurrection. He was asked, 'O Messenger of Allāh! When is it justified?' He said, 'You slaughter it and eat it, but do not cut its head and discard its body (i.e. for sport only).'"

Also, An-Nasai'ī narrated that the Messenger of Allāh ﷺ said:

« من قَتَلَ عُصْفورًا عَبَثًا، عَجَّ إلى الله يقول: يارب؛ إن فلانًا قتلني عَبَثًا، ولم

يقتلْني لِمَنْفَعة »

"Whoever kills a bird for fun, the bird will complain to Allāh, 'O my Lord, Such and such person killed me for fun, not for a useful purpose.'"

Bird meat is hot and dry, constipates and stimulates semen production. Bird meat soup constipates and helps the joints. If one eats birds' brain with ginger and onion, it excites the sexual desire. The mixtures that bird's produce is not favorable.

Pigeon Meat

Pigeon meat is hot and wet, although the meat of wild pigeons is less wet. The meat of pigeon chicks is more humid, especially the chicks of domesticated pigeons. Young pigeons are less meaty but a better food. The meat of male pigeons is a good cure for numbness, narcosis, apoplexy and convulsive shaking or trembles. Pigeon chick meat is favorable for the sexual drive and the kidneys and produces more blood.

Sand Grouse Meat

This type of meat is dry and causes black bile and constipation. It is not a good food, except that it helps cure dropsy.

Quail Meat

Quail meat is hot and dry and helps the joints. It harms the hot kidney unless it is taken with vinegar and coriander. Eating the meat of the quails that live in filthy areas should be avoided.

Fowl meats are all more easily digested than cattle meat. The parts of the birds that are the most easily digested are the necks and the wings. Also, the brains of the fowls are a better food than cattle brains.

Locust Meat

In the *Sahihain* it is narrated that 'Abdullāh bin Abi Awfa رَضِيَ الله عَنْهُ said, "We went to seven battles with the Messenger of Allāh during which we used to eat locust." The Musnad also narrated that the Messenger of Allāh said:

« أُحِلَّتْ لَنَا مَيْتَتَانِ ودمَانِ: الحوتُ والجرادُ، والكِبدُ والطِّحالُ »

"We were allowed two types of dead animals and two bloods: fish and locust; liver and spleen."

This *Hadith* is also related from Ibn 'Umar رَضِيَ الله عَنْهُ.

Locust meat is hot and dry and not very nutritious. Also, eating locust meat regularly makes the body thin, emaciated. The smoke of burnt locust helps in cases of dysuria (impaired ability to pass urine), especially for women, and is favorable for hemorrhoids. Eating fat wingless locust roasted is a good cure for scorpion stings. Also, locust meat is not favorable for those suffering from epilepsy and produces septic mixtures in the stomach.

There is a difference on allowing eating locust when it is dead, where the majority of the scholars except Mālik allow it. Yet, there is no difference that it is allowed if the locust died because of a reason, such as being burnt or pressed.

It is not good for the health to eat meat on a regular basis because it causes bloody sanguineous illnesses and various types of allergies. Hippocrates once said, "Do not turn your stomachs to a graveyard for animals."

2. Laban (Milk)

Allāh said:

﴿ وَإِنَّ لَكُمْ فِي ٱلْأَنْعَمِ لَعِبْرَةً نُّسْقِيكُم مِّمَّا فِي بُطُونِهِۦ مِنۢ بَيْنِ فَرْثٍ وَدَمٍ لَّبَنًا خَالِصًا سَآئِغًا لِّلشَّرِبِينَ ﴾

"And verily, in the cattle, there is a lesson for you. We give you to drink of that which is in their bellies, from between excretions and blood, pure milk; palatable to the drinkers." (16:66)

Also Allāh said, while describing Paradise:

﴿ فِيهَآ أَنْهَرٌ مِّن مَّآءٍ غَيْرِ ءَاسِنٍ وَأَنْهَرٌ مِّن لَّبَنٍ لَّمْ يَتَغَيَّرْ طَعْمُهُۥ ﴾

"In it are rivers of water the taste and smell of which are not changed, rivers of milk of which the taste never changes." (47:15)

In the *Sunan* it is also narrated:

« مَنْ أَطْعَمَه الله طَعَامًا، فَلْيَقُلْ: اللَّهُمَّ؛ بارِكْ لنا فيه، وارزُقْنا خيرًا منه . ومَنْ سقاه الله لَبَنًا، فليقل: اللهم بارِكْ لنا فيه، وزِدْنا منه . فإني لا أعلم ما يُجزِيءُ من الطَّعام والشراب، إلا اللَّبَنَ »

"Whoever Allāh gives some type of food, let him supplicate, 'O Allāh! Bless it for us and grant us what is better.' Whoever Allāh grants some Laban, let him say, 'O Allāh! Bless it for us and grant us more of it,' for I do not know of a more complete food or drink than milk.'"

Although milk is a simple type of food, it is very natural to the body as it contains three major substances: cheese, fat and water. Cheese is cold and wet and provides good nutrition. The fat contained in the milk is mild regarding warmth and wetness, and it very beneficial for healthy bodies.

The water part contained in milk is hot and wet, and it softens the stomach and provides the body with beneficial moistures. *Laban* in general is mild regarding warmth and wetness, although there are other opinions in this regard.

Milk is best when it has just been milked, and its value decreases by the passage of time thereafter. When it is freshly milked, milk is less cold and more humid. Sour milk is the opposite. Also, milk is better forty days after the animal has given birth. The best type of milk is the most white in color, as it has a good scent, delicious taste, mildly sweet, less fat and light consistency. It is also best when young healthy animals are milked, especially those that have less meat and which graze in healthy grazing lands. Milk is good and produces red blood, brings wetness to the body and is also a nutritious food. Also, milk helps relieve depression, obsession and black bile ailments. When milk is drunk with honey, it will help cleanse the insides of septic materials. Drinking milk with sugar makes the color of the skin fairer. Milk helps the body regain its strength after sexual intercourse and is also favorable for the chest, the lungs and for those suffering from tuberculosis.

Further, milk is not favorable for the head, the stomach, the liver and the spleen. Also, drinking milk excessively is harmful for the teeth and the gums, and this is why it is better to rinse the mouth after one drinks it. In the *Sahihain* it is narrated that the Prophet ﷺ once drank some milk and then asked for some water and rinsed his mouth, saying: "It has fat."

Milk is not good for those suffering from fever and headaches and is not favorable for the weakness in the head and the brain. Excessive drinking of milk causes darkness in the sight, sight impairment, gout, kidney clogs and swelling in the stomach and the intestines. These side effects will be neutralized when mixing milk with honey, ginger, and so forth, for those who are not used to drinking it.

Sheep Milk

Sheep milk is the most watery, and it has more fat and bad odor than goat or cow milk. Sheep milk produces phlegm and causes white spots or stains on the skin if one drinks it on a regular basis. This is why it is better that sheep milk is mixed with water so that its concentration becomes less. Sheep milk quenches the thirst quicker and cools the body faster than other milks.

Goat Milk

Goat milk is mild and light, works as a mild laxative, is wet for dry bodies and helps cure mouth cankers, dry cough and epistaxis (nosebleeds).

Milk in general is the most beneficial drink for the body due to its nutritional value and closeness to the nature of the body and to the childhood of mankind. In the *Sahihain* it is narrated:

« أن رسولَ الله صلى الله عليه وسلم أُتيَ ليلةَ أُسريَ به، بقَدَح من خَمْر، وقدح من لَبَن. فنظر إليهما، ثم أخذ اللَّبن فقال جبرائيلُ عليه السلام: الحمد لله الَّذي هداك للفِطْرة؛ لو أخذتَ الخَمْر: غوتْ أُمَّتُك »

"The night of the Isrā' (the Prophet's journey from Makkah to Jerusalem and then to heaven), the Messenger of Allāh ﷺ was given two cups, one containing milk and the other wine. The Prophet ﷺ looked at them and then took the cup of milk. Gabriel said, 'You have accepted what is natural, (True Religion i.e. Islam) and if you had taken the wine, your followers would have gone astray.'"

Sour goat milk is not digested quickly and produces unfavorable mixtures. The hot tempered stomach benefits from goat milk, though, and easily digests it.

Cow Milk

Cow milk provides nutrition for the body and is also a mild laxative. Cow milk is one of the best milks, between sheep milk and goat milk regarding thickness and fat.

'Abdullāh bin Mas'ud narrated that the Prophet ﷺ once said:

« عليكم بألبانِ البَقَرِ؛ فإنها تَرْتَمُ من كل الشَّجَرِ »

"Drink cow milk because it grazes on all types of trees."

Camel Milk

We mentioned camel milk in the beginning of the chapter, so there is no need to repeat it.

3. *Luban* (Frankincense), which is the Kundur

It was reported that once a man complained to 'Ali رَضِيَ اللهُ عَنْهُ that he forgets and that 'Ali رَضِيَ اللهُ عَنْهُ said to him, "Resort to the Luban, because it strengthens the heart and does away with forgetfulness."

Also, it was reported that Ibn 'Abbās رَضِيَ اللهُ عَنْهُ said, "Drinking Luban with sugar on an empty stomach is favorable for the urine and helps against forgetfulness." Also, it was reported that Anas رَضِيَ اللهُ عَنْهُ said to a man who complained to him of forgetfulness, "Resort to Kundur! Soak it overnight and in the morning take a sip of it on an empty stomach, because it is good against forgetfulness."

There is an apparent reason for this benefit. Forgetfulness is the result of cold, humid, bad moods that affect the brain in a way that makes the brain not recall the memory easily. In this case, *Luban* helps. When forgetfulness is a result of other physical causes, refreshing drinks help in that case. The difference between the two cases is that dry substances help one stay up at night and recall old memories rather than current memories. The wet drinks have the opposite effect.

Sometimes forgetfulness occurs because of cupping on the back of the head and excessive eating of wet coriander and sour apples. Also, depression, sadness, looking at stagnant water for a long time and urinating in it might cause forgetfulness. Also, looking at crucified people, reading grave commemorations, walking between two tarred camels, eating mice wastes by mistake, all cause forgetfulness.

Luban is hot in the second degree and dry in the first degree. It is also a mild constipation agent. It is very beneficial and its side effects are minimal. Among the benefits of the *Luban* is that it stops and heals bleeding, stomach ache, diarrhea, helps digest the food, gets rid of flatulence, cures eye sores, helps the body grow flesh on most ulcers and strengthens the weak stomach. *Luban* also dries the phlegm and the moistures accumulating in the chest, cures eyesight impairment and prevents malignant sores from progressing.

When *Luban* is chewed alone or mixed with Persian thyme, it will provoke phlegm, release and relax the tongue muscles and help the mind become sharper. When the *Luban* is burnt, it helps cure some illnesses and makes the air smell fresh.

The Letter *Mim*

1. *Maa'* (Water)

Maa' (Water), is the resource of life, the best drink there is, and one of the pillars of existence. Rather it is the most important pillar of life, as Allāh has created every living thing from water.

There is a difference of opinion if water is a source of nutrition for the body, or if it only helps wash down and dissolve the food. Water is a wet, cold substance that removes heat, preserves the body's moisture, restores the moisture that the body has lost, makes the food softer and helps carry it through the blood vessels.

There are ten standards with which we test water's freshness. First, its color should be crystal clear. Second, water should not have any odor at all. Third, water should be sweet and fresh just as the water of the Nile and the Euphrates. Fourth, water should be light. Fifth, water sources should be pure and not stagnant. Sixth, water is fresher when its source is deeper or farther. Seventh, water should be exposed to the wind and the sun, not hidden under the earth. Eighth, water sources should not be stagnant and should be fast running. Ninth, water should be plentiful which helps purify whatever impurities it might carry. Tenth, water source should be running north to south or west to east.

When all these characteristics are sought together, they will all be found in four rivers, the Nile, the Euphrates, Say'han (or Sayhoun) and Jay'han (or Jayhoun). In the Sahihain it is narrated that Abu Hurairah related from the Prophet ﷺ that he said:

« سَيْحَانُ وَجَيْحَانُ وَالنِّيلُ وَالفُرَات، كُلُّها من أنهارِ الجنة »

"Sayhan, Jayhun, the Nile and the Euphrates are all among the rivers of Paradise."

As for the water being light, there are three methods to verify it. First, water should easily absorb the cold and the heat. Hippocrates said, "The water that becomes hot or cold easily is the lightest water." Second; by weight. Third; when one wets two pieces of cotton, which are exactly the same weight, with water from two different sources, and then both pieces are dried and weighed. The one that has the lightest weight indicates the water it absorbed was the lightest.

The environment that the water passes through has a profound effect on the water. For instance, water sources that are located to the north are generally cooler and their water is generally thicker due to the northern wind. Also, the water that passes through mineral rich rocks is affected by this fact.

Fresh water is beneficial for both the ill and the healthy. Cool or chilled water is the most beneficial and has the best taste. Yet, one should not drink water soon after he wakes up, after sex, taking a bath or eating fruit. There is no harm if one drinks water while eating, but not excessively. Rather, having a few sips of water in this case is better and does not harm the stomach but strengthens it, excites the sexual drive and quenches the thirst.

Warm water, on the other hand, swells the stomach and causes the opposite effects that we mentioned regarding cold water. Old warm water is better than fresh warm water.

Cold water is better than warm water inside the body, as it cleanses the blood and clears the head. Also, cold water removes rot and is mild and favorable for the teeth, the mood and hot weather. Yet, cold water is not good for those suffering from colds or swelling, since such cases need heat to decompose. Very cold water harms the teeth and drinking it on a regular basis could cause bronchitis and chest pains.

Very hot and very cold waters are very harmful to the nerves and most of the limbs and body organs. One of them decomposes (hot water), while the other concentrates moistures. Warm water relieves hot mixtures, decomposes, matures and extracts excrement and brings wetness and hotness, but does not help the digestion as the food then floats up close to the upper side of the stomach. Warm water also does not quench the thirst quickly, weakens the body and causes many harmful illnesses. Yet, warm water is good for old people and those suffering from epilepsy, cold headaches and ophthalmia (inflammation of the eye).

There are no *Hadith* about sun heated water, nor did any of the renowned doctors of old discourage drinking it. Yet, very hot water dissolves the fat around the kidneys.

We talked about rainwater when we talked about the letter Ghayn.

Water contained in ice and hail.

In the *Sahihain* it is narrated that the Prophet ﷺ used to say the following supplication after starting the prayer:

« اللهم، اغسلني مِن خَطَايايَ بماءٍ وَالثَّلج والبَرَدِ »

"O Allāh! Wash my sins with water (rain), snow and hail."

Snow is accumulated due to the moisture in the air. We mentioned the wisdom in asking Allāh to wash the sins with snow, as the heart needs the coolness and its strength. We stated before the subject of curing the ills of the heart and treating them with their opposites and neutralizers.

Hail water is sweeter than snow water, while the quality of melted ice water depends on its source.

We should mention that the quality of the snow is affected by the area and the mountains that it falls on.

One should avoid drinking icy water after taking a bath, having sex, sports activity, eating hot foods, when coughing and having chest pains, weak liver and cool tempers.

Water from wells and ground water

Well water is not favorable, while underground water is heavy. This is because the first one (well water) rarely escapes rot, while underground water is not exposed to fresh air. Hence, one should not drink such types of water until exposing the water to air for at least a night. The worst type of well or underground water is that which runs through lead-rich stones and unused wells, especially if its soil is not good.

Zamzam Water

Zamzam water is the best, freshest, most beneficial, most beloved and most precious water there is. Further, Zamzam water was dug up by Jibril and the source that Prophet Isma'il عليه السلام drank from.

In the *Sahihain* it is narrated that the Prophet ﷺ said to Abu Tharr, who remained at the Ka'bah for forty days without food (or drink) living on Zamzam water: "It is a nutritious food." Muslim added that the Prophet ﷺ said:

« وشِفاءُ سُقْمٍ »

"And a cure from ailment."

Furthermore, Ibn Mājah narrated that Jabir bin 'Abdullāh related from the Prophet ﷺ that he said:

« ماءُ زمزمَ لِما شُرِب له »

"Zamzam water is for whatever was intended behind drinking it."

We were told that 'Abdullāh bin Al-Mubarak once said, "O Allāh! Ibn Al-Mu'ammil told us that Muhammad bin Al-Munkadir related from Jabir رَضِيَ الله عَنْهُ that your Prophet ﷺ said:

« ماءُ زمزمَ لِما شُرِب له . فإني أشرِب لِظَمَإٍ يوم القيامة»

"The water of Zamzam is for the purpose it is drank for, and I drink it to relieve my thirst on the Day of Resurrection."

This *Hadith* is of the Hasan (Sound) type.

Many other people and I have tried drinking from Zamzam water for the purpose of being cured from various illnesses, and by the will of Allāh, I was indeed cured from several illnesses. I also saw some people who lived on Zamzam water for a long time, fifteen days or a little longer without complaining from hunger. Such people would perform *Tawaf* with other people at a normal pace. Someone even told me that Zamzam water was his only food and drink for forty days and that he still had enough strength to have sex with his wife, fast and perform *Tawaf* many times.

The Nile

The Nile is one of the rivers of Paradise that flows from deep inside Ethiopia. It is collected from the rainfall and the floods that supply it with water. Then, Allāh directs this river that flows with water to dry areas, causing the vegetation, on which people and animals live, to grow and flourish.

The land that the river flows to is dry and does not keep rainwater that falls on it, which is insufficient to grow vegetation anyway. On the other hand, when such a land receives more than the normal rainfall, the houses and life will be destroyed. Allāh has caused the rain to fall on far lands and then directed this rain to flow in a huge river in sufficient amounts that would benefit the people and the animals. When the river provides enough water for farming and to grow vegetation, the water level then decreases so that the people are able to tend and harvest the vegetation. The water of the Nile has the ten characteristics that we mentioned before, and this is why it is among the lightest, sweetest and freshest waters.

Seawater

The Prophet ﷺ said about the sea:

« هُوَ الطَّهُورُ ماؤُهُ الحِلُّ ميتَتُه »

"Its water is pure and its dead is allowed (to eat)."

Allāh has made the sea salty for the benefit of the people and the animals of the earth. Seawater is plentiful and has sufficient amounts of animals [and fish] that die but do not get buried in it. If the seawater is fresh and sweet, the animals that would die in it would make it rotten, adversely affecting the quality of the air on the earth. Allāh's wisdom has decided that seawater is salty, that even if the entire dead corpses produced on the earth were thrown in it, it would still be fresh until Allāh brings this world to its inevitable end. This is one of the reasons why seawater is salty, along with its soil and sand also being salty.

Taking a bath in seawater helps relieve many illnesses and infections that appear on the skin. Drinking seawater is harmful, it causes diarrhea, weakens the body and causes rashes, mange and thirst.

Those who have to drink seawater do so for certain medicinal purposes. In this case, seawater should be boiled in a pot that is covered by wool, which will absorb the water vapor. Then, the collected water should be squeezed out of the wool and consumed when there is sufficient amount of it. Meanwhile, the salt and the minerals will remain in the pot.

Also, one could dig a hole near the seashore to collect the water through several parallel tunnels that would make the water fresh at the end [when it passes through them repeatedly].

If one has to drink seawater, he should first mix it with apricot pips, burning coal, Armenian argil (type of earth), oak wood or fine wheat flour. This way, most of the minerals and mud will be collected in the bottom of the pot or the cup.

2. Misk (Musk)

Muslim narrated that Abu Sa'id Al-Khudri said that the Prophet ﷺ said:

«أَطْيَبُ الطِّيبِ : المِسكُ »

"The best type of perfume is Musk."

In the *Sahihain* it is also narrated that 'Âishah رَضِيَ الله عَنْها said, "I used to anoint the Prophet ﷺ with perfumed Musk before assuming Ihram, on the Day of the Sacrifice and before performing *Tawaf* around the (Sacred) House."

Musk is the king of all perfumes, it has the best aroma. Other types of perfumes are usually compared to Musk, but Misk is never compared to them. Also, the hills and sands of Paradise are made of Musk.

Musk is a hot, dry substance of the second degree, and it brings comfort and joy to the hearts and strengthens the inner organs when it is drunk or smelled. Musk also brings strength and comfort to the external organs when anointed with it. Musk is profitable for old people and those who have excessive skin moistures, especially during winter, and also helps against fainting, shaking and the general weakness in the body as it excites the instinctive heat. Musk clears the white part in the eye and dries excess moisture in it, and also dissipates swelling in various organs. Musk also works as an antidote for some poisons, and helps against snakebite. It has many other benefits.

3. Marzanjush (Marjoram)

Marzanjush is hot in the third degree and dry in the second degree, and when its aroma is smelled, it relieves cold headache caused by phlegm, colds, black bile and thick flatulence pressure. It also relieves the congestion, and clogs in the nose and head and dissipates most cold, wet swellings.

When *Marzanjush* is used as suppository, it will increase the blood flow during menstruation and is favorable during pregnancies. When its dry leaves are crushed and used as a bandage, it will relieve blood traces that appear under the eye. It also helps relieve the pain of scorpion stings when it is mixed with vinegar [and then the affected area is bandaged with it].

Marzanjush ointment also helps relieve backache, knee pain and fatigue. Those who are used to smelling *Marzanjush* aroma will not suffer from water accumulation in the eye, cataract. When one administers its extract or water blended with the essence of bitter almonds in the nose, and helps against stuffiness that affects the nose and the head.

4. *Milh* (Salt)

Al-Bazzar narrated that the Prophet ﷺ said:

« سَيُوشِكُ أن تَكُونوا في الناس كالمِلْح في الطَّعام ولا يصلُح الطعام إلا بالمِلْح »

"You will soon be to the people just like what the salt represents to food, and the food's flavor doesn't become favorable unless there is salt in it."

Al-Baghawi said in his commentary on the Qur'ān that 'Abdullāh bin 'Umar رَضِيَ الله عَنْهُ related from the Prophet ﷺ that he said, "There are four blessings that Allāh has sent down to the earth from the heavens: iron, fire, water and salt." This *Hadith* should only be related from Ibn 'Umar رَضِيَ الله عَنْهما.

Salt is favorable for people's bodies and food. Further, salt is favorable and beneficial when blended with any substance, including gold and silver, as it makes gold more yellowish and whitens silver. Salt decomposes, cleanses, dries the thick humidity, strengthens and purifies the body and helps against open mangy sores.

When used as eyeliner salt, especially gem salt, will remove the excess fat or flesh and the yellowish color from the eye. Salt also prevents malignant infections from spreading, works as a laxative and helps against pleurisy when the stomach is anointed with it. Salt cleanses the teeth, prevents them from decaying, and strengthens the gums and makes them firm. There are many other benefits for the salt.

The Letter *Noon*

1. The *Nakhl* (Date Palm)

The date palm is mentioned in the Qur'ān in several places. In the *Sahihain* it is narrated that Ibn 'Umar رَضِيَ الله عَنْهما said, "We were with the Prophet ﷺ and a spadix of date-palm was brought to him. On that he said, 'Among the trees, there is a tree which resembles the Muslim.' I wanted to say that it was the date-palm tree but as I was the youngest of all (of them) I kept quiet. And then the Prophet ﷺ said, 'It is the date-palm tree.' I mentioned what happened to 'Umar رَضِيَ اللهُ عَنْهُ, and he said, 'Had you said it that would have been better to me than such and such.'"

This *Hadith* contains many benefits, such as the scholar training his students by asking them questions and testing their knowledge. It also contains parables and demonstrates the shyness of the Prophet's companions, the leaders and the commoners among them, as they all kept quite and were shy to answer the Prophet's question. The *Hadith* also demonstrates that the parent would be happy if his child does something right. The *Hadith* also demonstrates that it is allowed for the children to answer questions in the presence of their parents, even if the father did not know the answer, as this does not constitute misbehaving with the father. Also, this *Hadith* compares the Muslim with the *Nakhlah*, the date palm, because of its tremendous benefit, constant shade and sweet fruit that it produces throughout the year.

Dates are eaten fresh, dried, ripe and unripe and are both a type of food and a cure. Dates are nutritious, a type of sweet, a drink and a fruit. The date-tree's trunk is used for building purposes, in making pots, and so forth and its leaves are used to make woven mats, baskets, vases and funnels, and so forth. Its fibers are used to make ropes and mattresses. Also, its stones are used as fodder for camels and as ingredients in various medicinal remedies and in Ku'hl. Also, the fruit of the date-tree is known for its beauty, refreshing shape, and the handsome way the fruits are arranged on their branches, which also brings comfort to the eye.

Merely looking at the fruits of the date tree reminds one of its Creator, Whose creation is both excellent and perfect, just as is His Wisdom. Therefore the date tree resembles the righteous believer, for he is pure goodness who brings about benefit both inwardly and outwardly.

Also, the *Nakhlah* was the tree trunk that yearned and longed for the Messenger of Allāh ﷺ when he no longer used it as a podium. The trunk yearned for the Prophet's closeness and for hearing his speech!

Also, we should mention that the tree that Mary took refuge under when she gave birth to Jesus was the date palm.

There is a difference of opinion regarding which is better the date-tree or the *Habalah* (vine tree). Allāh has mentioned both trees together in several *Āyāt* (Verses) in His Book (the Qur'ān). Also, both trees are truly similar to each other, although each is at its prime in its natural habitat and the land that accepts it the most.

2. *Narjis* (Narcissus)

The *Narjis* is hot and dry in the second degree and its stems are used to relieve deep cankers that reach the nerves. Also, *Narjis* cleanses and extracts septic substances. If the Narjis is cooked and one drinks its water, or boils it and eats it, it will cause vomiting and will extract the moistures that reside in the bottom of the stomach. When the *Narjis* is cooked with lentil plant and honey, it will cleanse the cankers from septic excretions and will cause the gastric ulcers to rupture.

Narjis blossoms are mild and beneficial against colds. They have a strong power of decomposition, open the nose and cerebral clogs, and help against headaches and black bile. Those who repeatedly smell *Narjis* during winter will have immunity form pleurisy during summer. Also, *Narjis* helps relieve headaches caused by phlegm and black bile. *Narjis* aroma sharpens the mind and the heart and helps relieve many of their ailments. The author of 'At-Taysir' once said, "Inhaling *Narjis* aroma heals against the epilepsy that attacks boys."

3. *Noorah* (slaked lime)

It is two parts lime and one part arsenic mixed with water and left to dry in the sun until it turns blue. Then one uses it as ointment and waits an hour until it starts its effect before touching water. Then one takes a bath and anoints himself with henna to remove the lime's hotness.

4. *Nabq* or *Nabiq*

It has several names: *Nabq*, Christ's thorn, lotus jujube, or rhamnus. Abu Nu'aym mentioned these in his book on Prophetic medicine, when he mentioned the *Hadith*,

« أَن آدم لَمَّا هَبَط إِلى الأرض، كان أَولَ شيء أَكلَ من ثِمارها النَّبَقُ »

"When Adam was sent down to earth, the first of its fruits he ate was Nabiq.*"*

Also, the Messenger of Allāh ﷺ mentioned the Nabq in a Hadith narrated by the Two *Muhaddithain,*

« أنه رأى سِدْرَةَ المُنْتَهى ليلةَ أُسْرِيَ به : وإذا نَبَقُها مِثلُ قِلالِ هَجَرٍ »

"On the night that I was taken on the Night Journey, I was shown Sidrat Al-Muntaha (a tree in the seventh heaven) and I saw its Nabq fruits which resembled the clay jugs of Hajr (a town in Arabia)"

Nabq is the fruit produced by the lote-tree. Nabq soothes the natural digestive process, helps against diarrhea, coats the stomach, relieves bile, provides nutrition for the body, taste to the food and causes phlegm. It also helps against inflammation caused by bile. Nabq is slowly digested while its flour strengthens the bowls and is favorable for bilious temperaments. The harm of the Nabq will be neutralized when eating honeycomb with it.

There is a conflict of opinion concerning if Nabq is wet or dry. The correct opinion is that wet Nabq is cold and wet while dry Nabq is cold and dry.

The Letter Haa'

Hindaba (Chicory)

Hindaba temperament changes according to the season. It is cold and wet in winter, hot and dry in summer and mild in spring and autumn. In general, Hindaba is cold and dry. Hindaba is beneficial and cools the stomach and causes constipation. When Hindaba, especially wild Hindaba, is cooked and eaten with vinegar, it constipates even more and is more favorable for the stomach and invigorating.

When Hindaba (chicory) is used as a bandage, it will relieve gastric inflammations, gout and hot ocular inflammations. In cases of scorpion stings, Hindaba helps when its leaves and stems are used as a bandage.

Hindaba also strengthens the stomach and opens the clogs in the kidneys, spleen, veins and intestines. It also clears and purifies the kidneys and helps them against the various hot and cold aches.

The sour Hindaba is the best for the liver, while its extract helps against icter (jaundice), especially when mixed with wet fennel extract. When *Hindaba* leaves are bruised and placed on hot swellings, it will cool and dissipate them. *Hindaba* also cleanses and clears the chest and dissipates the heat of irritated blood and bile.

The best way to eat *Hindaba* is without washing it so as to preserve its effective ingredients. *Hindaba* works as an effective antidote against most poisons.

When *Hindaba* extract is used as eyeliner, it will clear and cleanse the eyes. *Hindaba* leaves are used in antidotes against scorpion stings, and against most poisons as we have stated. When the *Hindaba* is squeezed and its water is mixed with oil, it will help against all toxic substances in general. When *Hindaba* stems are squeezed and their water drunk, it will help against scorpion and hornet stings and against snakebite. Finally, the sap of its stems whitens the white area in the eye.

The Letter *Waw*

1. *Warss* (Ceylon Cornel tree)

Umm Salamah رَضِيَ اللهُ عَنْها narrated, "The woman who has just delivered would remain for forty days afterwards [without praying or fasting]. One of us would then overlay *Warss* on her face to help against spots." Abu Hanifah, a linguist, said, "*Warss* does not grow in the wild. Rather, it is cultivated. I think that it is only grown in the Arab lands, especially in Yemen."

Warss is dry and hot in the second degree. The best type of Warss is the red *Warss*, which is soft in the hand and does not have much bran. *Warss* is used as an ointment to treat spots, rashes and pimples that appear on the surface of the skin. Warss constipates, has a dyeing quality and helps against leprosy when taken as a drink.

Warss has similar benefits to sea Qust, and if it is used as an ointment it relieves vitiligo (skin condition of unknown cause, characterized by patchy loss of pigment), rashes, pimples and ulcers. When the clothes are dyed with *Warss*, they strengthen the sexual drive.

2. *Wasmah* (Woad)

Wasmah is similar to the Nile's leaves and it is used to dye the hair black. We mentioned the subject of dying the hair black before.

The letter *Yaa*

Yaqtin (Gourd)

Yaqtin means gourd or pumpkin, although the word Yaqtin entails more meanings than these two. *Yaqtin* in Arabic entails every tree that does not have a stem, such as watermelon and cucumbers. Allāh said:

$$\text{﴿ وَأَنبَتْنَا عَلَيْهِ شَجَرَةً مِّن يَقْطِينٍ ﴾}$$

"And We caused a plant of gourd to grow over him." (37:146)

If someone says that the word tree means every plant that has a stem or a trunk and that which does not have a stem or a trunk is called *Najm,* not a tree. Hence, why did Allāh say,

$$\text{﴿ شَجَرَةً مِّن يَقْطِينٍ ﴾}$$

"A plant of gourd to grow over him." (37:146)

We answer this question by stating that the word 'tree' describes the plants that have stems in general. Yet sometimes, this word is meant to describe something specific [to describe *Yaqtin* for instance]. Understanding the areas where the texts speak in general terms and the areas where a specific meaning is meant is a great door to understanding the Arabic Language. The *Yaqtin* mentioned in the Qur'ân is the pumpkin, which is also called *Dubbaa, Qar'* and *Yaqtin.*

In the *Sahihain* it is narrated by Anas bin Malik رَضِيَ الله عَنْهُ that a tailor once invited the Messenger of Allāh ﷺ to eat from some food that he made. So I (Anas) went with the Messenger of Allāh ﷺ, and the tailor brought forth some bread made from barley and some soup that had *Dubbaa* and dried meat. I saw the Messenger of Allāh ﷺ follow the traces of the *Dubbaa* all around the edge of the pot, which made me love *Dubbaa* ever since that day."

Abu Talut also said, "I entered upon Anas bin Malik رَضِيَ الله عَنْهُ while he was eating *Dubbaa* and saying [referring to the *Yaqtin* tree], 'You are a tree that is so dear to me because the Messenger of Allāh ﷺ used to like eating you.'"

Yaqtin is a type of cold and wet plant and a light food that is easily digested. If the gourd was not spoiled in the stomach before being completely digested, it produces a good mixture in the stomach, especially when one eats similar or compatible types of food with it. For example, mixing mustard and pumpkin produces bitter humor, while eating it with salt makes it salty and with constrictive substances makes it constipate. When it is cooked with Safarjal (quince), it will provide good nutrition for the body.

Gourd is light on the stomach, especially for those who do not suffer from phlegm or cold condition. The wetness contained in this plant helps ease the thirst and headaches if one drinks its extract or washes his head with it. Also, gourd soothes the stomach however one uses it, and is very beneficial for those who have hot temperaments.

Also, when the *Yaqtin* is kneaded with dough and baked in the oven and then its extract is mixed with some light drinks, it helps cool down fever, quenches the thirst and constitutes a good, nutritious food. If it was mixed with quince jam and Manna, it eliminates bile.

When pumpkin is cooked and its juice is mixed with some honey and Natron, it will cause phlegm and acid. If gourd was ground and then the head is bandaged with it, it will help ease the hot swellings in the cerebral.

When the gourd rinds are squeezed and the extract is mixed with rose oil and used as ear drops, it will help against hot tumors. Also, its rind helps ease the swelling of hot eye infections and against gout.

Also, gourd is very useful for those who have hot temperaments and those suffering from fever. When gourd finds some spoiled mixtures in the stomach it also gets spoiled causing harmful mixtures in the stomach. In this case, one should treat this condition with vinegar and sour substances.

In general, gourd is one of the lightest foods and the most easily digested. Anas رَضِيَ اللهُ عَنهُ narrated that the Messenger of Allāh ﷺ used to like eating it.

Conclusion *

I thought that the best way to end this chapter is by mentioning a general advice concerning preventive measures so as to complete the book's benefit.

This is a chapter that Ibn Masawayh has collected in his book, Al-Mahathir. He said,

"Whoever eats onion for forty days and then his face becomes full of spots, has only himself to blame.

Those who want to economize and eat salted foods will have only themselves to blame if they catch mange or vitiligo.

Those who eat fish and eggs will have only themselves to blame if they catch hemiplegia (paralysis affecting only one side of the body) or facial paralysis."

Those who catch hemiplegia when they take a bath with their stomach full [of food], will have only themselves to blame.

Those who eat milk and fish will have only themselves to blame if they catch leprosy, gecko or gout.

* Whoever mixes milk and wine and then catches gecko or gout has only himself to blame. Whoever has a wet dream but does not take a bath until he has sex with his wife and then if his wife gives birth to a retarded child, will have only himself to blame.

* Whoever eats his full of cold, boiled eggs and then catches Asthma will have only himself to blame.

* Whoever has sexual intercourse but did not wait until he ejaculates and then catches urinary calculus, (stone like mass that may form in the body under abnormal conditions), will have himself to blame. And

---

* **Editor's note**: Some of the advices contained in this chapter are not based upon evidence from Qur'an and sunnah, but are merely wide spread notions about health that were popular in the author's time. Some of these will be clearly recognized by the reader as superstitions. Thus it is important for the reader to remember that only that which can be substantiated by sound proof from Qur'an and authentic hadeeths should be depended upon religiously. A.W

whoever looks at himself in the mirror at night and then catches facial paralysis or another disease will have only himself to blame."

Also, Ibn Bukhtayshu' said, "Beware of eating eggs and fish together because they cause constipation, hemorrhoids and toothache. Also, eating eggs excessively begets spots on the face. Further, eating salted foods and salted fish and having venesection (puncturing of a vein) after one takes a bath causes vitiligo and mange. Eating goat kidney on a regular basis will cause the prostate to be sterile, while taking a bath with cold water after eating soft-meat fish causes facial paralysis. Also, having sex with a menstruating woman causes leprosy, and sexual intercourse that is not followed by taking a bath causes stones. Finally, spending too much time while answering the call of nature causes serious ailments."

Hippocrates said, "Less of a harmful substance is better than too much of a beneficial substance." He also said, "Preserve good health by preferring tiresome activity to laziness and abandoning having your fill of foods and drinks."

Further, a wise man once said, "Whoever wants to be healthy, let him eat good food, preserve cleanness and purity while eating, drink while thirsty, refrain from drinking excessive amounts of water and take a rest after lunch. Also, let him walk after dinner and avoid going to sleep before first answering the call of nature or taking a bath after eating his fill. Further taking a bath once during summer is better than ten times during winter. Eating dried jerky meat at night helps bring about death. Having sex with old women brings the person closer to old age and sickens the healthy body." These words were falsely attributed to Ali. However, some of these words are from Al-Harith bin Kaladah the renowned Arab doctor.

Al-Harith said, "Whoever seeks longevity, although eternal living is not possible, should have lunch and dinner early, wear light clothes and refrain from excessive sexual activity."

He also said, "Four things weaken the body: sexual intercourse when one is hungry, taking a bath when one is full, eating dried meat and having sexual intercourse with an old woman."

When Al-Harith was dying, some people visited him and said, "Give us an advise that we could use after you." He said, "Only marry young women, eat ripe fruits when in season and refrain from seeking medications when you can bear the illness. Clean your stomachs once a month (i.e. vomit intentionally), so as to dissipate the phlegm and the bile and to allow the flesh to grow. When one of you eats lunch, let him lay down for an hour and when he eats dinner, let him walk at least forty steps."

A king once said to his doctor, "You might not remain with me for ever, so give me a prescription that I can use after you." He said, "Only marry young women, eat fresh meat and take medication when you are ill. Eat the fruit when ripe and in season and chew the food well. If you eat during the day, there is no harm if you lay down. If you eat at night, do not sleep until you walk even fifty steps. Do not eat except when hungry and do not force yourself to have sex or refrain from urinating. Cool hotness because it causes you tiredness. Do not eat food when your stomach already has food, nor eat what your teeth cannot chew, because your stomach will not be able to digest that food. Try to vomit once a week to cleanse your body. What a good treasure the blood in your body is, so do not cup it without necessity. Finally, take a bath, because it rids you of what the medication cannot rid you of."

In addition, Imam Shafi'i said,

– "Four matters bring strength to the body:

* eating meat, smelling perfume, taking baths without having sexual intercourse and wearing Kittan (linen).

– Four matters weaken the body:

* excessive sexual intercourse, depression, drinking water repeatedly while the stomach is empty and consuming too much sour foods.

– Four matters strengthen the sight:

* sitting next to the Ka'bah, using Kohl before going to sleep, looking at green things and cleaning up the sitting area [in the house].

– Four maters weaken the sight:

* looking at dirt, crucified persons,' a woman's vagina and sitting while your back is to the Qiblah (direction of the prayer).

– Four matters increase sexual power:

* eating fowl-meat, the large Itreefal (a non-Arabic medication for

constipation), pistachio and carob.

– Four matters sharpen mind power:

* avoiding unnecessary speech, using *Siwak,* and sitting with righteous people and with the scholars."

Plato said, "Five matters dissipate the strength of the body and might lead to death:

* weekness, leaving loved ones behind, rage, rejecting good advice and the clever persons falling victim to deceit by ignorant people."

The doctor of Al-Ma'mun said, "Hold fast to five characteristics that whoever preserves them would never catch a disease other than death:

* Do not eat food while there is still food in your stomach.

* Do not eat a type of food that your teeth cannot chew, because then your stomach would not be able to digest it. Refrain from excessive sexual activity because it shortens life.

* Do not have sex with an old woman because it leads to sudden death.

* Do not revert to cupping without necessity. Vomit during the summer."

Hippocrates also said,

* "Everything that is excessive is unnatural."

Galinus was once told:

* "Why do you not get sick that often?" He said, "I do not mix two types of unfavorable food together, nor eat food while not hungry, nor keep a food in my stomach which is bothering it."

* Excessiveness in four matters causes sickness:

* speech, sexual activity, sleep and eating habits.

* Excessive speech weakens the mind and hastens old age.

* Excessive sleep turns the face yellow, blinds the heart, irritates the eyes, makes one lazy to work and causes excess humidity in the body.

* Excessive eating habits spoil the orifice of the stomach, weaken the body, cause thick flatulence and difficult ailments.

* Having sexual intercourse excessively depletes the strength,

weakens the body, dries the moistures in the body, adversely relaxes the nerves, causes various clogs and harms the entire body, especially the brain because of the psychological effects it will have on it. Weakness in the brain, which will also weaken the soul, is worse than weakness in any other organ.

* The best time to have sex is when one feels a strong desire for a lawful partner (wife) who is beautiful, especially when the spouse is young, ready and excited. Also, occasional legal sex makes it more desirable, especially when one does not have any concerns and does not use it excessively. Also, legal sex is best when one is not full or hungry, not after conducting serious physical activity and not during extremely hot or cold weather. When one takes care of these ten matters we mentioned, sex will be most beneficial. Otherwise, if some of these matters were ignored, harm might be caused according to the seriousness of the matters that were ignored. If one does not take care of all these ten matters, he will be faced with a shorter life span.

* Excessive diet is as dangerous to the healthy person as excessive eating habits when one is ill.

* Galinus said to some of his companions, "Beware of three matters and seek four matters, and you will not need a doctor.

* Avoid dust, smoke and foul odors. Seek nutritious foods, good scents (or aromas), sweets and take baths. Do not eat above your fill, nor pickle Batharuj (a plant) and basil, and do not eat walnuts at night. Whoever caught a cold should not sleep on his back nor should a depressed person eat sour foods.

* Whoever had venesection (puncturing of a vein), should not walk fast because this might cause death.

* Those who have an ache in the eye should not vomit.

* Do not eat too much meat during summer.

* Whoever is suffering from fever should not sleep in the sun. Do not eat old, seeded eggplant.

* Those who drink a cup of warm water every day during winter will save themselves from illness.

* Those who rub their bodies with pomegranate rind while taking a

bath will not catch a rash or mange.

* Whoever eats five flowers of iris with Greek mastic, roe aloes and Musk, will persevere the strength and health of his stomach the rest of his life.

* Eating watermelon seeds with sugar will cleanse the stomach from stones and will prevent burning sensation while urinating."

Four matters bring demise to the body:

* depression, sadness, hunger and staying up late at night

Four matters bring joy:

* looking at greenery, running water, loved ones and fruits.

Four matters bring darkness to the sight:

* walking bare footed, seeing hated faces mornings and afternoons or seeing the enemy, excessive crying and looking at thin lines for extended periods of time.

Four matters bring strength to the body:

* wearing soft clothes, taking a bath moderately, eating sweet and nutritious food and smelling good scents.

Four matters harden the face and rid it of its youth and health:

* lying, rudeness, asking too many questions without knowledge [or useful purpose] and sinning.

Four matters increase the youth of the face:

* chivalry, faithfulness, generosity and fear of Allāh.

Four matters bring about anger and hatred:

* arrogance, envy, lying and spreading calumnies.

Four matters bring sustenance:

* standing up in prayer at night, seeking forgiveness [of Allāh] often at night, giving away in charity and remembering Allāh morning and evening.

Four matters prevent sustenance:

* sleeping in the morning, not praying often, laziness and treachery.

Four matters harm the mind and the intellect:

* eating sour foods and fruits excessively, sleeping on the back,

depression and sadness.

Four matters strengthen the intellect and the mind:

* when the heart is not busy [or concerned], consuming moderate amounts of food and drink, dieting on good combinations of sweets and nutritious foods and getting rid of the harmful substances in the body.

There are some matters that harm the mind:

* eating onions, beans, olives and eggplant excessively, having too much sexual intercourse, loneliness, worrying, intoxication, excessive laughing and depression.

Some wise men also said, "I became tired three times and could not find a reason for that except for three matters:

* I ate too much eggplant one day, olives another day and beans a third day."

We have mentioned several beneficial basics of the medicinal sciences that one might not be able to find except in this book. We also affirmed that the religion and medicinal science are close to each other. We also stated that Prophetic medicine cannot and should not be compared to the medicine of the doctors just as the medicine of the doctors cannot be compared to folk medicine.

This matter is deeper and more serious than we explained, but we mentioned what is sufficient for the reader to recognize its importance. Those whom Allāh did not endow with sound comprehension in such matters let them know the difference between the power that is supported by divine intervention and knowledge, strong mind and sound comprehension that Allāh has endowed the Prophets with, and between what all others have in this regard.

Someone might ask, "What does the guidance of the Prophet ﷺ have to do with the subject of medicines and cures and preserving the health?"

This question exposes the lack of understanding of such people, because this subject and many others are among what the Prophet ﷺ was sent with and what he has directed us to do. Sound understanding and knowledge of Allāh and His Messenger are a bounty that Allāh endows to whom He will among His creation.

We have explained the three principal basics of medicine in the Qur'ān. How can anyone deny that the religion of he who was sent with the righteousness of this and the Next Life also contains what preserves the body? How can anyone deny that the religion also directs us to the best methods of staying healthy, just as it directs to the best methods of preserving the heart and preventing sicknesses that might attack them? These cures [that the religion contains] are mentioned in general terms and the specifics are left to those of correct minds and pure hearts to seek and implement, just as one does regarding matters of *Fiqh*. Do not be among those who reject something simply because they have no knowledge of it.*

When the slave is endowed with sufficient knowledge of Allāh's Book and the *Sunnah* of His Messenger ﷺ, along with sound comprehension of the Texts [of the Qur'ān and *Sunnah*], he will rely on these sources and would not need anything else. Also, he will be able to acquire all types of good knowledge from these sources.

All types of knowledge depends on knowing Allāh, His Commands and creation. The Messengers of Allāh ﷺ are the only source that we can acquire such knowledge from, because they have the best knowledge of Allāh, His Commandments and creation. The Messengers also have the best knowledge of the wisdom behind Allāh's creation and Commandments.

This is why the remedies provided by the followers of the Prophets are better and more efficient than the remedies of all others. Also, the remedies provided by the followers of the best and the master of the Prophets, Muhammad bin 'Abdullāh, are the best, most sufficient and beneficial remedies.

Only those who have true knowledge of the science of medicine and doctors and the medicine offered by the Prophets, can know the

---

* **Editor's note**: The author is telling the people that vision and subject are noted then the scholars or professionals who are most competent in those fields should follow these guidelines to further wisdom. This was the same method applied to jurisprudence and the wisdom that was realized from this method was well known and understood among the people. His basic message is follow the Prophet Muhammad, there is no better guide.

difference between them. The Prophets are those with the best minds, purest ways and deepest knowledge. They are the nearest to the truth among the creation. They are the best of mankind that Allāh has chosen, just as the Messenger, Muhammad ﷺ, is the best among all the Messengers. The knowledge that Allāh has endowed the Prophets and Messengers with and the wisdom and forbearing puts them in a category that does not permit comparison. Imam Ahmad narrated that the Messenger of Allāh ﷺ said:

« أَنتُم تُوَفُّونَ سبعينَ أُمَّةً؛ أَنتُم خيرُها و أَكرمُها علَى اللهِ »

"You (mankind) are seventy nations (or distinct communities); you (Muslims) are the best and most honored among them to Allāh."

This honor that Allāh has endowed the Muslims with has appeared in their knowledge, minds, intellects and natural ways. The Muslims are the ones who searched through the knowledge of all other nations before them and also their wisdom, progress and their works, then added this knowledge to their own knowledge, forbearing and wisdom that Allāh has endowed them with.

This is why the Christians are set aback by their silliness, lack of intelligence and apathy, while the Jews are set aback by their sadness, grief and anguish. Muslims, on the other hand, are endowed with sound minds, courage, understanding, joy, happiness and the tendency to help those in distress.

These are some secrets and facts that can only be comprehended by those who have sound minds, sharp intellect, deep knowledge and acquaintance with what the people have [of wisdom, knowledge, and so forth]. All success comes from Allāh.